The Year Ahead

A century ago marked the beginning of a new, exuberant era: the "Roaring Twenties." New technologies promised better ways of living. A hopeful optimism led Americans to cast aside traditional moral standards, valuing conspicuous consumption over austerity. Radio shows brought fresh ideas and music into homes and cars transported Americans from their family farms to new opportunities in the city. Americans weren't the only beneficiaries of all this growth. Europeans enjoyed great economic prosperity in the aftermath of World War I, while South America became a beneficiary of new oil production. It seemed as though the good times might last forever.

But the Roaring Twenties also brought Prohibition, a short-sighted regulatory attempt to shape American society that resulted in the rise of organized crime and kingpins like Al Capone. Fascism, authoritarian dictators and civil wars erupted in Eastern Europe and China in the aftermath of collapsed empires. Technological innovations, like the Panama Canal, moving assembly lines and wide-scale electric power transmission, had created new wealth but it wasn't evenly distributed. More than two-thirds of Americans survived on wages too low to sustain everyday living, and they didn't have a safety net. High valuations and the promise of massive returns lured enthusiastic investors, who bought company shares—lots of them—using questionable loans. When share prices began their inevitable decline, people panicked. By October 1929, the stock market crashed, setting in motion a Great Depression, a rise in xenophobia and far-right extremism, and eventually, another world war.

It's difficult not to see unsettling parallels to our present-day world. But we are positioned to make better choices this time around. A century ago, the tools of modern strategic foresight hadn't been invented yet. There was no method of researching and categorizing trends that might influence the future. Rather than studying plausible long-term implications, leaders made decisions in the moment. Or they didn't actively make decisions at all.

With the benefit of both hindsight and strategic foresight, we now have frameworks and methods to identify risk and capitalize on emerging opportunity. In fact, you're holding one of those tools in your hand: our 2020 Tech Trends Report. It's vitally important to make connections between emerging trends, your industry and society, especially this year as we reach a tipping point for a number of technologies and trends that will shape the world of tomorrow.

A sample of them include:

- *A.I. systems that can be trained in hours rather than weeks*
- *Widespread availability of algorithmically-traded funds*
- *Off-planet human civilization*
- *Bioengineered animals, plant-based proteins and indoor robot-powered farms*
- *Autonomous cars, trucks, ships and fighter jets*
- *Exascale computing*
- *Quantum computing*
- *Functional 5G networks*

Connections must also be made between technologies and many external uncertainties that will continue to loom:

- *The outcome of the 2020 U.S. election*
- *A heightened scrutiny of chief executives and boards*
- *Frequent extreme weather events*
- *The proliferation of superbugs and new epidemics*
- *The rise of extreme political movements and ideologies*
- *Unstable U.S.-China relations*
- *Unresolved tensions between Russia and the West*
- *An ongoing clash between old laws and new technologies*

We cannot know how future historians will remember the 2020s or what they will name this decade. We can, however, choose to put forth our best efforts to plan strategically for an era of technological innovation, measured growth, distributed prosperity and solutions that will propel humankind forward.

Now, more than ever, your organization should examine the potential near and long-term impact of tech trends. You must factor the trends in this report into your strategic thinking for the coming year, and adjust your planning, operations and business models accordingly. Failing to monitor trends in a meaningful way will put your competitive advantage, growth and survivability at risk.

Think exponentially. Act incrementally. Always remember that the future isn't yet written. You and your team have the power to build your best possible futures today.

Sincerely,

Amy Webb
Founder, The Future Today Institute
Writing from my New York office on January 13, 2020

Key Takeaways

○ **Welcome to the Synthetic Decade.**

From digital twins to engineered DNA to plant-based pork sausages, a deep push to develop synthetic versions of life is already underway. We will look back on the 2020s as an era that brought us synthetic media, such as A.I.-generated characters whose storylines we follow on social media and humanlike virtual assistants who make our appointments and screen our calls. Soon, we will produce "designer" molecules in a range of host cells on demand and at scale, which will lead to transformational improvements in vaccine production, tissue production and medical treatments. Scientists will start to build entire human chromosomes, and they will design programmable proteins. Foods made from synthetic techniques rather than artificial ingredients will make their way to the mainstream, and you'll have a wide array of choices: humanely engineered foie gras, flora-derived ice cream and molecular whiskey made in a lab. Every industry will be impacted as our synthetic decade brings new business opportunities and strategic risks. Companies will need to ask challenging ethical questions and examine the security risks for synthetic material in order to earn public acceptance, government approvals and commercial appeal.

○ **You'll soon have augmented hearing and sight.**

While you shouldn't expect to see everyone wearing smart glasses by this time next year, you will certainly start to notice some important developments throughout 2020, beginning with audio augmented reality (or AAR). Think of it as augmented reality for audio. Smart earbuds and glasses will digitally overlay audio (like directions, notifications, and verbal descriptions of what — or who — you're looking at) without others hearing and while you continue to hear what's going on around you. Not only will AAR help runners stay safe, it offers a sophisticated alternative to traditional hearing aids. Smart glasses won't look like the minimalistic Google Glass headband, but rather a stylish pair of frames you'd find at your local optometrist's office. Google, Amazon, Apple, Microsoft and Facebook all have connected systems on their product roadmaps. The connected glasses and AAR ecosystem offer tremendous new business opportunities—and could signal disruption to longtime market leaders in frames, prescription lenses, hearing aids and headphones.

○ **A.I.-as-a-Service and Data-as-a-Service will reshape business.**

The future of digital transformation is rooted in two key areas: A.I.-as-a-Service and Data-as-a-Service. Microsoft, IBM, Google, Amazon, Facebook and Apple are all developing new services and tools ranging from robotic process automation to offering GPUs (graphics processing unit) in the cloud. Amazon's upcoming project, AWS For Everyone—a low-code/no-code platform built to enable anyone to create business applications using their company data—will be a huge differentiator when it launches.

○ **China has created a new world order.**

The growth of China's economy might be slowing, but it would be a mistake to assume that the People's Republic of China has lost its influence. In the past two decades, China overtook the U.S. as the world's dominant exporter on every continent with the exception of North America. Its imports matter, too: This year China should surpass the U.S. and become the world's largest movie market, with a projected $10 billion in revenue. China has a rapidly-expanding middle class, an educated and trained workforce and a government that executes on long-term plans. China will continue to assert prolific dominance in 2020 across multiple areas: diplomacy throughout Southeast Asia, Africa, Latin and South America and Europe; the development of critical digital infrastructure; artificial intelligence; data collection and scoring; bioengineering and space.

○ **Home and office automation is nearing the mainstream.**

An Alexa in every pot and a self-driving car in every garage? Nearly 100 years ago Herbert Hoover promised Americans they would prosper under his presidency: a chicken in every pot, and a car in every garage. Today, A.I.-powered digital assistants, home security systems and voice-controlled microwaves are being manufactured—and priced—for the masses. Robots used to be the stuff of science fiction, but this year major appliance manufacturers, component makers, and of course, the big tech companies will make compelling arguments for why our homes and offices should be outfitted with sensors, cameras and microphones. Next-generation network infrastructure should speed adoption. The global market could reach $214 billion by 2025. Which company's operating system controls all those devices, and what happens to the data being collected, will spark public debate.

○ **Everyone alive today is being scored.**

In order for our automated systems to work, they need both our data and a framework for making decisions. We're shedding data just by virtue of being alive. From our social media posts, to our unique biology (posture, bone and capillary structures, vocal pitch and cadence), to our credit card debt, to our travel habits, thousands of data points are analyzed to score us. Automated systems use our scores to make decisions for or about us, whether it's what price to show us on e-commerce sites or if we might pose a security risk at a football game. We anticipate that in the coming year, regulators will take a deeper interest in scoring.

○ **We've traded FOMO for abject fear.**

In the 2010s Facebook, Instagram, Snapchat, Reddit, Foursquare and Twitter caused a "fear of missing out." Those very same networks (save for the now-defunct mobile social app Foursquare) are being used for intentional—and sometimes unwitting—scaremongering. On Facebook, Baltimore Mayor Bernard "Jack" Young helped propagate a wild—and totally false—story on Facebook about a white van abducting girls for human trafficking and for selling body parts. Numerous times, President Donald Trump has used Twitter to stoke fear, telling the public about armed "large [sic] Caravans" that were "invading" America. On Twitter, he has publicly threatened the leaders of other countries:

"I will totally destroy and obliterate the [sic] Economy of Turkey" – October 7, 2019

"North Korean Leader Kim Jong Un just stated that the "Nuclear Button is on his desk at all times." Will someone from his depleted and food starved regime please inform him that I too have a Nuclear Button, but it is a much bigger & more powerful one than his, and my Button works!" – January 2, 2018

"To Iranian President Rouhani: NEVER, EVER THREATEN THE UNITED STATES AGAIN OR YOU WILL SUFFER CONSEQUENCES THE LIKES OF WHICH FEW THROUGHOUT HISTORY HAVE EVER SUFFERED BEFORE. WE ARE NO LONGER A COUNTRY THAT WILL STAND FOR YOUR DEMENTED WORDS OF VIOLENCE & DEATH. BE CAUTIOUS!" – July 22, 2018

Social media posts like these are often repeated at rallies and protests, which only serve to amplify our fear. The Anti-Defamation League discovered a 226% increase in acts of vandalism and hate crimes in the counties hosting Trump rallies. We're continually told that we need protection: from unsafe countries, people and even our neighbors. Fear is good for business. Amazon bought smart doorbell company Ring for $1 billion, and it now has lucrative partnerships with more than 400 U.S. police departments to share recognition tech and surveillance video from users' homes.

○ **It's the end of forgetting.**

After a decade of posting photos, videos and written messages on social media, it's now clear that our recent histories will persist far into the future. It isn't possible to truly delete or erase our pasts. A centerpiece of the European Union's landmark internet laws, the "right to be forgotten," emerged as a standard intended to force search engines to delete links to personal information if it wasn't in the public interest. But in 2019, the European Court of Justice ruled in Google's favor, making it much harder for people to request that negative, private or misleading information about them is removed from internet searches. A Google search team member put it more bluntly: "We're not a truth engine."

○ **Our new trust economy is being formed.**

We will soon see a host of new tools built to engender and ensure—but also manipulate—our trust. In the wake of deepfake videos and other manipulated content, a new ecosystem devoted to trust is in the process of being formed. There's a lot at stake: After hearing an A.I. fake his CEO's voice on the phone, a gullible employee transferred $243,000 to a scammer. In the coming year, sentinel surveillance systems will algorithmically detect manipulated content—for a fee. Meanwhile, governments and interest groups around the world will try to shape the future development of A.I. and blockchain technology, proposing legislation and "bill of rights" manifestos.

Table of Contents

Table of Contents

Table of Contents

How to Use Our Report

Each trend offers eight important strategic insights for your organization.

The Future Today Institute's 13th annual Tech Trends Report positions organizations to see disruption before it fully erupts. Use our trend analysis, scenarios and foresight frameworks as a springboard for deeper strategic planning. This report will help you identify new business opportunities, emerging threats to your organization, and potential partners and collaborators in and adjacent to your industry.

We recommend using our 2020 Tech Trends Report as part of a formalized strategic foresight process within your organization.

For a complete list of trends by industry, and to search by individual technology, visit futuretodayinstitute.com/trends.

SECOND YEAR ON THE LIST — 1

Precision Agriculture

New tools will help farmers predict crop yields based on environmental factors.

Key Insight — 2

Using sensors, algorithms, and optimization analytics, farmers can now quantify the progress of every single crop—down to a single cherry tomato hanging on a particular vine.

Why It Matters — 3

Precision agriculture can help increase crop yields and profitability while reducing the costs associated with watering, fertilizing and treating crops for pests.

Examples — 4

The **University of Georgia** became one of the first research institutions to apply big data to farming in the mid-1990s. This new farm management approach involves a variety of technologies, including GPS, sensors, collaborative robotics, autonomous vehicles, autonomous soil sampling, telematics, and lots of machine learning. Vestiges of precision agriculture have been around since farmers started using GPS alongside their tractors, but advancements in robotics, data collection, and insights have meant new opportunities. Farmers can now vary irrigation and fertilizer automatically using new technologies.

What's Next — 5

Modern agriculture relies on efficient management and accurate predictions. Researchers at the **University of Illinois** combined seasonal climate data and satellite images with the USDA's **World Agricultural Supply and Demand Estimates** to build new kinds of prediction models—they hope this will help farmers predict crop yields in advance given environmental factors. **South Dakota State University** invested $46 million in a new facility to study the future of precision agriculture and is developing new precision ag courses set to start in 2021. New technologies on the near-future horizon include drones equipped with smart cameras, data mining to understand crop blossoming and ripeness, and new analytics dashboards to help farmers make smarter decisions.

The Impact — 6

As 5G becomes more widely available this year, precision agriculture applications will improve and usage will expand.

Watchlist — 7

Amazon, Arable, Blue River Technology, Bosch, CropMetrics, Descartes Labs, DuPont, Farmers Business Network, Farmers Edge, Google, Honeywell, Planet Labs, SAP, Semios, Sentera, Smart Ag, Syngenta, TerrAvion, University of Georgia College of Agricultural and Environmental Sciences, University of Georgia's Center for Agribusiness and Economic Development, University of Illinois, United States Department of Agriculture.

8 —

HIGH DEGREE OF CERTAINTY

	INFORMS STRATEGY	ACT NOW	
LONGER-TERM IMPACT			IMMEDIATE IMPACT
	REVISIT LATER	KEEP VIGILANT WATCH	

LOW DEGREE OF CERTAINTY

---

1. Years On The List

The number of years we have been tracking this trend as it has evolved. This measurement is an indication of how the trend is progressing.

2. Key Insight

Concise description of this trend that can be easily understood and repeated to others.

3. Why It Matters

Explanation of this trend's significance to you and your organization.

4. Examples

Real-world use cases, some of which should be familiar to you.

5. What's Next

FTI's analysis of how this trend will develop over time.

6. The Impact

Describing the next-order implications of this trend.

7. Watchlist

Individuals, research teams and organizations most deeply involved in this trend.

8. Action Matrix

FTI's analysis of what action your organization should take. Our quadrants include:

Act Now
Ample evidence and data.
This trend is already mature.

Informs Strategy
Mounting evidence and data.
Longer-term uncertainties remain.

Keep Vigilant Watch
Mounting evidence and data.
However, the impact is likely nearer-term.

Revisit Later
Less evidence and data.
However, this trend has the potential to cause great disruption.

Scenarios Describe Plausible Outcomes Relevant to Your Organization

In this report, you will find many scenarios imagining future worlds as these trends evolve and converge. Scenarios offer you fresh perspective on emerging trends and choices that still have yet to be made. They challenge you to ask "what if," and illuminate ways opportunities to prevent, mitigate, leverage or capitalize on change in the future. The Future Today Institute uses a wide variety of data across numerous sources to create our scenarios: statistics, patent filings, academic and archival research, policy briefings, conference papers, structured interviews with lots of people and even critical design and speculative fiction.

1. Headline
A short description offering you a glimpse into future changes.

2. Temporal and Emotive Tags
A label explaining both when in the future this scenario is set and whether it is optimistic, neutral, pessimistic or catastrophic.

3. Descriptive Elements
A narrative of our imagined world, with a description of what developments led us to this point in our future history.

1

SCENARIO • AMY WEBB

When There's Truly Nowhere to Hide

2

MID-FUTURE CATASTROPHIC SCENARIO

3

All of the cameras and sensors seem futuristic and fantastic at the beginning, promising to optimize your diets and keep intruders at bay. We spend a decade acquiring new technologies that make our lives a little more easy and convenient, and so we silence those nagging voices asking us what we're giving up in exchange for all those new features. Eventually, we realize that while we weren't paying attention, our homes were turned into ventures for marketing, which is now constant and intrusive. We see custom video advertisements everywhere there's a screen: the smart mirrors in your bathroom and closets, the retractable screens we carry in our pockets, even the smart window panes we had to install in our houses to block out extreme solar heat. There is nowhere to hide anymore, because some entity is always watching, always listening, always there. We're uncomfortable in our own homes, the one place we used to feel most safe and relaxed.

Strategic Questions to Ask

To make practical use of this year's report, readers should ask and answer some fundamental questions about what these trends mean to their organization in the near future. Don't discount a trend simply because, at first glance, it doesn't seem to connect directly to you or your field. As you review the analysis in this report with your cross-functional team, ask and answer the following questions when it comes to:

Guiding our strategic planning process

- How does this trend support or challenge our current strategic direction?

- What new emerging threats or existential risks might result from the evolution of this trend?

- What are the consequences if our organization fails to take action on this trend?

- Considering this research, is our strategic planning process too limited in scope or in timing?

Informing our decisions

- How can our organization make incremental decisions on this trend today and ongoing, as it evolves?

- How might global events—politics, climate change, economic shifts—impact this trend, and as a result, our organization?

- Can we use this research to build support and alignment for our decision-making process?

Making future investments

- What is our current business model, and how must it change as this trend evolves?

- Where should we invest our resources as this trend evolves?

- Are there opportunities to acquire startups, research teams and those at the forefront of this trend?

Growing our business

- How is our strategy providing a competitive edge and helping to move our organization forward into the future?

- How will the wants, needs and expectations of our consumers, customers and partners change as a result of this trend?

- How does this trend help us think about innovation?

Facilitating strong partnerships

- Where does this trend create potential new partners or collaborators for us?

- How does this trend introduce new adversaries we've never seen before?

- How are organizations in adjacent industries addressing this trend?

What can we learn from their failures and best practices?

Supporting my team/ business unit

- Does this trend signal emerging disruption to our organization's culture, practices and cherished beliefs?

- Does this trend indicate future disruption to the established roles and responsibilities within our organization?

- Will our workforce need to change because of this trend? If so, does our current operating structure allow us to make the necessary changes, whether that means downsizing or upskilling? If we must attract new talent, are we positioned to attract and retain the workers we will need?

Leading our industry into the future

- How does this trend impact our industry and all of its parts?

- What new uncertainties—about our industry, organization, customers, partners—can our organization now address after reading this report?

- How do we leverage this trend in a positive way for both our organizations and the greater good?

Decision Matrix

Taking Strategic Actions on Trends

Many organizations prefer to take a "wait and see" approach after seeing new research, and that's a mistake. We recognize how difficult it is to take risks during a time of political, technological and economic uncertainty. Your team must take some action, even if it's small, to build momentum so that you may confront the future on your own terms.

For that reason, the Future Today Institute created a simple framework for our clients. We have a singular goal: think exponentially, act incrementally.

NEED ACTIONS ———————————————— NEED INSIGHTS ———

MORE →

CERTAINTY ABOUT TRENDS

BUILD CAPABILITIES

How will we develop expertise to act? How do our stakeholders understand these trends, and what are their expectations of us?

Sample Action

Develop an assessment to learn how well positioned your current team is to address this trend. Determine what changes are necessary.

DEVELOP STRATEGY

How do these trends support or challenge our current strategic direction?

Sample Action

Ask your teams to look at your current strategy through the lenses of these trends. Have each develop a list of questions and recommendations.

FIND DISRUPTION

Where can we find emerging threats and risks as these trends evolve? In what new and novel ways could our operations be jeopardized in the future?

Sample Action

Host a disaster scenario writing workshop. Identify plausible pessimistic and catastrophic outcomes.

BRAINSTORM IDEAS

How can we develop a new product or service that leverages these trends as they evolve? Where opportunities are on the horizon?

Sample Action

Host a design thinking workshop. Challenge teams to invent new concepts, ideas and solutions to society's future problems.

← LESS

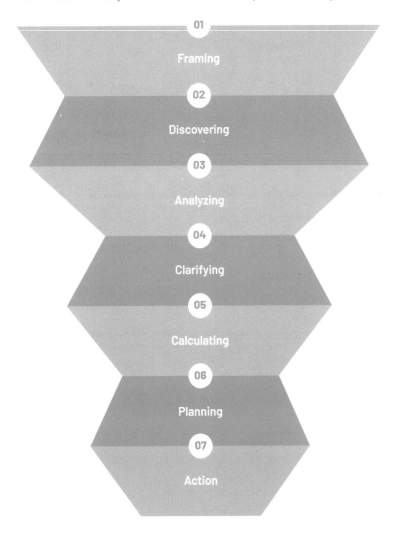

The Future Today Institute's Seven-Step Forecasting Funnel

01 Framing
02 Discovering
03 Analyzing
04 Clarifying
05 Calculating
06 Planning
07 Action

Methodology

The Future Today Institute's strategic forecasting model uses quantitative and qualitative data to identify weak signals and map their trajectories into tech trends. Our seven steps alternate between broad and narrow scopes, which include: framing your work, identifying weak signals at the fringe, spotting patterns, developing trend candidates, calculating a trend's velocity, developing scenarios, and finally, backcasting preferred outcomes.

The steps of our methodology can be used independently to surface new trends or to generate scenarios, or they can be used to guide your strategic planning process. To identify trends, use steps 1 – 4. To imagine future worlds, use steps 1 and 5.

1. **Converge:** Determine your questions, time horizons and stakeholders.

2. **Diverge:** Listen for weak signals at the fringe. Make observations and harness information from the broadest possible array of sources and on a wide variety of topics.

3. **Converge:** Uncover hidden patterns in the previous step. Use FTI's CIPHER framework to identify trends. Look for contradictions, inflections, practices, hacks, extremes and rarities.

4. **Diverge:** Ask questions to learn how the trends you've identified intersect with your industry and all of its parts.

5. **Converge:** Calculate the velocity and trajectory of change that are both internal and external to your organization.

6. **Diverge:** Write scenarios to describe impacts and outcomes in the future.

7. **Converge:** Backcast preferred outcomes. Define your desired future and then work backwards to identify the strategic actions connecting that future to your present.

The Four Laws of Technology Trends were first published in _The Signals Are Talking: Why Today's Fringe Is Tomorrow's Mainstream,_ by Amy Webb.

Trend vs. Trendy: Knowing the Difference

It isn't always easy to distinguish between trend and trendy, especially now as we transition to ambient computing, autonomous machines and a wide variety of digital voices. You need to make sound decisions today, but that's a difficult ask since much of our technological ecosystem is still being developed.

The easiest way to cut through hype is to remember that trends are driven by fundamental shifts in demographics, the economy, technology, politics and social movements. They are new manifestations representing our fundamental human needs. Trends form steadily over many years, and they do not necessarily follow a linear path. Trendy phenomena (or fads) are much more transient. They appear suddenly, capture our attention and distract us with intense possibilities—only to burn out just as quickly as they arrived. Fads move along a common cycle: insider discovery, trending on social networks, influencer bragging, media hysteria and mainstream acceptance, until we are disillusioned because the fads never meet our broader expectations.

Strategic trends share a set of conspicuous, universal features, which we call FTI's Four Laws of Tech Trends.

The Four Laws of Tech Trends

1. Trends are driven by basic human needs.

2. Trends are timely, but they persist.

3. Trends are the convergence of weak signals over time.

4. Trends evolve as they emerge.

Typically all four features are present in an authentic strategic trend.

Future Forces Theory:
The 11 Macro Sources of Disruption

FTI's Future Forces Theory explains how disruption usually stems from influential sources of macro change. It is a way of understanding where disruption is coming from and where it's headed next. The sources of macro change represent external uncertainties—factors that broadly affect business, governing and society. They can skew positive, neutral and negative.

We use a simple tool to apply the future forces theory to organizations as they are developing strategic thinking on trends. It lists 11 sources of macro change that are typically outside of a leader's control. For example: as we think about the evolution of artificial intelligence, how will geopolitics and infrastructure impact development?

Organizations must pay attention to all 11 as they track trends. Leaders must connect the dots back to their industries and companies and position teams to take incremental actions.

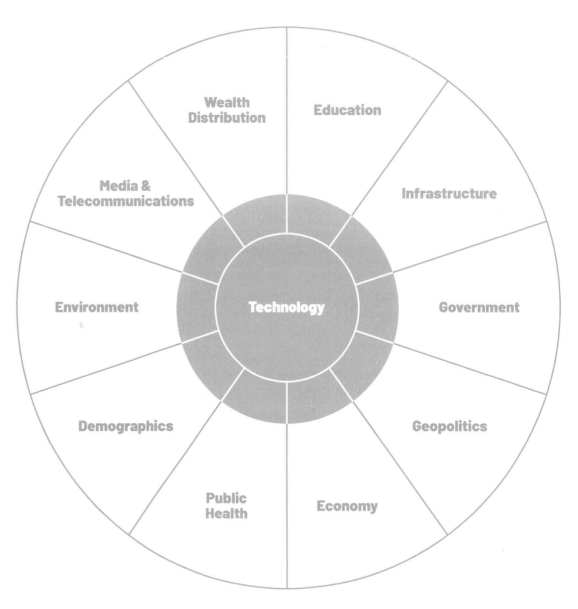

The 11 Macro Sources of Disruption

The 11 Macro Sources of Disruption Include:

Wealth Distribution

The distribution of income across a population's households, the concentration of assets in various communities, the ability for individuals to move up from their existing financial circumstances and the gap between the top and bottom brackets within an economy.

Education

Access and quality of primary, secondary, and post-secondary education, workforce training, trade apprenticeships, certification programs, the ways in which people are learning and the tools they're using and what people are interested in studying.

Infrastructure

Physical, organizational, and digital structures needed for society to operate (bridges, power grids, roads, wifi towers, closed-circuit security cameras), the ways in which the infrastructure of a city, state or country might impact another's.

Government

Local, state, national, and international governing bodies, their planning cycles, their elections and the regulatory decisions they make.

Geopolitics

The relationships between the leaders, militaries and governments of different countries, the risk faced by investors, companies and elected leaders in response to regulatory, economic or military actions.

Economy

Shifts in standard macroeconomic and microeconomic factors.

Public Health

Changes in the health and behavior of a community's population in response to lifestyles, popular culture, disease, government regulation, warfare or conflict and religious beliefs.

Demographics

Observing how birth and death rates, income, population density, human migration, disease and other dynamics are shifting communities.

Environment

Changes to the natural world or to specific geographic areas, including extreme weather events, climate fluctuations, sea level rise, drought, high or low temperatures and more. (We include agricultural production in this category.)

Media and Telecommunications

All of the ways in which we send and receive information and learn about the world. This includes social networks, news organizations, digital platforms, video streaming services, gaming and e-sports systems, 5G and the boundless other ways in which we connect with each other.

Technology

We recognize technology not as an isolated source of macro change, but rather, as the connective tissue linking business, government and society. For that reason, we always look for emerging tech developments, as well as tech signals within the other sources of change.

How To Do Strategic Planning Like A Futurist

For any given uncertainty about the future—whether that's risk, opportunity or growth—it's best to think in the short and long-term simultaneously. To do this, the Future Today Institute uses a framework that measures certainty and charts actions, rather than simply marking the passage of time as quarters or years. That's why our timelines aren't actually lines at all—they are cones.

As we think about the future, we build a cone with four distinct categories:

1. Tactics

2. Strategy

3. Vision

4. Systems-Level Evolution

We start by defining the cone's edge using highly probable events for which there is already data or evidence. The amount of time varies for every project, organization and industry. In this example, we've used 12-24 months as a place to start. Because we can identify trends and probable events (both within a company and external to it), the kind of planning that can be done is *tactical* in nature, and the corresponding actions could include things like redesigning products or identifying and targeting a new customer segment.

Tactical decisions must fit into an organization's strategy. At this point in the cone, we are a little less certain of outcomes, because we're looking at the next 24 months to five years. This area should be most familiar to strategy officers and their teams: We're describing traditional strategy and the direction the organization will take. Our actions include defining priorities, setting resource allocation, making any personnel changes needed and the like.

Lots of teams get stuck cycling between strategy and tactics, and that makes their organizations vulnerable to disruption. If you aren't simultaneously articulating your vision and a systems-level evolution, another organization will drag you into their version of the future.

Think exponentially. Act incrementally.

The Future Today Institute's Time Cone for Strategic Planning

The Time Cone represents years and certainty on the axes, and it represents actions and work streams in the interior space. The years are malleable, depending on a project's parameters and scope. At the start of every foresight project, we calibrate the Time Cone to each organization.

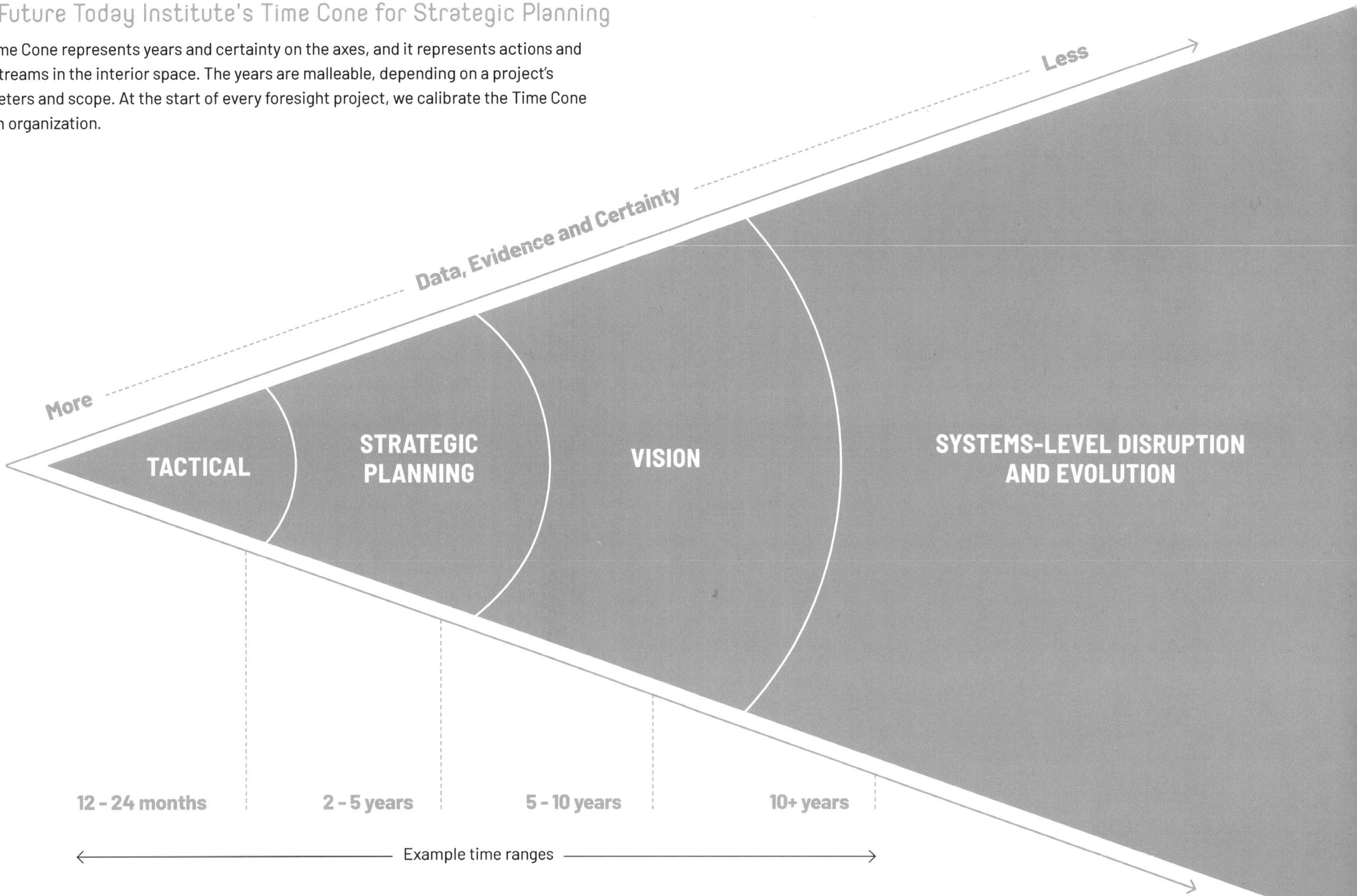

Less

Data, Evidence and Certainty

More

TACTICAL

STRATEGIC PLANNING

VISION

SYSTEMS-LEVEL DISRUPTION AND EVOLUTION

12 – 24 months

2 – 5 years

5 – 10 years

10+ years

←———————— Example time ranges ————————→

21

Disclaimer

The views expressed herein are the authors own and are not representative of the greater organizations in which they have been employed. The names of companies, services and products mentioned in this report are not necessarily intended as endorsements by the Future Today Institute or this report's authors.

The Future Today Institute's 2020 Trends Report relies on data, analysis and modeling from a number of sources, which includes: sources within public and private companies, securities filings, patents, academic research, government agencies, market research firms, conference presentations and papers, and news media stories. Additionally, this report draws from the Future Today Institute's 2020 EMT Trends Report and from earlier editions of the FTI Trend Report. FTI's reports are occasionally updated on the FTI website.

FTI advises hundreds of companies and organizations, some of which are referenced in this report. FTI does not own any equity position in any of the entities listed in this presentation.

Any trademarks or service marks used in this report are the marks of their respective owners and who do not endorse the statements in this report. All rights in marks are reserved by their respective owners. We disclaim any and all warranties, express or implied, with respect to this report.

Using and Sharing The Material In This Report

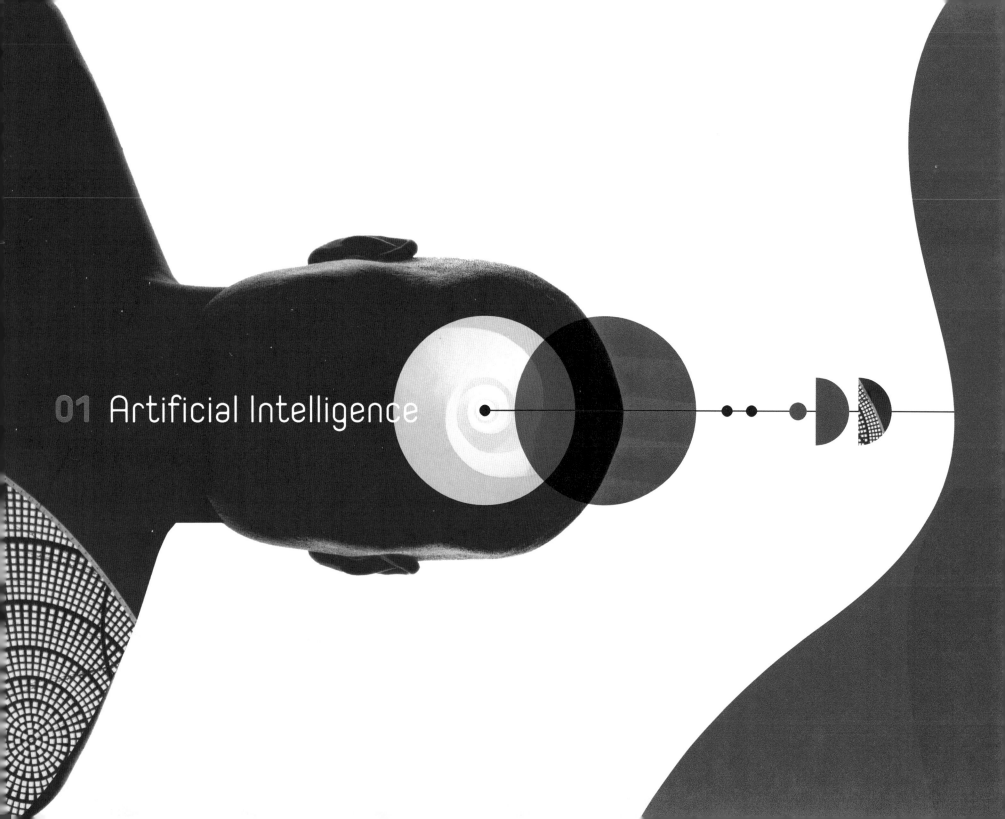

01 Artificial Intelligence

Artificial Intelligence

HIGH DEGREE OF CERTAINTY

	LONGER-TERM IMPACT		IMMEDIATE IMPACT
	INFORMS STRATEGY	ACT NOW	
	REVISIT LATER	KEEP VIGILANT WATCH	

LOW DEGREE OF CERTAINTY

A.I. represents the third era of computing.

KEY INSIGHT

Artificial intelligence (A.I.) represents the third era of computing, one that could usher in a new period of productivity and prosperity for all. It has potential to act as a force multiplier for good, helping to address humanity's most complex challenges: how to mitigate climate change, how to increase the global food supply, how to develop safer infrastructure, how to manage cyberse-curity threats and how to diagnose and eradicate diseases. However, A.I. also carries risks: gender, race and ethnic bias continues to negatively influence the crim-inal justice system; countries differ in their regulatory approaches; it enables the cre-ation and spread of fake news and misinfor-mation; it threatens privacy and security; and it will inevitably displace swaths of the workforce. There is no central agreement on how A.I. should develop during the next several decades. Many facets of artificial intelligence have made our list since we first started publishing this report 13 years ago. Because A.I. itself isn't the trend, we identified different themes within A.I. that you should be following. You will also find the technology intersecting with other trends throughout this report.

WHAT YOU NEED TO KNOW

In its most basic form, artificial intelligence is a system that makes autonomous deci-sions. A.I. is a branch of computer science in which computers are programmed to do things that normally require human intel-ligence. This includes learning, reasoning, problem solving, understanding language and perceiving a situation or environment. A.I. is an extremely large, broad field, which uses its own computer languages and relies on computer networks modeled on our human brains.

WHY IT MATTERS

The global A.I. market should grow 20% an-nually between 2020 and 2024, while global economic growth generated by A.I. could reach $16 trillion by the end of this decade.

Weak and Strong A.I.

There are two kinds of A.I.—weak (or "narrow") and strong (or "general"). Narrow A.I. systems make decisions within very narrow parameters at the same level as a human or better, and we use them all day long without even realizing it. The anti-lock brakes in your car, the spam filter and autocomplete functions in your email and the fraud detection that authenticates you as you make a credit card purchase— these are all examples of artificial narrow intelligence. Artificial general intelligence (AGI) describes systems capable of decision-making outside of narrow specialties. Dolores in *Westworld*, the Samantha operating system in *Her*, and the H.A.L. supercomputer from *2001: A Space Odyssey* are anthropomorphized representations of AGI—but the actual technology doesn't necessarily require humanlike appearances or voices.

There is no single standard that marks the distinction between weak and strong A.I.

This is problematic for researchers covering A.I. developments and for managers who must make decisions about A.I.

In fact, we have already started to see real-world examples of functioning AGI. In 2017 researchers at **DeepMind**, a lab owned by the same parent company as **Google**, announced that A.I. had taught itself how to play chess, shogi (a **Japanese** version of chess) and Go (an abstract strategy board game)—all without any human intervention. The system, named AlphaZero, quickly became the strongest player in history for each game. The team has been publishing important discoveries at an impressively fast pace. Last year, the DeepMind team taught A.I. agents to play complex games, such as the capture the flag "game mode" inside the video game Quake III. They, like humans, had learned skills specific to the game as well as when and how to collaborate with other teammates. The A.I. agents had matched human player ability using reinforcement learning, in which machines learn not unlike we do—by trial and error.

While we haven't seen an anthropomorphic A.I. walk out of DeepMind's lab, we should consider these projects as part of a long transition between the narrow A.I of today and the strong A.I. of tomorrow.

Neural Networks and Deep Neural Networks

A neural network is the part of a system in which information is sent and received, and a program is the set of meticulous instructions that tell a system precisely what to do so that it will accomplish a specific task. How you want the computer to get from start to finish—essentially, a set of rules—is the "algorithm."

A deep neural network is one that has many hidden layers. There's no set number of layers required to make a network "deep." Deep neural networks tend to work better and are more powerful than traditional neural networks (which can be recurrent or feedforward).

Machine Learning and Deep Learning

A.I. pioneer **Arthur Samuel** popularized the idea of machine learning in 1959, explaining how computers could learn without being explicitly programmed. This would mean developing an algorithm that could someday extract patterns from data sets and use those patterns to predict and make real-time decisions automatically. It took many years for reality to catch up with Samuel's idea, but today machine learning is a primary driver of growth in A.I.

Deep learning is a relatively new branch of machine learning. Programmers use special deep learning algorithms alongside a corpus of data—typically many terabytes of text, images, videos, speech and the like. Often, these systems are trained to learn on their own, and they can sort through a variety of unstructured data, whether it's making sense of typed text in documents or audio clips or video. In practical terms, this means that more and more human processes will be automated, including the writing of software, which computers will soon start to do themselves.

27

Artificial Intelligence cont.

Nvidia's A.I. turns your hand-scrawled doodles into photorealistic landscapes.

Companies Building the Future of A.I.

Nine big tech companies—six American, and three Chinese—overwhelmingly drive the future of artificial intelligence. In the U.S., it's the G-MAFIA: **Google**, **Microsoft**, **Amazon**, **Facebook**, **IBM** and **Apple**. In **China** it's the **BAT**: **Baidu**, **Alibaba** and **Tencent**. Those nine companies drive the majority of research, funding, government involvement and consumer-grade applications of A.I. University researchers and labs rely on these companies for data, tools and funding. The Big Nine A.I. companies also wield huge influence over A.I. mergers and acquisitions, funding A.I. startups and supporting the next generation of developers.

Artificial Intelligence and Personal Data

Artificial intelligence requires robust, clean data sets. For example, manufacturers with large data sets can build machine learning models to help them optimize their supply chain. Logistics companies with route maps, real-time traffic information and weather data can use A.I. to make deliveries more efficient.

But a significant amount of our personal data is also driving the growth of A.I. Called "personally identifiable information," or PIIs, these are discrete units of data we shed simply by using our computers, phones and smart speakers. Our personal data is treated differently around the world. The **California Consumer Privacy Act (CCPA)**, which took effect in January of 2020, limits the ways in which companies can use personal data, while the **European Union's General Data Protection Regulation (GDPR)** requires companies to gain consent before collecting and processing someone's personal data.

From Small Bits to Huge Bytes

As smart gadgets become affordable and recognition systems more common in the workplace and public spaces, a significant amount of personal data will be collected – orders of magnitude more than is today. By 2025, it is estimated that 463 exabytes of data will be created every single day – that's equivalent to 77 billion Netflix movie streams. However, more data isn't necessarily better, especially when data saturation doesn't effectively tell a complete story.

For this reason, we believe that companies will eventually unify our PIIs into more comprehensive "personal data records," or PDRs for short. This single unifying ledger would pull together all of our PIIs, i.e. all of the data we create as a result of our digital usage (think internet and mobile phones). But it would also include other sources of information: our school and work histories (diplomas, previous and current employers); our legal records (marriages, divorces, arrests); our financial records (home mortgages, credit scores, loans, taxes); travel information (countries visited, visas); dating history (online apps); health information (electronic health records, genetic screening results, exercise habits); and shopping history (online retailers, in-store coupon use).

Who Will Own Your Data in the Future?

Ideally, you would be the owner of your PDR. It would be fully interoperable between systems, and the big tech companies would simply act as custodians. However, given the lack of enforceable norms, standards and guardrails, we believe that in the future your PDRs would be owned and held by one of the big tech companies.

During his 2020 presidential run, businessman **Andrew Yang** proposed that Congress pass a new law establishing data as a property right for individuals, giving them the right to protect how it is collected and used, and a way for them to share in the economic value generated as a result of their data.

Enabling Future Generations to Inherit Your Data

Your PDR could be heritable—a comprehensive record passed down to and used by your children. This would enable an A.I. system to learn from your family's health data, which could someday aid in precision medicine. It could also help track and untangle a family member's finances after their death. Heritable PDRs could also help families pass down memories of loved ones to further generations.

Imagine being able to set permissions on all of the content you consume—news stories, movies, songs, sporting events, lectures—and then passing down insights to your children or other loved ones. The content we consume shapes our worldviews and actions, and a window into that content could help others more deeply understand you, for better or worse.

THE IMPACT

The long-term impact of A.I. will depend on choices we make in the present. As **ANI (artificial narrow intelligence)** becomes a ubiquitous presence in business, education, research and governing, it is imperative that leaders make informed decisions.

Artificial Intelligence cont.

WATCHLIST FOR SECTION

Algorithmia, Algorithmic Warfare Cross-Functional Team, Alibaba Cloud, Alibaba, Alipay, Allianz, Amazon Polly, Amazon SageMaker Autopilot, Amazon A9 team, Amazon AWS Lambda, Amazon DeepComposer, Amazon Rekognition, Apple, Arria NLG, Automated Insights, Automation Anyware, Autoregressive Quantile Networks for Generative Modeling, AWS, AWS Textract, Baidu Cloud, Baidu, Baidu Text-to-Speech, Blue Prism, Bonseyes, Brazil's eight national AI laboratories, California Consumer Privacy Act (CCPA), Carnegie Mellon University, Central Intelligence Agency, Cerebras Systems, Child Exploitation Image Analytics program, China's Belt and Road Initiative, China's C.E.I.E.C., China's New Generation Artificial Intelligence Development Plan, China's People's Liberation Army, China's state broadcaster CCTV, Citi, CloudSight, Columbia University, Crosscheq, CycleGAN, Defense Advanced Research Projects Agency, DeepMind, Descript, Drift, Electronic Frontier Foundation, Electronic Privacy Information Center, European Union's AI Alliance, European Union's General Data Protection Regulation, Facebook and Carnegie Mellon University's Pluribus Networks, Facebook,

Facebook AI lab, Facebook Soumith Chintala, Federal Bureau of Investigation, Federal Trade Commission, France's AI for Humanity strategy, Future of Life Institute, General Language Understanding Evaluation competition, GenesisAI, Germany's national AI framework, GitHub, Google Cloud, Google Ventures, Google's Bidirectional Encoder Representations from Transformers, Google Brain, Google Cloud AutoML, Google Cloud Natural Language API, Google Coral Project, Google DeepMind team, Google Duplex team, Graphcore, Harvard University, HireVue, Huawei, IBM Project Debater, IBM Research, IBM Watson Text-to-Speech, Immigration and Customs Enforcement, In-Q-Tel, Intel, Intel Capital, International Computer Science Institute, Israel's national A.I. plan, Italy's interdisciplinary A.I. task force, Joint Enterprise Defense Infrastructure (JEDI), Kenya's A.I. taskforce, LaPlaya Insurance, Lyrebird, Mayo Clinic, McDonald's Dynamic Yield, Megvii, MGH and BWH Center for Clinical Data Science, Michigan State University, Microsoft Azure Text-to-Speech API, Microsoft Azure, Microsoft Machine Reading Comprehension dataset, Microsoft's HoloLens, Massachusetts Institute of Technology (MIT), MIT and Harvard's Giant

Language Model Test Room (GLTR), MIT-IBM Watson AI Lab, MIT's Computer Science and Artificial Intelligence Laboratory, Mohamed bin Zayed University of Artificial Intelligence in Abu Dhabi, Molly, Multiple Encounter Dataset, Mythic, Narrative Science, National Institute of Informatics in Tokyo, National Science Foundation, New York University Stern School of Business Professor Arun Sundararajan, New York University, Nike's Celect and Invertex, Nuance AI Marketplace, Nvidia, Nvidia's EGX platform, Nvidia's GauGAN, ObEN, OpenAI, Oracle, Organisation for Economic Co-operation and Development, Palantir, Pan-Canadian Artificial Intelligence Strategy, Princeton, PyTorch, Qualcomm, Quantiacs, Reddit, Resemble AI, Russia's Agency for Strategic Initiatives, Russia's Federal Security Service, Russia's Ministry of Defense, Russia's National AI strategy, Salesforce, SambaNova Systems, Samsung, Samsung AI Center, Samsung Ventures, SAP, Saudi Arabia's national AI strategy, Sensetime, Siemens MindSphere, Singapore's AI national strategy, Skolkovo Institute of Science and Technology, Stanford University, Tamedia, Tencent, Turing Award, Twitter, U.K. Parliament's Select Committee on AI, U.K.'s House of Com-

mons Science and Technology Committee, U.S. Army Futures Command, U.S. Army Research Laboratory, U.S. Department of Energy, U.S. Joint AI Center, U.S. National Artificial Intelligence Research and Development Strategic Plan, U.S. National Institute of Standards and Technology (NIST), U.S. National Security Commission on AI, U.S. National Security Strategy and National Security Commission on AI, U.S. presidential candidate Andrew Yang, U.S. Space Force, Uber, United Arab Emirates's Minister of State for Artificial Intelligence Omar Sultan Al Olama, United Arab Emirates's sweeping AI policy initiatives, University of British Columbia Department of Chemistry, University of California-Berkeley, University of Copenhagen, University of Maryland; University of Montreal, University of Texas at Arlington's algorithmic fact-checking research, Victor Dibia, applied AI researcher at Cloudera Fast Forward Labs, Wave Computing, Wikipedia, Y Combinator.

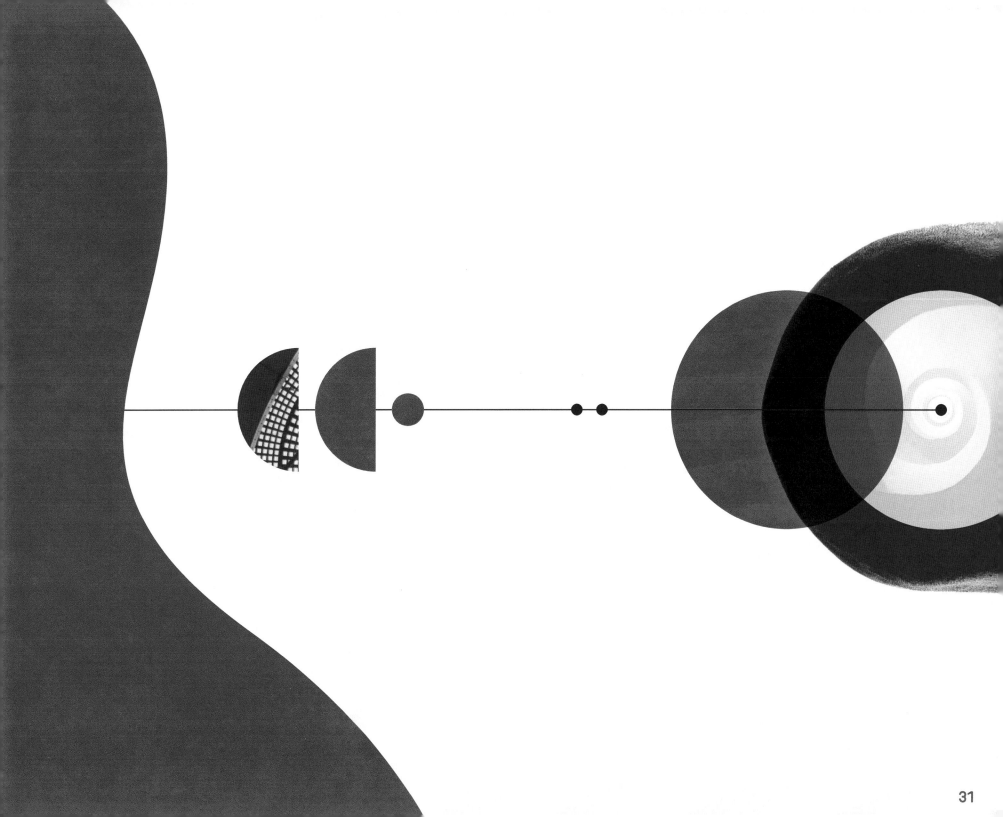

Enterprise

China's CCTV featured digital twin hosts on a popular TV show.

⟳ TRENDS

Using A.I. to Speed the Process of Scientific Discovery

Running experiments with several variables often requires tiny, methodical tweaks to measurements, materials and inputs. Graduate students might spend hundreds of tedious hours making small adjustments again and again until a solution is found—a waste of their cognitive abilities. Increasingly, A.I. systems are being used in research labs to speed the process of scientific discovery. Materials scientists at the **University of British Columbia** used a robot overseen by an A.I. algorithm to rapidly test a new kind of solar cell and log results. Based on what each experiment revealed, an algorithm determined what to change next. A process that might have taken 9–12 months was completed in five days. **Google's DeepMind** developed a way of testing and modeling the complex folding patterns of long chains of amino acids, solving a problem that has vexed scientists for many years. DeepMind's system, AlphaFold, will allow scientists to synthesize new drugs to treat diseases and develop enzymes that might someday break down pollution.

A.I. in the Cloud

Corporate leaders within the A.I. ecosystem have been racing to capture A.I. cloud-share—and to become the most trusted provider of A.I. on remote servers. Enterprise customers are likely to stick with their initial vendor, because the more data that a machine learning system has access to, the better decisions it will learn to make over time. For that reason, the race is on. In the West, the field is led by **Amazon**, **Microsoft** and **Google**, followed by companies including **Apple**, **IBM**, **Salesforce**, **SAP** and **Oracle**. In Asian markets, **Alibaba** and **Baidu** dominate the A.I. cloud, although in January of 2020 telecom equipment and smartphone maker **Huawei** announced a management change to focus on what it calls a "full-stake cloud platform." It's a $250 billion industry and quickly growing. **NYU Stern School of Business** professor **Arun Sundararajan** says it best: "The prize will be to become the operating system of the next era of tech."

A.I. at the Edge (or A.I. *Not* in the Cloud)

Imagine a self-driving car in a busy neighborhood: A car driving 25 miles per hour is moving 36.7 feet per second. For a car to capture an image of a stop sign, process it in the cloud and then make a decision would require a consistently fast connection. But if that image capture and analysis happened on-site, it would likely not only be faster, but safer. For that reason, such companies as **Google** and **Nvidia** are building networks that can make these kinds of local A.I.-driven processing and decision-making on devices, without any interaction of data in the cloud or the Internet—a technique that uses what's known as "edge computing." Processing data directly on devices will be important in the future for health care, automotive and manufacturing applications, because it would potentially be faster, and therefore safer.

Robotic Process Automation

Robotic Process Automation (RPA) enables businesses to automate certain tasks and processes within offices, which allows employees to spend time on higher-value work.

Google's Duplex, which is a bot designed to make routine phone calls to other people, is an example of an RPA. **Amazon** uses RPA to sift through resumes before prioritizing top candidates for review. In banking, **Blue Prism** and **Automation Anywhere** help staff with repetitive work functions. RPA will eventually augment staff and shift their productivity into higher gear. This will allow media and entertainment companies to make better real-time predictive decisions in a host of different areas, from customer service to cost savings.

Digital Twins and Cognitive Twins in the Enterprise

Digital twins are virtual representations of real-world environments, products or assets, used for a host of purposes. Manufacturers use digital twins to manage the performance and effectiveness of machines and plants, while city planners use them to simulate the impact of new developments and roads. The **Singapore** government uses them for urban operations. **Siemens MindSphere** supports digital twins for a number of industries. What's on the horizon: cognitive twins, which not only simulate environments but help design solutions.

Robots with Cognitive Skills

As humans and machines work more closely together, there are opportunities for robots to learn and adapt new skills based on their environments. Machine learning, deep reinforcement learning, computer vision and advancements in simulated environments will soon lead to robots with early-stage cognitive abilities. Applications include environmental cleanups, exploring dangerous terrain and assisting first responders.

Advanced A.I. Chipsets

Today's neural networks have long required an enormous amount of computing power, have taken a very long time to train, and have relied on data centers and computers that consume hundreds of kilowatts of power. That ecosystem is starting to change. Enter a suite of new processors found on a SoC—"system on a chip." Big tech companies like **Huawei**, **Apple**, **Microsoft**, **Facebook**, **Alphabet**, **IBM**, **Nvidia**, **Intel** and **Qualcomm**, as well as startups like **Graphcore**, **Mythic**, **Wave Computing**, **SambaNova Systems** and **Cerebras Systems**, are all working on new systems architecture and SoCs, and some of which come pre-trained. In short, this means that the chips are more readily able to work on A.I. projects and should promise faster and more secure processing. Projects that might otherwise take weeks could instead be accomplished in a matter of hours. Cerebras has built an A.I. chip with 1.2 trillion transistors, 400,000 processor cores, 18 gigabytes of SRAM and interconnects (tiny connection nodes) that can move 100 quadrillion bits per second. (That's an astounding amount of components and power.) **Amazon**'s homegrown A.I. chip, called Inferentia, and **Google**'s Tensor Processing Unit (or TPU) were specifically built for the companies' cloud services.

Market research company **Tractica** estimates that the A.I. chip market will quadruple to $6.7 billion in 2022, from $1.66 billion in 2018. While marketing pre-trained chips to businesses will speed up commercialization and, as a result, will further R&D, the challenge is that developers might need to wrestle with many different frameworks rather than a handful of standard frameworks in the near-future, especially if the various device manufacturers all decide to start creating unique protocols. We do anticipate an eventual consolidation, pitting just a few companies—and their SoCs and languages—against each other.

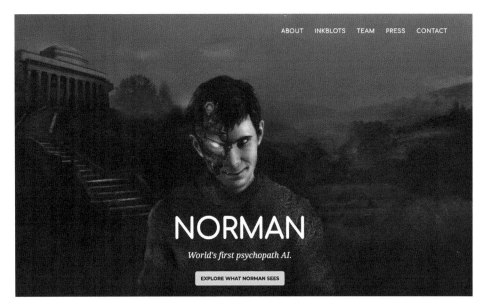

Scientists at MIT trained an A.I. psychopath named "Norman" using only the image captions from a subreddit that's known for disturbing content.

Serverless Computing

Amazon Web Services, **Alibaba Cloud**, **Microsoft's Azure**, **Google Cloud** and **Baidu Cloud** are rolling out new offerings and packages for developers, hoping to make it easier and more affordable for a wide swath of A.I. startups to launch their ideas into the marketplace. **Amazon's AWS Lambda** lets teams run code for virtually any type of application or backend service—without provisioning or managing servers or hands-on administration. **Microsoft's Functions** architecture for **Azure** supports myriad programming languages, scales on demand and only charges for active compute time. This isn't sitting well with some engineers, though, who are worried about losing control.

Proprietary, Homegrown A.I. Languages

Python is a leading language with lots of pre-built libraries and frameworks. Julia, a language developed by **MIT**, is an open-source language that focuses on numerical computing. And of course there's Lisp, created by modern A.I. 's foreparent John McCarthy in 1958. Companies are starting to build and release their own software packages now, as well as unique programming languages for A.I. applications. **Uber** released its own probabilistic programming language, Pyro, which it wrote in Python. It's a move that signals likely fragmentation in the future of the A.I. ecosystem, not unlike our current rivalry of **OSX** vs **Android**, and earlier Mac vs PC camps. Businesses will find it increasingly cost-prohibitive and difficult to switch between A.I. frameworks and languages.

Proliferation of Franken-Algorithms

Algorithms are simply rules that define and automate the treatment of data. They are built using "if this, then that" logic that a computer can understand and process. Here's an easy example: If a website reader's IP address is based in Baltimore, the rules allow that reader to freely access the site; if the IP address is based in Belgium, the rules first show a GDPR screen stating privacy and cookie policies. While a single algorithm might be easily described and deployed as expected, systems of algorithms all working together can sometimes pose problems. Developers don't always know in advance how one algorithm will function alongside other algorithms. Sometimes, several teams of developers are all working independently on different algorithms and data sets and only see their work once it is deployed. This has been the cause of recent stock market glitches and e-commerce website wonkiness. Indeed, it is a challenge for big companies like **Facebook**, which have billions of algorithms working together at any given time.

Companies Manipulating A.I. Systems for Competitive Advantage

Amazon, Google and Facebook have all come under fire in the past few years for manipulating their search systems to prioritize results that are more profitable for their companies. For example, Google has been accused of de-ranking websites and promoting news stories from preferred partners. Late in 2019 researchers found that Amazon had optimized its search algorithm to boost the visibility of Amazon's own brands. Tweaks to search algorithms have a significant impact on what internet users see, whether that is news, products for sale or advertising. The U.S. and E.U. are currently investigating Amazon's simultaneous roles as a search engine, marketplace operator and seller of its own products. Lawmakers are not yet aligned on whether manipulating algorithms for competitive advantage meets the criteria for antitrust activity.

Corporate Biometric Spoofing

Companies might want to think twice before implementing A.I. systems to monitor and authenticate staff. New techniques in machine learning have led to synthetic fingerprints and other automatically-generating bioidentifiers capable of fooling monitoring systems. Researchers at **Michigan State University** and **New York University** built an algorithm that can generate fake biometric credentials, signaling the potential for innovation-related vulnerabilities on our horizon. One such instance might be a malicious system generating millions of fingerprints in a brute force attack to remotely open a door or unlock a laptop.

Bots

The term "bot" has become part of our mainstream vocabulary, and you can expect to hear more about them as America completes its 2020 election cycle. Bots, at the most basic level, are software applications designed to automate a specified task. They can be text or audio-based and can be deployed across various platforms. News bots can help aggregate and automatically alert a user about a specified event, whereas productivity bots are tools companies use to automate and streamline their day-to-day operations. Chatbots are now fully mainstream, and they're deployed by all kinds of organizations, especially in customer service functions. In fact, research from **Survey Monkey** and live chat provider **Drift** revealed that only 38% of consumers actually want to talk with a human when engaging with a brand.

The next big advancement in bots won't be technical in nature—it will be regulatory. During 2018's campaign cycles, we saw a resurgence of botnets, which are networks of computers designed to send out misleading content. That, coupled with concerns that bots are increasingly leading to widespread deception, led to a new law in **California** that requires bots to disclose that they are not humans in their interactions with people. The law went into effect on July 1, 2019 and requires the disclosure to be "clear, conspicuous, and reasonably designed to inform persons with whom the bot communicates or interacts that it is a bot." The success of this new regulation could become the basis for other state and national laws, especially if conversational bots like **Google's Duplex** reach critical mass within the marketplace.

Business Ecosystem

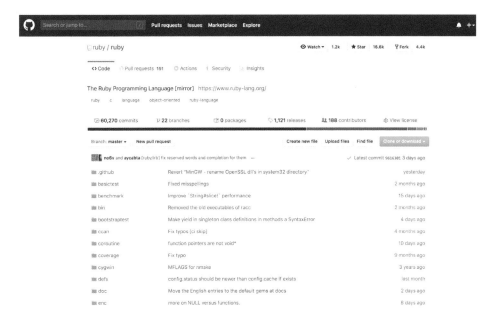

Github is a popular platform allowing anyone to host and review code.

Global Rush to Fund A.I.

There is a well-reported shortage of A.I. talent, and every sector is hoping to integrate A.I. into their core business functions. As a result, there is a global race to fund A.I. research and to acquire startups. In 2019, investors put $136.5 billion into 10,777 deals worldwide. Seed or pre-seed rounds made up half of those deals, while 21% were Series A and 12% were Series B. U.S. tech giants like **Apple**, **Google** and **Microsoft** are acquiring A.I. companies at a rapid clip, and non-tech companies are gobbling A.I. startups too: **McDonald's** acquired personalization platform **Dynamic Yield**, while **Nike** acquired inventory management company **Celect** and guided shopping experience platform **Invertex**. The **U.S. Department of Energy** is reportedly planning to ask **Congress** for $3 - $4 billion over the next 10 years to build next-generation exascale computers that use A.I. to speed scientific discoveries. In July of 2019, **Japanese** conglomerate **Softbank** launched Vision Fund 2, a $108 billion fund designated specifically for A.I. startups.

Algorithm Marketplaces

In the 2010s, big tech companies, startups and communities of developers used algorithm marketplaces to share and sell their work. In 2018, **Microsoft** paid $7.5 billion to buy **GitHub**, a popular development platform allowing anyone to host and review code, to collaborate with other developers and to build all kinds of projects. **Amazon's AWS** hosts its own marketplace, offering models and algorithms for computer vision, speech recognition, and text—and its base of sellers includes **Intel**, **CloudSight** and many others. (Think of AWS Marketplace as an Amazon for algorithms and models.) There are marketplaces for generalists, like **GenesisAI** and **Algorithmia**, where developers can upload their work and receive payment when others pay to access it. Now there are specialized marketplaces for specific use cases: **Nuance AI Marketplace** offers A.I. developers a single API to connect their algorithms to radiologists at 6,500 healthcare facilities. **Quantiacs** allows developers to build algorithmic trading systems, and it matches their algorithms up with capital from institutional investors. **Bonseyes** is a **European**-specific marketplace to buy and sell A.I. tools.

Marketplace Consolidation

As much as the A.I. ecosystem is booming, a rush of acquisitions means consolidation, too. Big companies now pick up startups long before they have time to mature—the average age at acquisition is three years old. Just nine big companies dominate the A.I. landscape: **Google**, **Amazon**, **Microsoft**, **IBM**, **Facebook** and **Apple** in the **U.S.** and Chinese behemoths **Baidu**, **Alibaba** and **Tencent**—with significant fortification and support from the **Chinese** government. On the investment side, **Qualcomm**, **Tencent**, **Intel Capital**, **Google Ventures**, **Nvidia**, **Salesforce**, **Samsung Ventures**, **Alibaba**, **Apple**, **Baidu**, **Citi** and **In-Q-Tel** fund much of the growth. When it comes to the future of A.I., we should ask whether consolidation makes sense for the greater good, and whether competition—and therefore access—will eventually be hindered as we've seen in other fields such as telecommunications and cable.

Fragmentation

The A.I. ecosystem spans hundreds of companies. They are building the network infrastructure, the custom chipsets, the consumer applications, the backend communications systems, the low-power radios in our smart home gadgets...we could go on. Meanwhile, a large number of policy groups, advocacy organizations and governments are all developing guidelines, norms and standards and policy frameworks hoping to guide the future development of A.I. As a result, the ecosystem is fragmented in two ways: infrastructure standards and governance.

Liability Insurance for A.I.

Who's to blame when machines behave badly? Our current legal systems were built to regulate human behavior, not the actions of unsupervised machines. As businesses rush to build and implement A.I. products and processes, they must plan ahead for emerging risks. For example, what happens if machine learning makes a company vulnerable to attackers injecting fake training data into a system? What if a healthcare company's A.I. misinterprets data and neglects to identify cancer among certain patients? These are the kinds of problems that could open a company up to lawsuits. **LaPlaya Insurance** and **Allianz** are now studying new liability insurance models that may help to address these issues.

Ambient Surveillance

What happens behind closed doors may not be secret for long, and executives should beware of new ambient surveillance methods. **MIT** computer vision scientists discovered how to use computer vision to track data from what they call "accidental cameras." Windows, mirrors, corners, houseplants and other common objects can be used, along with A.I., to track subtle changes in light, shadow and vibrations. The result? We all may soon have x-ray vision capabilities—which may not be great news for companies working on sensitive projects. Those working in information security and risk management should pay especially close attention to advancements in computer vision.

Processes, Systems and Computational Neuroscience

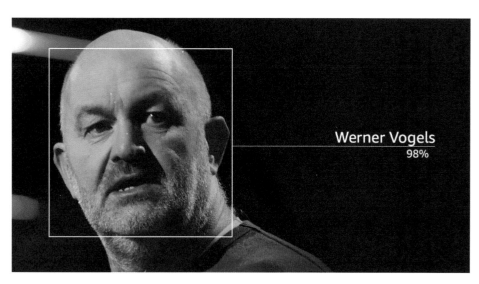

Amazon's Rekognition identifies well-known people to help you "catalogue footage and photos for marketing, advertising and media industry use cases."

Creating 3D Models from Flat 2D Images

Last year, Nvidia trained a neural network to autonomously generate fully-textured 3D models based on a single photo. Researchers trained a neural network using a large corpus of 3D models, images that had been transformed into 3D models, and 2D images showing an object from various angles. The result: a new system that can render 3D models without any need for human intervention. Practical applications include robots that can autonomously generate realistic models of their environments using only 2D images.

Neuro-Symbolic A.I. Algorithms and Systems

The development of A.I. has been on two conceptual tracks since the 1950s: symbolic (machines use a base of knowledge and rules that represent concepts) and non-symbolic (machines use raw data to create their own patterns and representations of concepts). Classic A.I. is the former, because it more closely represents how we understand human thought—and the original intent was to teach machines to think like us. Researchers are working on new ways to combine both learning and logic using neural networks, which would understand data through symbols rather than always relying on human programmers to sort, tag and catalogue data for them. Symbolic algorithms will aid the process, which should eventually lead to robust systems that don't always require a human for training.

Real-Time Machine Learning

One big challenge in A.I. is building machines that can proactively collect and interpret data, spot patterns and incorporate context, and ultimately learn in real time. New research into real-time machine learning (RTML) shows that it's possible to use a continual flow of transactional data and adjust models in real-time. This signals a big change in how data moves, and in how we retrieve information. The **National Science Foundation** launched a $10 million grant program to catalyze research in this area, though all of the big tech companies are working closely to advance RTML too.

Natural Language Understanding (NLU)

Last year, **Amazon** released updates to its Transcribe Medical system, a natural language understanding (NLU) system that recognizes speech used by doctors and medical professionals in real time—no small achievement. Getting machines to understand exactly what or who someone is referring to has been a challenge for conversational A.I. systems like **Siri** and **Alexa**. At best, the systems are trained to reference the last pronoun spoken. If a consumer asks "What time is *The Lion King* playing at Cinemark Theater?" and follows with "parking near there," the system infers that "there" means "Cinemark Theater." In technical terms, this process is called "slot carryover," and it uses syntactic context to understand what our pronouns mean. The process works, unless we speak in complex sentences with many different pronouns. The fact is that in real conversation, most of us are messy talkers. We start and stop sentences without warning, we misuse words, and sometimes we rely on our tone to convey something we don't want to say in

actual words. We tend to speak in unstructured text. One of the things that makes reference resolution especially complicated for a large A.I. system like Alexa is that different Alexa services use different names—or *slots*—for the same data. A movie-finding service, for instance, might tag location data with the slot name Theater_Location, while a restaurant-finding service might use the slot name Landmark_Address. Over the course of a conversation, Alexa has to determine which slots used by one service should inherit data from which slots used by another.

NLU allows researchers to quantify and learn from all of that text by extracting concepts, mapping relationships and analyzing emotion, and they made some impressive advancements in the past year. The **General Language Understanding Evaluation competition** (or GLUE) is seen as a high-water mark in how well an A.I. system understands human language. **China's Baidu** unseated **Google** and **Microsoft** in the most recent competition and became the first to develop techniques for understanding not only English, but Chinese as well.

Machine Reading Comprehension (MRC)

For A.I. researchers, machine reading comprehension (MRC) has been a challenging goal, but an important one. MRC makes it possible for systems to read, infer meaning and immediately deliver answers while sifting through enormous data sets. Last year, China's **Alibaba** outperformed humans when tested by the **Microsoft Machine Reading Comprehension dataset** (or MS MARCO for short), which assessed its ability to use natural language to answer real questions posed by humans. Alibaba's system delivered answers to search queries posted by people to **Microsoft's Bing**, like "how many carbs are in an English muffin?" and "how do you grow hops?"

One practical application of MRC on the consumer side: When you perform a search query, wouldn't you rather have a system offer you a precise answer than just a list of URLs where you can go to hunt down more specifics—even showing you where, on the page, that information comes from? If you are an airline mechanic and you're trying to troubleshoot a tricky engine problem without further delaying a flight, it would

be easier if you had a computer read all of the technical documentation for you and suggest likely fixes. Or, better yet, let the machines figure out what's wrong on their own, by making all technical manuals and documentation available to them for reading and analysis. That's the promise of MRC, which represents a necessary step in realizing artificial general intelligence, and in the near-term could potentially turn everything from technical manuals to historical maps to our medical records into easily searchable repositories of information.

Natural Language Generation (NLG)

With the growing popularity of digital assistants, consumers want the ability to have natural conversations with machines. But training A.I. systems require a tremendous amount of data. Natural language generation (NLG) systems automatically detect, parse, visualize and then narrate key data. **Google's Cloud Natural Language API**, the **Azure Text-to-Speech API**, **IBM Watson Text-to-Speech**, **Amazon Polly** and **Baidu's Text-to-Speech** system are all advancing the field of NLG. Companies like **Arria NLG**, **Narrative Science** and **Automated Insights** have products that help non-data science people make better sense of what's happening within their organizations. One possibility for NLG: developing a system that can use plain language to explain itself, and the decisions it makes, to others.

Real-Time Context in Machine Learning

The world is awash with information, misinformation and superficial thinking. Last year, **IBM** unveiled **Project Debater**, an A.I. system capable of incorporating context in real-time learning systems and debating humans on complex topics. Designed to help people practice their reasoning, develop well-informed arguments and reach reliable conclusions, Project Debater shows how machine learning systems can use an array of source material alongside real-time data to form arguments.

General Reinforcement Learning Algorithms

Researchers are developing single algorithms that can learn multiple tasks. **DeepMind**, the team behind **AlphaGo**, which learned how to play Go with the skill level of a human grandmaster, has developed an innovative new algorithm: **AlphaZero**. It is capable of achieving superhuman performance not only in Go, but in other games as well, including chess and shogi (Japanese chess). This one algorithm starts with no knowledge except for the rules of the game and eventually develops its own strategies to beat other players. In January of 2020, DeepMind published new research showing how reinforcement learning techniques could be used to improve our understanding of mental health and motivation.

Deep Learning Scales

In the 1980s, **Geoffrey Hinton** and a team of researchers at **Carnegie Mellon University** hypothesized a back propagation-based training method that could someday lead to an unsupervised A.I. network. It took a few decades to build and train the massive data sets, recognition algorithms and powerful computer systems that could make good on that idea. Last year, **Facebook's Yann LeCun**, the **University of Montreal's Yoshua Bengio** and Hinton (now at **Google**) won the Turing Award for their research in deep learning, and this subfield of A.I. is finally taking off in earnest. Programmers use special deep learning algorithms alongside a corpus of data—typically many terabytes of text, images, videos, speech and the like—and the system is trained to learn on its own. Though conceptually deep learning isn't new, what's changed recently is the amount of compute and the volume of data that's become available. In practical terms, this means that more and more human processes will be automated, including the writing of software, which computers will soon start to do themselves. Deep learning (DL) has been limited by the processing power of computer networks, however new chipsets and faster processors will help DNNs perform at superhuman speeds. (See trend #7: Advanced AI chipsets.)

Faster and More Powerful Open Source Frameworks

Research lab **OpenAI** develops and deploys open source A.I. language systems, while **Google** and **Facebook**'s open source frameworks are used widely. The open source **PyTorch**, created by **Soumith Chintala** at **Facebook**, is among the most popular machine learning frameworks used in the world. In 2018, Google open-sourced its technique for training general purpose language representation models using the enormous amount of unannotated text on the web (known as pre-training). Named **Bidirectional Encoder Representations from Transformers** (or BERT), it is a question answering system that can be trained in about 30 minutes. Hardware upgrades and faster chips should help make open source frameworks even faster—and popular—in the years to come.

Reinforcement Learning and Hierarchical RL

Reinforcement learning (RL) is a powerful tool for sorting out decision-making problems, and it's being used to train A.I. systems to achieve superhuman capabilities. Inside of a computer simulation, a system tries, fails, learns, experiments and then tries again, in rapid succession, altering its future attempts each time. It's because of RL that **AlphaGo**, a computer developed by **DeepMind** (part of **Alphabet**), learned how to beat the greatest Go players in the world. One problem with RL: agents have difficulty when they don't have enough supervision, or when their objective is to run scenarios for a very long time horizon. In 2020 and beyond, researchers will try to solve those problems using **hierarchical reinforcement learning**, which discovers high-level actions and methodically works through learning challenges to master new tasks at speeds we humans can't imagine. This is important for non-techies, too: RL will improve the "intelligence" in our A.I. systems, helping cars learn to drive in unusual conditions and helping military drones perform complicated maneuvers that have never been attempted before in the physical world.

Continuous Learning

At the moment, deep learning techniques have helped systems learn to solve complex tasks in a way that more closely matches what humans can do—but those tasks are still specific, such as beating a human at a game. And they require a rigid sequence: gather data, determine the goal, deploy an algorithm. This process requires humans and can be time-consuming, especially during early phases when supervised training is required. Continuous learning

(CL) is more about autonomous and incremental skill building and development, and researchers will continue to push the limits of what's possible in this field.

Multitask Learning

In the past year, researchers at **Carnegie Mellon University** and **Facebook's AI lab** released a superhuman A.I. for multiplayer poker called **Pluribus**, and by the end of 10,000 hands against 12 professional players, it got very good at bluffing. It marked a significant milestone in A.I. research. Winning at games like checkers and chess entails computational challenges. In poker, there is an information challenge, since what's needed to win is hidden from other players. Poker also pits multiple players against each other and achieving victory is more complex than capturing game pieces. Pluribus learned to do several things at once and built its own strategy to win.

Generative Adversarial Networks (GANs)

Facebook AI research director **Yann LeCun** has called generative adversarial networks (GANs) the most interesting idea of the

decade—and in the past few years, there have been tremendous advancements in GANs. Think of a GAN as the Turing test but without any humans involved. GANs are unsupervised deep learning systems comprised of two competing neural networks trained on the same data—such as images of people. For example, the first A.I. creates photos of a woman that seem realistic, while the second A.I. compares the generated photos with photos of real women. Based on the judgment of the second A.I., the first one goes back and makes tweaks to its process. This happens again and again, until the first A.I. is automatically generating all kinds of images of a woman that look entirely realistic. Last year alone saw a number of interesting experiments involving GANs. Researchers from **Nvidia**, the **MGH and BWH Center for Clinical Data Science** and the **Mayo Clinic** collaborated on a GAN that generates synthetic MRIs showing cancerous tumors. Researchers at the **Skolkovo Institute of Science and Technology** and the **Samsung AI Center** made living deepfakes—the Mona Lisa moved her head and Rasputin sang "Halo" by Beyonce. (Naturally, it's this same GAN technology that's behind deepfakes in general.)

New Generative Modeling Techniques

Autoregressive Implicit Quantile Networks (or AIQN for short) sound complicated, but it's an innovative idea to help improve algorithms and make them more stable. The implication: This could quicken the pace of advancements in A.I.—and that could mean faster opportunities and innovations within the whole ecosystem.

Probabilistic Programming Languages

Probabilistic programming languages alleviate some of the strain and tedium of developing probability models. These newer languages allow developers to build, reuse and share their model libraries, while still accommodating incomplete information.

Machine Image Completion

If a computer system has access to enough images—millions and millions, say—it can patch and fill in holes in pictures. This capability has practical applications for professional photographers as well as everyone who wants to take a better selfie.

Processes, Systems and Computational Neuroscience cont.

Researcher Victor Dibia trained a DCGAN model (deep convolutional generative adversarial network) to generate African Masks.

Soon, if the foreground of a mountain is out of focus, or if your skin has an unsightly blemish, another version can be swapped in to generate the perfect picture. But what are the next-order scenarios and implications? How will we draw the line between reality and enhancement? How much image completion should be allowed without tacking on a warning label or disclosure? Online daters, journalists and marketers should be asking these questions. But so should policymakers. Image completion is also a useful tool for law enforcement and military intelligence officers—computers can now assist them in identifying who or what is in the frame. Given the bias we've already seen across machine learning algorithms and data sets, image completion could become part of a future debate about privacy and our devices.

Hybrid Human–Computer Vision Analysis

A.I. isn't yet capable of fully functioning without human assistance. Hybrid intelligence systems combine humans and A.I. systems to achieve greater accuracy. New research from the **U.S. Army Research Laboratory** shows a system that uses a brain-computer interface armed with computer vision technology that allows a person to rapidly see and sort images within their line of sight. **CloudSight**, a **Los Angeles**-based technology company specializing in image captioning, is working on a hybrid crowdsourced computer vision system. **Microsoft** researchers have proposed hybrid human-in-the-loop and machine learning methods (codenamed Pandora) that facilitate the process of describing and explaining failures in machine learning systems.

Predictive Machine Vision

In 2019, the **DeepMind** team developed a generative adversarial network that generates videos from images. For example: Imagine a photo of a person holding a basketball. Based on their posture, face and other data within the picture, the GAN figures out what likely happened next and generates a video clip of the action. Earlier, researchers at **MIT's Computer Science and Artificial Intelligence Laboratory** (CSAIL) trained computers to not only recognize what's in a video, but to predict what humans will do next using YouTube videos and TV shows such as "The Office" and "Desperate Housewives." CSAIL's system predicts whether two people are likely to

hug, kiss, shake hands or slap a high five. This research will someday enable robots to more easily navigate human environments—and to interact with us humans by taking cues from our own body language. It could also be used in retail environments, while we're operating machinery, or while we're in classrooms learning.

Automated Machine Learning (AutoML)

Some organizations want to move away from traditional machine learning methods, which are time-consuming and difficult and require data scientists, specialists in A.I. fields and engineers. Automated machine learning, or AutoML, is a new approach: A process in which raw data and models are matched together to reveal the most relevant information. **Google**, **Amazon** and **Microsoft** now offer a host of AutoML products and services.

Customized Machine Learning

Soon, individual users will upload their own data to customize existing A.I. models. For example, tools like **Google's Cloud AutoML** and **Amazon SageMaker Autopilot** allow

organizations to train custom machine learning models without highly-trained staff.

Graph Neural Networks

Predicting the way something will smell is incredibly complex. That's because we perceive scents using the millions of sensory neurons in our brains—and because scents are multi-faceted. For example, how would you describe the smell of an orange? Sweet? Bright? Grassy? Each descriptor is unique. Classifying smell is tricky because it requires a multi-label system. Researchers at **Google** are building graph neural networks—a particular type of deep neural network that operates on graphs as inputs—to predict odors at a molecular level.

Intelligent Optical Character Recognition

An ongoing challenge is getting machines to recognize the various ways we express ourselves in writing. Optical character recognition (OCR) works in fixed, recognizable formats like highway signs and the text from a book. But often, OCR isn't smart enough to recognize different fonts, unique notations or spreadsheets with fields specific only to

one company. Researchers are training A.I. systems to recognize patterns, even if they show up in unusual places. For example, **AWS's Textract** system now recognizes both text and context.

Content and Creativity

Amazon's DeepComposer system composes music "automagically."

A.I. for the Creative Process

Generative adversarial networks (GANs) are capable of far more than generating deepfake videos. Researchers are partnering with artists and musicians to generate entirely new forms of creative expression. From synthesizing African tribal masks to building fantastical, fictional galaxies, A.I. is being used to explore new ideas. Last year, **Nvidia** launched **GauGAN** (named after post-Impressionist painter **Paul Gauguin**), a generative adversarial A.I. system that lets users create lifelike landscape images that never existed. The **National Institute of Informatics in Tokyo** built an A.I. lyricist, while **Amazon** released its **DeepComposer** system, which composes music "automagically." These A.I.s aren't intended to replace artists, but rather to enhance their creative process.

Generative Algorithms for Content Production

For some time, we've been training computers to watch videos and predict corresponding sounds in our physical world. For example, what sound is generated when a wooden drumstick taps a couch? A pile of leaves? A glass windowpane? The focus of this research, underway at **MIT's Computer Science and Artificial Intelligence Laboratory** (CSAIL), is to help systems understand how objects interact with each other in the physical realm. Numerous projects are now underway to make it easier to automatically generate voices, videos and even storylines.

Generating Virtual Environments from Short Videos

Chip designer **Nvidia** is teaching A.I. to build realistic 3D environments from short video clips. The method builds on previous research on generative adversarial networks (GANs). Nvidia's system generated graphics taken from open-source data sets used by the autonomous driving field. Using short clips segmented into various categories (buildings, sky, vehicles, signs, trees, people) the GAN was trained to generate new, different versions of these objects. Future applications of automatically-generated virtual environments are vast: think training environments for logistics (warehouses, factories, shipping centers), urban planning simulations, even testing customer flow scenarios within amusement parks and shopping centers.

Automated Versioning

Journalists at **Switzerland**-based **Tamedia** experimented with generative techniques during their country's 2018 election. A decision-tree algorithm Tamedia named "Tobi" generated automated articles detailing vote results for each of the municipalities covered by the private media group's 30 newspapers, and it produced content simultaneously in multiple languages. In total, Tobi generated 39,996 different versions of election stories averaging 250 words in length and published to Tamedia's online platforms. Each story carried a special byline alerting readers that the story had been written by an algorithm. With more experiments underway, we expect to see news and entertainment media companies developing multiple versions of the same content to reach wider audiences or to produce massive amounts of content at scale.

Automatic Voice Cloning and Dubbing

Anyone who's ever recorded a podcast is familiar with editing challenges, such as guests talking over each other, random sirens or outdoor noise suddenly blaring in the background, or moments when a speaker sneezes or coughs. It can interrupt momentum or stop a conversation cold. But what if you could edit a spoken conversation the way you edit a word document? That's the promise of A.I. Companies like **Lyrebird**, **Resemble AI** and **Descript**, which make it possible to clone voices—which means that soon you might see Keanu Reeves in a movie and also hear him, in his own voice, speaking in Italian. There's a dark side to this technology, however. Last year, hackers used voice cloning tools to trick an employee into thinking he was speaking on the phone to his CEO—he then transferred $243,000 to a scammer's bank account.

Spotting Machine-Written Text

In the past year, researchers showed how A.I. could be used to compose text so good that humans couldn't tell it was machine written. The team at **OpenAI** demonstrated the many reasons why this was problematic, from mass-generating salacious social media posts and fake reviews to forging documents by world leaders. It turns out that A.I. can also be used to detect when text was machine generated, even if we humans can't spot the fake. That's because

an essay written by A.I. tends to rely on statistical patterns in text and doesn't have much linguistic variation. Researchers at the **MIT-IBM Watson AI Lab** and at **Harvard University** developed the Giant Language Model Test Room (GLTR), which looks for words that are likely to appear in a particular order. This is good news for those concerned about the spread of automated misinformation campaigns.

Algorithmic Fact Checking

Misleading and outright false information has polluted the internet and our social media channels, and everyday consumers struggle to cope. While we've seen tremendous global efforts to fact-check various governmental officials, algorithms designed to propagate lies can work faster than human fact-checkers. Researchers at the **University of Texas at Arlington** and **Google** have been working on automated techniques using frame semantics. A frame is a schematic that describes a particular kind of event, situation, object or relation along with its participants. Researchers extended a system called **FrameNet** to include new frames built specifically for automated fact checking.

Datamining Crowds

Well after citizens in the **U.K.** voted for **Brexit**, they continued to Google "What is the EU" and "What is Brexit." In the nearly four years after the initial vote, this passive data has continued to tell an interesting story. This is just one example of what we're now able to learn from the crowd by monitoring various networks. Our smartphone ownership has reached critical mass, and so has our use of various networks. Our data not only follows us around, it's often available for anyone to search, collect and analyze. We anticipate that more news organizations—as well as marketers, activists and other groups—will start harnessing this data in creative ways. That's because our thinking results in behavior (like searching for "what is the EU?"), and our behavior results in data—and that data can be used to learn something about us.

Deep Linking

Deep mobile linking has been around since the beginning of smartphones, and it makes it easier to find and share data across all of the apps in your phone. Deep links are now being used in ways that obscure information from consumers. In 2019, **Yelp** restaurant

listings showed accurate direct contact information within its mobile app, but when a customer clicked through they were deep-linked through to order on the **Grubhub** app. Even if customers bypassed the app and wanted to dial the number, the app instead routed them through a Grubhub-owned number, which allowed Grubhub to categorize the interaction as a "marketing call" and to charge restaurants a hefty commission fee. There are three kinds of deep links: traditional, deferred and contextual. Traditional deep links reroute you from one app or site to another: If you click on a **Baltimore Sun** link someone posts on **Twitter**, theoretically it should automatically open in the Baltimore Sun app, as long as you have it installed. Deferred deep links either link straight to content if the app is installed, or to an app store for you to download the app first. Contextual deep links offer much more robust information—they take you from site to app, app to site, site to site or app to app, and they can also include personalized information. This is what happened with the Yelp and Grubhub example, though the process was purposely hidden from consumers.

Consumer Products and Services

Drug companies ramped up research to determine if A.I. could be used at every phase of drug development.

Ambient Computing Expands

Also known as "zero-UIs," our modern interfaces are becoming more and more like ambient music—able to do more for us with fewer direct actions, yet still able to captivate our attention. Rather than relying on a single input screen, or even a series of screens, we'll instead interact with computers with less friction. In our modern age of information, the average adult now makes more than 20,000 decisions a day—some big, such as whether or not to invest in the stock market, and some small, such as whether to glance at your mobile phone when you see the screen light up. Ambient computing systems promise to prioritize those decisions, delegate them on our behalf, and even to autonomously answer for us, depending on the circumstance. Much of this invisible decision-making will happen without your direct supervision or input. What makes ambient design so tantalizing is that it should require us to make fewer and fewer decisions in the near-future. Think of it as a sort of autocomplete for intention.

Ubiquitous Digital Assistants

Digital assistants (DAs)—like Siri, Alexa, and their Chinese counterpart Tiān Māo from Alibaba—use semantic and natural language processing, along with our data, in order to anticipate what we want or need to do next, sometimes before we even know to ask. Alibaba's highly advanced DA can not only interact with real humans, but also deftly handle interruptions and open-ended answers. Similar to Google's Duplex, Alibaba's DA can make calls on your behalf, but it also understands intent. So if you're trying to schedule an appointment and you mention you're usually commuting in the morning, the system understands that you aren't available even though you never explicitly said that. In 2017, FTI's model projected that nearly half of Americans would own and use a digital assistant by the year 2020, and our model continues to track in that direction. Amazon and Google dominate the smart speaker market, but digital assistants can be found in many places. There are now thousands of applications and gadgets that track and respond to DAs. News organizations, entertainment companies, marketers, credit card companies, banks, local government agencies (police, highway administration), political campaigns and many others can harness DAs to both surface and deliver critical information.

A.I. for Drug Development

In 2018 and 2019, drug companies ramped up research to determine if A.I. could be used at every phase of drug development, from hypotheses, picking better compounds and identifying better drug targets to designing more successful clinical trials and tracking real-world outcomes. Microsoft and Novartis announced a collaboration for A.I.-driven drug discovery, Pfizer intends to use IBM's Watson, and Alphabet's DeepMind proved last year how a tech company could beat a roomful of biologists in predicting the shape of a protein based on its genetic code. Nearly every major pharmaceutical company inked deals with A.I. drug discovery startups, too, including Johnson & Johnson, Novartis, Merck, AstraZeneca and GlaxoSmithKline. And investors poured $2.4 billion into hundreds of such startups between 2013 and 2019, according to data by **PitchBook**. Much of the potential in A.I. stems from deep learning's ability to sort through huge volumes of information and to learn and extrapolate from that information. The upshot: A.I. can think faster than humans—sorting data in months versus years—and see patterns that we may not. Still, drug discovery is tricky, because the algorithms rely on drug targets that must be published in research journals and have well-characterized metabolic mechanisms. Most data about potential compounds, too, isn't always readily available, and when it is, it isn't always complete or reliable. Filling in the gaps and cleaning up that data takes time and money. It also requires data sharing—and most drug data is proprietary and locked up by big drug makers. Despite the frenzy in the industry about the technology's potential, no A.I.-driven drugs have been created yet. But the industry may be inching closer: In September of 2019, **Deep Genomics** in **Canada** successfully used A.I. to decipher more precisely how one gene mutation fails to create a protein, one of hundreds of genes that leads to Wilson's disease, a life-threatening genetic disorder in which the body's ability to properly distribute copper is impaired. Deep Genomics used another set of algorithms to analyze billions of molecules and ultimately identify 12 drug candidates, which appeared to work in both cell models and mice. The company will take one of them, known as DG12P1, to human clinical trials in 2021. The process took 18 months, instead of the traditional 3 to 6 years. If A.I. works for drug development, it will dramatically alter the field's needed skills in the future: drug developers must not only know biology but computer science and statistics, too. Then there's the **Food and Drug Administration** approval process. Using algorithms for drug development brings up a host of ethical questions. Will bias invade drug discovery much like it has other arenas of A.I., thereby marginalizing certain patients or diseases? Do algorithms need their own clinical trials? Could A.I. be used to take shortcuts and undermine the value of the science being done inside the laboratory? Advocates say A.I. will make drug development and clinical trials more efficient, thereby cutting drug prices and paving the way for more personalized medicine.

A.I. for Interviews

Recognition systems can now be deployed to watch you being interviewed, to gauge your enthusiasm, tenacity and poise. Algorithms analyze hundreds of details, such as the tone of your voice, your facial expressions and your mannerisms to try and predict how you'll fit in to the culture of a community. Startups such as **HireVue** use A.I. systems to help companies decide which candidates to hire. But this kind of recognition technology has practical applications well beyond job interviews: It can detect when someone is likely to make a purchase—or attempt to shoplift—in a store, whether someone is lying, and whether someone is receptive to new suggestions and ideas. Unlike security cameras, which tend to have a light indicating they're recording, algorithms work invisibly, which means that this is an area that could face regulatory scrutiny. Consumer advocacy organization **EPIC** filed a complaint with the **Federal Trade Commission** asking the FTC to investigate **HireVue**, alleging its tools produce results that are "biased, unprovable, and not replicable" through algorithmic models.

Consumer-Grade A.I. Applications

We're now seeing a shift from highly technical A.I. applications that are used by professional researchers to more lightweight, user-friendly apps intended for tech-savvy consumers. New automated machine learning platforms make it possible for non-experts to build and deploy predictive models. Many hope that in the near future, we'll use various A.I. applications as part of our everyday work, just as we do **Microsoft Office** or **Google Docs** today.

Digital Twins Mean Never Having to Call Customer Service Again

NEAR-FUTURE OPTIMISTIC SCENARIO

Imagine the last time you were on the phone with your health insurance trying to settle a claim. What about the last time you tried to dispute a charge with your credit card company? Chances are at least part of your interaction involved a bot. What if you had your own bot to negotiate on your behalf for lower premiums and better rates? This scenario may arrive sooner than you think. Multiple startups are developing customer-advocacy bots to interact with corporate bots in a number of industries.

Humans Failing the Human Test

NEAR-FUTURE OPTIMISTIC SCENARIO

Have you noticed that CAPTCHA tests have become increasingly hard to solve? That's because bots are getting better at cracking those frustratingly difficult, warped word puzzles. According to research from Google, computers could solve the hardest distorted text CAPTCHAs with 99% accuracy, while humans could only solve with a 33% accuracy. This has led to increasingly difficult CAPTCHA tests that have significant accessibility issues for individuals who are blind, deaf or have cognitive impairments. In the future, CAPTCHAs will evolve into more sophisticated tests that only humans can pass. These tests need to be easy enough for any human to complete without compromising privacy or personally identifiable information such as a DNA sample or a fingerprint. With more and more sophisticated sensors being incorporated into our digital devices, what if CAPTCHAs evolve to be breathalyzers, body heat sensors or heartbeat monitors on your computer screen?

Geopolitics, Geoeconomics and Warfare

Google employees protested the company's A.I. work on a U.S. military project.

The New Mil-Tech Industrial Complex

In the past few years, some of the biggest A.I. companies in the U.S. started partnering with the military to advance research, find efficiencies and develop new technological systems that can be deployed under a variety of circumstances. The reason: The public sector cannot advance its technology without help from outside companies. Plus, there is a lot of money to be made. Both **Amazon** and **Microsoft** made headlines over a $10 billion, 10-year government tech contract called the **Joint Enterprise Defense Infrastructure**, or JEDI. In addition to **Amazon** and **Microsoft**, several others, including **IBM**, **Oracle** and **Google**, competed to transform the military's cloud computing systems. Meanwhile, the **Central Intelligence Agency** awarded Amazon a $600 million cloud services contract, while Microsoft won a $480 million contract to build HoloLens headsets for the **Army**. The contracts prompted employee protests. In 2017, the **Department of Defense** established an **Algorithmic Warfare Cross-Functional Team** to work on something called **Project Maven**—a computer vision and deep-learning system that autonomously recognizes objects from still images and videos. The team didn't have the necessary A.I. capabilities, so the DOD contracted with Google for help training A.I. systems to analyze drone footage. But the Google employees assigned to the project didn't know they'd actually been working on a military project, and that resulted in high-profile backlash. As many as 4,000 Google employees signed a petition objecting to Project Maven. They took out a full-page ad in **The New York Times**, and ultimately dozens of employees resigned. Eventually, Google said it wouldn't renew its contract with the DOD. Google eventually launched a set of ethical principles governing its development and use of A.I., including a provision that prohibits any systems from being used for "weapons or other technologies whose principal purpose or implementation is to cause or directly facilitate injury to people."

National A.I. Strategies

Over the past few years, the danger of artificial intelligence has been thrown into sharp relief. From self-driving car accidents to electioneering through disinformation campaigns to political repression enhanced by facial recognition and automated sur-

Former Google CEO Eric Schmidt (left) shakes hands with former Secretary of Defense Ash Carter. Last fall, Schmidt warned that the U.S. must invest more into A.I. or face security threats from countries like China.

veillance, it is clear that A.I. is transforming the security environment for nation-states, firms and citizens alike. Few guardrails now exist for a technology that will touch every facet of humanity, and countries around the world are racing to develop and publish their own strategies and guidelines for A.I. The **European Union** developed an **AI Alliance** and plan of cooperation between member countries; the **United Nations** has a number of ongoing initiatives on A.I.; **Brazil** is creating a national strategy and establishing eight A.I. laboratories; **Canada** already has a national A.I. strategy called the **Pan-Canadian Artificial Intelligence Strategy**; **China** passed its **"New Generation Artificial Intelligence Development Plan"** with aggressive benchmarks to become the world's dominant A.I. player within 10 years; **Estonia** is developing a legal framework governing the use of A.I. within the country; **France** adopted a national strategy called **"AI for Humanity;"** **Germany** adopted a national framework in 2018; **Italy** has an interdisciplinary A.I. task force; **Kenya** has an A.I. and blockchain taskforce; **Saudi Arabia** has both a strategy and a legal framework giving citizenship to robots; **Singapore** launched its national A.I. strategy in 2019; and perhaps the farthest

ahead, the **United Arab Emirates** has a sweeping set of policy initiatives on A.I. and appointed **Omar Sultan Al Olama** as its minister of state for artificial intelligence.

In the **U.S.**, numerous initiatives, cells and centers work independently on the future of A.I. on behalf of the nation. Those efforts, however, lack interagency collaboration and coordinated efforts to streamline goals, outcomes, R&D efforts and funding. The **National Institute of Standards and Technology** (NIST) and various congressional offices attempt to define technical specifications for A.I., while the **Joint AI Center** and the **National Security Commission on AI** each focus on national security and defense. When it comes to A.I. planning, the **National Artificial Intelligence Research and Development Strategic Plan** duplicates the **National Security Strategy** and **National Security Commission on AI.** Top tech executives are often asked to serve on multiple commissions or to engage in similar efforts across government. Paradoxically, this creates a gap: with so many groups working either redundantly or even at odds with each other, the U.S. will miss strategic opportunities to coordinate efforts between the tech, finance and government sectors so that significant forward progress can be made within a reasonable timeframe.

The Race to Establish A.I. Rules

Last year, **China** moved into position to lead the first set of global norms and standards to govern the future of artificial intelligence. In 2019, China published a report on technical standards that would allow companies to collaborate and make their systems interoperable. The **European Union** and the **Organisation for Economic Co-operation and Development** similarly published their own guidelines, and the **Trump Administration** signed an executive order to spur the development of standards in the U.S. While the result of these efforts could introduce new ways to safeguard against bias and to ensure trust, they also attempt to create a strategic advantage for each stakeholder. As A.I. continues to develop according to different rules in China, the E.U. and the U.S., one of the hallmarks of the field—global academic collaboration—could drastically decline.

Algorithmic Warfare

Our future wars will be fought in code, using data and algorithms as powerful weapons. The current global order is being shaped by artificial intelligence, and the same countries leading the world in A.I. research – the **U.S.**, **China**, **Israel**, **France**, **Russia**, the **U.K.**, and **South Korea** – are also developing weapons systems that include at least some autonomous functionality. Israel uses autonomous drones for border patrol, while China developed stealth drones capable of autonomous airstrikes. Our FTI analysis shows that the future of warfare encompasses more than traditional weapons. Using A.I. techniques, a military can "win" by destabilizing an economy rather than demolishing countrysides and city centers. From that perspective, and given China's unified march advancing artificial intelligence, China is dangerously far ahead of the West.

Making A.I. Explain Itself

You've undoubtedly heard someone argue that A.I. is becoming a "black box"—that even those researchers working in the field don't understand how our newest systems work. That's not entirely true, however there is growing concern voiced by computer scientists, journalists and legal scholars who argue that A.I. systems shouldn't be so secretive. In August 2019, **IBM Research** launched AI Explainability 360, an open-source toolkit of algorithms that support explainability of machine learning models. It's open source so that other researchers can build on and explain models that are more transparent. This isn't a panacea—there are only a few algorithms in the toolkit—but it's a public attempt to quantify and measure explainability. Broadly speaking, there are a few challenges that will need to be overcome. Requiring transparency in A.I. could reveal a company's trade secrets. Asking the systems to simultaneously explain their decision-making process could also degrade the speed and quality of output. It's plausible that new regulations requiring explainability will be enacted in various countries in the coming years. Imagine sitting beside a genius mathematician who gives you correct answers in Italy, but receiving her answers across the border in France would mean asking her to stop and show her work, and so on every time she was asked to share her answers in a new country.

Using A.I. in Critical Systems

Machine learning promises efficiencies and new safeguards in our critical infrastructure systems. For that reason, government researchers are exploring ways to spearhead A.I. development for critical systems use: road and rail transportation systems, power generation and distribution and predicting routes for such public safety vehicles as ambulances and firetrucks. Rather than shunning A.I. systems, there is new interest in using the technology to prevent disasters and improve safety.

China's A.I. Rules

Sensetime, one of the world's most valuable A.I. startups, is helping China build its futuristic panopticon.

❯ DEEPER DIVE

If you think of China as a country that copies rather than innovates—think again.

China Rules

China is a global leader in artificial intelligence. Under **President Xi Jinping**, the country has made tremendous strides in many fields, but especially in A.I. Businesses and government have collaborated on a sweeping plan to make China the world's primary A.I. innovation center by 2030, and it's already making serious progress toward that goal. That plan is unlikely to be repealed by a new government; last March, China abolished Xi's term limits and will effectively allow him to remain in power for life.

That gives China an incredible advantage over the West. It also gives three of China's biggest companies—**Baidu**, **Alibaba**, and **Tencent**—superpowers. Collectively, they're known as the **BAT**, and they're all part of the country's well-capitalized, highly organized A.I. plan. The BAT is important to you even if you've never used them and don't do any business in China.

That's because these companies are now well established in **Seattle** and around **San Francisco**, and they are investing significantly in **U.S.** startups. **Alibaba**, China's version of **Amazon**, will invest $15 billion into A.I. research over the next three years, planting research centers in seven cities worldwide, including **San Mateo, California**, and **Bellevue, Washington**. **Baidu** (a Chinese search-engine company often likened to Google) established an A.I. research center in **Silicon Valley**, and **Tencent** (the developer of the mega-popular messaging app **WeChat**) began hunting for American talent when it opened an A.I. lab in **Seattle** two years ago. It has since upped its stakes in companies like **Tesla** and **Snap**. The payoff for the Chinese is not just a typical return on investment—Chinese firms expect IP as well. **China**-based A.I. startups now account for nearly half of all AI. investments globally.

China's Rules

In late 2019, China began requiring all citizens to submit to facial recognition in order to apply for new internet or mobile services, and telecommunications companies must deploy A.I. to check the identities of people registering SIM cards. Chinese social media platforms require users to sign up with their "real-name identities." In Chinese schools, surveillance cameras outfitted with computer vision systems are in widespread use and track whether students are paying attention, whether they are attempting to cheat or sleep, and how focused they are during lectures. These and other national standards make it easier for the government to track its citizens. China's social credit system, an algorithmic reputation system developed by the government, will standardize assessments of citizens' and businesses' behavior and activity. It's expected to be fully operational in the next year.

Numerous complaints have criticized China's use of personal data, from allegations of tracking, detaining and abusing the **Uighur Muslim** community to myriad other human rights abuses in factories, where smart cameras find unproductive workers and alert human minders to physically strike them as "encouragement." In November 2019, a professor filed a lawsuit against the use of facial recognition technology. **Professor Guo Bing** of **Zhejiang Sci-Tech University** alleged that when an amusement park scanned his face without consent, it violated the country's consumer rights protection law. It is the first lawsuit of its kind in China.

China's Data Surplus

The country's massive population—nearing 1.4 billion people—offers researchers and startups there command of what may be the most valuable natural resource in the future—human data—without the privacy and security restrictions common in much of the rest of the world. If data is the new oil, then China is the new OPEC. The kind of rich data the Chinese are mining can be used to train A.I. to detect patterns used in everything from education and manufacturing to retail and military applications. The Chinese startup **Sensetime** is pioneering myriad recognition technologies, such as a system that provides advertisers real-time feedback on what people are watching, technology that can extract customer information and carry out statistical analysis in crowded areas like shopping malls and supermarkets, and simultaneous recognition of everything in a scene, whether it's people, pets, automobiles, trees or soda cans.

Risk Profile

We have failed and are continuing to fail to see China as a militaristic, economic, and diplomatic pacing threat when it comes to A.I. China has already used its **Belt and Road Initiative** as a platform to build international partnerships in both physical and digital infrastructure, and it is making surveillance technologies available to countries with authoritarian regimes. **Ecuador's** surveillance system, called **ECU-911**, was built by two Chinese companies: the state-controlled **C.E.I.E.C.** and **Huawei**. The system promised to curb high murder rates and drug crime, but it was too expensive an investment. As a result, a deal was struck for a Chinese-built surveillance system financed with Chinese loans. It was an entrée to a much more lucrative deal: Ecuador eventually signed away big portions of its oil reserves to China to help finance infrastructure projects. Similar package deals have been brokered in **Venezuela** and **Bolivia**.

China is quietly weaponizing A.I., too. China's **People Liberation Army** is catching up to the U.S. when it comes to military applications, using A.I. for such tasks as spotting hidden images with drones. The Chinese military is equipping helicopters and jet fighters with A.I., the government created a top-secret military lab—a Chinese version of **DARPA** in the U.S.—and it's building billion-dollar A.I. national laboratories. China's military is achieving remarkable A.I. successes, including a recent test of "swarm intelligence," that can automate dozens of armed drones.

The Bottom Line

有备则无患 is a Chinese proverb that roughly translates to "forewarned is forearmed." Now that you know what's coming, reframe your thinking of China as simply the world's factory.

—Amy Webb

Society

Researchers at Loving A.I. and Hanson Technologies are teaching machines unconditional love, active listening and empathy.

Artificial Emotional Intelligence

Research teams at **Loving AI** and **Hanson Technologies** are teaching machines unconditional love, active listening and empathy. In the future, machines will convincingly exhibit human emotions like love, happiness, fear and sadness—begging the question, what is an authentic emotion? Theory of mind refers to the ability to imagine the mental state of others. This has long been considered a trait unique to humans and certain primates. A.I. researchers are working to train machines to build theory of mind models of their own. This technology could improve existing A.I. therapy applications such as **WoeBot**. By designing machines to respond with empathy and concern, digital assistants like **Alexa** will become more and more a part of one's family. This technology could eventually end up in hospitals, schools and prisons, providing emotional support robots to patients, students and inmates. According to research from health service organization **Cigna**, the rate of loneliness in the **U.S.** has doubled in the last 50 years. Two years ago, former **U.K. Prime Minister Theresa May** created a new cabinet position, the world's first **Minister of Loneliness**. In our increasingly connected world, people report feeling more isolated. In the future, governments struggling with a massive mental health crisis, such as **South Korea**, may turn to emotional support robots to address this issue at scale.

Personal Digital Twins

Last year's Spring Festival Gala on **China's** state broadcaster (**CCTV**) featured four well-known human hosts—**Beining Sa**, **Xun Zhu**, **Bo Gao**, and **Yang Long**—alongside their digital twins. With an estimated billion people watching, the A.I. copies mimicked their human counterparts without pre-scripted behaviors, speeches or routines. There are a number of startups building customizable, trainable platforms that are capable of learning from you—and then representing you online via personal digital twins. **ObEN** created the twins for CCTV, while **Molly**, a **Y Combinator**-backed startup, answers questions via text. The near-future could include digital twins for professionals across a range of fields, including health and education.

Problematic Data Sets

In 2018, researchers at **MIT** revealed "Norman," an A.I. trained to perform image captioning, a deep learning method of generating a textual description of an image. They trained Norman using only the image captions from a subreddit that's known for content that's disturbing. When Norman was ready, they unleashed him against a similar neural network that had been trained using standard data. Researchers fed both systems Rorschach inkblots and asked them to caption what they saw, and the results were striking: Where the standard system saw "a black and white photo of a baseball glove," Norman saw "a man murdered by machine gun in broad daylight." The point of the experiment was to prove that A.I. isn't inherently biased, but that data input methods—and the people inputting that data—can significantly alter an A.I.'s behavior.

In 2019, new pre-trained systems built for natural language generation were released—and the conversations they learned from were scraped from **Reddit** and **Amazon** reviews. This is problematic: Both Reddit and Amazon commenters skew white and male, which means that their use of language isn't representative of everyone. But it illustrates an ongoing challenge within the developer community. It is already difficult to get authentic data from real people to train systems, and with new privacy restrictions, developers may choose to rely more on public—and problematic—data sets.

A.I. to Catch Cheaters

A.I. is also being used to catch cheaters. ECRI Institute's Crosscheq uses machine learning and data analytics to look for hyperbole and misleading information during the hiring process. Drexel University researchers built an app that uses biometrics to predict when dieters are likely to stray from their prescribed regimen. Researchers at the University of Copenhagen created a machine learning system to spot cheating on essays with, they say, a 90% accuracy rate.

Algorithms Designed to Target Vulnerable Populations

In countries around the world, A.I. is being used at border crossings, within poor neighborhoods, and in school districts where delinquency is a problem. Most of the time, the technology is billed as a solution, but it serves to disenfranchise vulnerable communities. In 2018, Amazon pitched Immigration and Customs Enforcement on an A.I. system capable of identifying and tracking immigrants and said its Rekognition face scanning platform could assist with homeland security investigations. The Multiple Encounter Dataset is a big database that contains two big sets of photos: people who have not yet committed a crime, and an FBI data set of deceased people. The dataset overindexes on people of color, which means that if law enforcement use the data to train algorithms, it's going to lead to bias. Image recognition is a particularly vexing challenge, because researchers need large datasets to perform their work. Often, images are used without consent. The Child Exploitation Image Analytics program—a data set used by facial recognition technology developers for testing—has been running since at least 2016 with images of "children who range in age from infant through adolescent" and the majority of which "feature coercion, abuse, and sexual activity," according to the program's own developer documentation. These images are considered particularly challenging for the software because of the greater variability of position, context, and more.

A.I. Still Has a Bias Problem

It's no secret A.I. has a serious and multifaceted bias problem. Just one example: The data sets used for training often come from places like Reddit, Amazon reviews and Wikipedia, a site inherently riddled with bias. The people building models tend to be homogeneous and aren't often aware of their own biases. As computer systems get better at making decisions, algorithms may sort each of us into groups that don't make any obvious sense to us—but could have massive repercussions. Every single day, you are creating unimaginable amounts of data, both actively (like when uploading and tagging photos on Facebook) and passively (driving to work, for example). Those data are mined and used, often without your direct knowledge or understanding, by algorithms. It is used to create advertising, to help potential employers predict our behaviors, to determine our mortgage rates and even to help law enforcement predict whether or not we're likely to commit a crime. Researchers at a number of universities—including the University of Maryland, Columbia University, Carnegie Mellon, MIT, Princeton, University of California-Berkeley, International Computer Science Institute, among others—are studying the side effects of automatic decision-making. You, or someone you know, could wind up on the wrong side of the algorithm and discover you're ineligible for a loan, or a particular medication, or the ability to rent an apartment, for reasons that aren't transparent or easy to understand. Increasingly, data is being harvested and sold to third parties without your knowledge. These biases can reinforce themselves over time. As A.I. applications become more ubiquitous, the negative effects of bias will have greater impact. The Apple card gave high credit limits for men versus women, in some cases, by a factor of 20. Wearables such as Google's Fitbit are considerably less accurate for darker skin-types because of how melanin absorbs green light. This is problematic when insurance companies use biased algorithms to track heart rates, blood pressure and risk rates for conditions like irregular heartbeats or a potential heart attack.

A.I. Systems Intentionally Hiding Data

Computers do exactly what they are told to do. Command a machine to win at a game, and it will do everything in its power to achieve that goal. Apparently that now includes cheating. Researchers at **Stanford** and **Google** discovered that an A.I. created to turn satellite images into usable maps was withholding certain data. Researchers were using a neural network called **CycleGAN**, which learns how to map image transformations. For example, it could take an old aerial photograph of a neighborhood, distinguish between streets, alleys, driveways, buildings and lamp posts, and generate a map that could be used by a GPS. Initially, they used an aerial photograph that hadn't been seen by the network. The resulting image looked very close to the original—suspiciously close. But on deeper inspection, the researchers found that there were lots of details in both the original image and the image generated that weren't visible in the map made by the A.I. It turns out that the system learned to hide information about the original image inside of the image it generated.

The Rise of Undocumented A.I. Accidents

There were a number of A.I.-related accidents in 2018 and 2019, but only a few made the headlines. An **Uber** self-driving car hit and killed a pedestrian in **Tempe, Arizona**—but there were countless more incidents that didn't result in death, and as a result, aren't known to the public. At the moment, researchers are not obligated to report accidents or incidents involving our data, or A.I. processes, unless a law is broken. While big companies must inform consumers if their personal data—credit card numbers, home addresses, passwords—have been stolen, they are not required to publicly document instances in which algorithms have learned to discriminate against someone on the basis of race or gender, for example.

A.I. and Digital Dividends

Artificial intelligence will inevitably lead to a shift in the global workforce, causing job losses across many industries. Researchers at **Oxford's Institute for Humanity**, researchers at the **Future Today Institute**, and **U.S. presidential candidate Andrew Yang** have all published works outlining different versions of a "digital dividend" – a way for companies to pay back to society a portion of the profits derived from A.I.

Prioritizing Accountability and Trust

We will soon reach a point when we will no longer be able to tell if a data set has been tampered with, either intentionally or accidentally. A.I. systems rely on our trust. If we no longer trust the outcome, decades of research and technological advancement will be for naught. Leaders in every sector—government, business, the nonprofit world and so on—must have confidence in the data and algorithms used. Building trust and accountability is a matter of showing the work performed. This is a complicated process, and, understandably, corporations, government offices, law enforcement agencies and other organizations want to keep data private. The scientific community is focusing on efforts to standardize guidelines for research reproducibility and data sets with open source tools such as **Qeresp** and crowd-sourced fact-checking by sites like **Melwy**. The ethics of how data is collected in the first place may also influence the trustworthiness and validity of scientific research, particularly in areas such as organ donations and medical research.

Committing to transparency in method would create trust without necessarily divulging any personal data. In addition, employing ethicists to work directly with managers and developers and ensuring developers themselves are diverse—representing different races, ethnicities and genders—will reduce inherent bias in A.I. systems.

A.I. Bans for Specific Industries

NEAR-FUTURE NEUTRAL SCENARIO

Because it's difficult to ensure that A.I. is not discriminating for or against certain populations in the United States, the use of A.I. is restricted or banned entirely from certain processes. That includes risk assessment for health insurance, bank loans, employee recruitment and hiring, and college admissions.

A.I. Becomes a Self-Fulfilling Prophecy

NEAR-FUTURE CATASTROPHIC SCENARIO

With increased investment in surveillance tools and continued use of social networks, companies gain access to larger and larger digital profiles of every individual customer. These profiles are fed into A.I. learning models to label, cluster and classify us into customer segments. Instead of broad categories with high variability (men over 40, women aged 18-30), hyper-targeted customer segments will become self-fulfilling prophecies and further ingrain our differences. A company has reams of data on, say, a 7-year-old boy living in a rural community—so much data that it can pre-classify him into a future customer segment and begin feeding him content, ads and products to further reinforce this label. Eventually, consumers don't know if they are exploring their own identities or simply assuming the identities assigned to them by A.I.

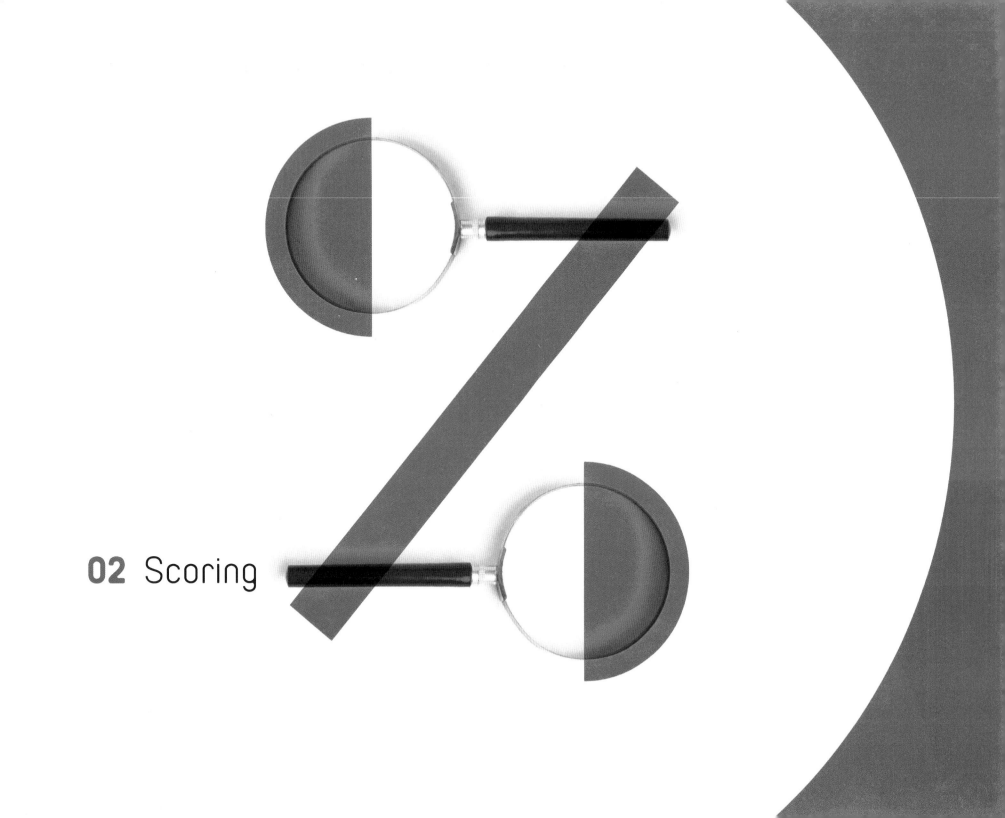

02 Scoring

Scoring

HIGH DEGREE OF CERTAINTY

INFORMS STRATEGY	**ACT NOW**
REVISIT LATER	**KEEP VIGILANT WATCH**

LONGER-TERM IMPACT · IMMEDIATE IMPACT

LOW DEGREE OF CERTAINTY

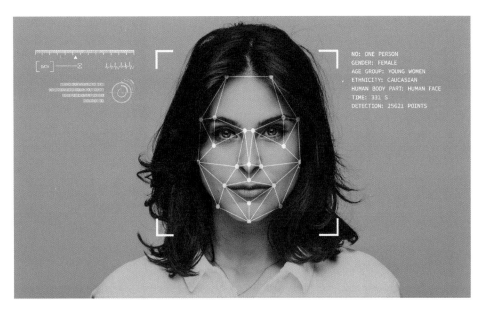

NO: ONE PERSON
GENDER: FEMALE
AGE GROUP: YOUNG WOMEN
ETHNICITY: CAUCASIAN
HUMAN BODY PART: HUMAN FACE
TIME: 331 S
DETECTION: 25621 POINTS

Quantifying and analyzing our biometric data can reveal patterns in our activities and, as a result, reveal a lot about who we are, what we're thinking and what we are likely to do next.

KEY INSIGHT

In order for our automated systems to work, they need both our data and a framework for making decisions. Everyone alive today is being scored.

WHAT YOU NEED TO KNOW

In the U.S., we have a credit reporting system that measures our creditworthiness. Banks, financial institutions and others use that score to determine the likelihood that we might default on a loan or mortgage. Financial credit scoring is tightly regulated and available to all consumers—we can request copies of our financial credit scores, check their accuracy and correct errors. Now, hundreds of types of data are being harnessed to assign us scores. However, unlike the credit reporting system, which is federally regulated and follows set processes, this kind of data isn't subject to enforceable rules. It can be impossible to find out what our scores are, how they are being calculated and how to correct them if there are inaccuracies.

WHY IT MATTERS

Recent advancements in data mining and artificial intelligence promise new opportunities for business intelligence and law enforcement. There are risks, too: China is selling its government-funded scoring tools to authoritarian regimes elsewhere in the world. We anticipate that in the coming year, regulators will take a deeper interest in scoring.

◯ DEEPER DIVE

The Age of Algorithmic Determinism

Our data are being mined, refined and productized to sort, tag and catalogue us. Why? To make it easier for systems to make decisions for, on behalf of and about us. We're living in a new age of algorithmic determinism, where we increasingly rely on A.I. systems to make choices—even if those systems score us without being able to understand our nuanced histories, special circumstances and the unique characteristics of our humanity.

The Price is Right—For Some

Algorithms can determine how likely we are to break the law, what kinds of mobile plans we should qualify for, what sort of news we should be shown and even how much we're willing to pay for a roll of toilet paper. Researchers at the **Consumer Education Foundation** found that when visiting e-commerce sites, anonymous shoppers were offered products at lower prices than the researchers themselves. For example, when browsing anonymously at **Walmart.com**, a box of ballpoint pens was listed for $4.15, but when **Walmart** had access to other data from the researchers, that price spiked to $9.69. Customers are being algorithmically assigned scores based on the predicted profit they might generate for the company, and served different prices accordingly.

China is Scoring its Citizens

By now, you are familiar with **China's Social Credit System**, a vast ranking system that this year will see a national rollout. First announced in 2014, it promises to make good on the government's stance that "keeping trust is glorious and breaking trust is disgraceful." The system will take some time to become fully operational nationwide, but already it's granting and restricting permissions for Chinese citizens algorithmically. Last year, the system determined that 13 million Chinese citizens are untrustworthy. Citizens are awarded or deducted points for a variety of activities, such as paying bills on time, spreading news contrary to the government's viewpoints or spending too much time playing video games.

In late 2019, a leak of highly classified government documents revealed an operations manual for detention camps in the far western region of **Xinjiang**, where scoring is used for predictive policing. It is in this region where **China's Muslim Uighur** community lives. **The International Consortium of Investigative Journalists** published a detailed report showing the scope and ambition of **Beijing's** scoring system, which awards points and punishments for inmates in the camps. China argues its "re-education camps" and scoring system were built to combat terrorists and radical religious extremism.

China is Scoring Companies, Too

A longstanding goal of China's Social Credit System is to create what the **Communist Party of China (CCP)** calls a "fair, transparent and predictable" business environment. To accomplish that goal starting in 2020, businesses that operate in China will begin to earn and lose points as part of China's corporate social credit system. The plan includes centralizing data from domestic and foreign companies in a government system that allows the CCP to monitor the activities of all entities operating in China.

The Sky is Watching

There's an old Chinese adage that says, "People are doing things, and the sky is watching." But it holds true for the West, too. Increasingly, everything we do is being watched and recorded. Algorithms assign us scores all the time, by governments in some countries and by the commercial sector in others.

THE IMPACT

Scoring presents tremendous opportunities to help businesses understand their customers better, which is why in 2020 every organization must develop a data governance strategy and ethics policy. For those who work in risk and compliance, 2020 will be the start of a newly complicated landscape. Organizations will need to hire compliance specialists who understand the complexities of using scoring systems.

For those in the public sector, massive-scale scoring impacts every facet of our daily lives, and it will soon influence geoeconomic relationships around the world. Chinese tech companies—**Huawei**, **Hikvision**, **Dahua** and **ZTE**—are building and supplying the scoring apparatus for 63 countries around the world. Of those, 36 have signed on to **China's Belt and Road Initiative**. It isn't just that China is exporting technology, it is actively creating an environment where the CCP can also export its influence.

Scoring cont.

In China, Megvii's Face++ system recognizes and scores your credit-worthiness before you walk into a bank or retail store.

⊘ TRENDS

Persistent Tracking and Scoring

Retailers hope to gain access to our homes to deliver purchases—and also to learn more about what we're likely to buy next. Now affordable, **Google's** various home automation systems make it easy for you to shop online and to take while traveling. Workers from both **Amazon.com** and **Walmart.com** will deliver packages indoors and even stock your refrigerator with groceries, and to allay fears of theft, those workers wear cameras. The problem? Amazon and Walmart will store video footage of the delivery, allowing them to develop computer vision analytics and other processes to gain insights from the millions of hours of video collected.

Scoring Agencies Are On the Rise

Hundreds of companies now score customers. Some, like **Iovation**, **Kount** and **Riskified**, focus on niche areas like fraud detection, while such companies as **Kustomer** score you more broadly to determine your purchasing power and your general frame of mind. **Retail Equation's** algorithms tell

Best Buy and **Sephora** whether to accept or reject a product you've purchased from them online. **Zeta Global** scores you based on how much money you're likely to spend, while **MaxMind** scores you based on your location in the real world. Collectively, these companies are mining thousands of your unique data points, including how many times you open apps on your phone, which devices you use, where you spend time, what kinds of food you order for delivery and insights from messages you've sent to **Uber** drivers and **Airbnb** hosts.

Vast Differences in Verification Systems

Unlike the three major credit agencies (**Equifax**, **Experian** and **TransUnion**), which produce scores that typically fall within roughly the same range, the systems that generate scores in the datascape each use different inputs and methodologies to arrive at their answers. Unlike finance, this new consumer scoring has no standardization, the algorithms are automated, and companies cloak methodologies under the premise of proprietary algorithms.

Behavioral Biometrics

Quantifying and analyzing our biometric data can reveal patterns in our activities—and as a result, reveal a lot about who we are, what we're thinking, and what we are likely to do next. This is why companies like **Facebook** have come under intense scrutiny in the past year. Behavioral biometrics tools can be used to map and measure how you type—what force you use to press down on screens, whether you fat finger your C's and V's on your phone and how quickly you tend to flick your fingers when hunting through search results. Those tools know your unique typing pattern on a physical keyboard, too: whether you're someone who constantly spells the word "behavioral" wrong on the first try, and whether you hold down or repeatedly tap on the delete button. You're not consciously aware that you have certain identifiable behaviors, but machines perceive them. We also don't realize that they will pose security vulnerabilities—as well as interesting new opportunities—in the near future. Imagine never having to use a password again; your bank would simply recognize it's you after typing a few sentences. The downside is that if your behavior is observable, at some point it will become repeatable, too.

Scoring Vulnerable Populations

A.I.-powered recognition tools have well-documented blind spots. They often return incorrect results for people of color and for trans, queer and nonbinary individuals. In November 2019, researchers at the **University of Colorado-Boulder** showed how scoring tools—including **Clarifai**, **Amazon's Rekognition system**, **IBM Watson**, **Megvii's Face++** and **Microsoft** facial analysis systems—habitually misidentified non-cisgender people. Another study, this one from the **MIT Media Lab**, found that 33% of the time, Rekognition misidentified women of color as men. Even so, companies and government agencies continue to score vulnerable communities. Law enforcement, immigration officials, banks, universities and even religious institutions now use scoring systems. The **Charlottesville Police Department** was publicly criticized early this year for placing smart cameras in communities with public housing and using A.I. systems to monitor activity.

Surveillance Scoring-as-a-Service (SSaaS)

Some of our largest tech giants are building comprehensive systems intended to optimize our daily lives, and those scoring systems have appeal beyond their original use cases. For example, **Amazon** applied for a U.S. patent for an unmanned aerial vehicle that can perform surveillance from the air and generate images that could be used by others. Surveillance Scoring-as-a-Service (SSaaS) would be a monetized byproduct of its drone delivery service, and it would fit into its broader constellation of surveillance scoring technologies. In February 2018, Amazon acquired the video-equipped smart doorbell company **Ring**, and three months later it launched **Neighbors**, a crime-reporting social network that encourages Ring users to upload videos from their security cameras and doorbells for others to see. Now, more than 400 law enforcement agencies in the U.S. use data from Ring.

Bias in Scoring Systems

It is no secret that many of our machine learning models—and the data they use to recognize others—are encoded with bias. That's because the people who built the models are themselves subject to unconscious bias, as well as more explicit homogeneous learning and working environments. Everyone seems to agree we have

China's social credit score is visible in many cities. In Rongcheng, photos of "civilized families" are displayed on public noticeboards. Photo credit: Simina Mistreanu.

a bias problem, but so far the tech industry still doesn't have a plan for how to address and solve for bias in recognition systems that are now scoring all of us continuously. The algorithmic bias problem will likely get worse, especially as more law enforcement agencies and the justice system adopt recognition technologies. To reduce bias, **Facebook** announced in June of 2019 that it was building an independent oversight board—a kind of "supreme court"—to judge itself. The board of 40 people would make content review decisions in small panels, in an effort to curtail false or misleading information, cyber bullying and meddling by governments wishing to harm countries and their citizens. Research scientists **Kate Crawford** and **Meredith Whittaker** founded the **AI Now Institute** to study bias in A.I. as well as the impacts the technology will have on human rights and labor. In response to a scathing investigative report by **ProPublica** on bias in the technologies used in the criminal justice system, the **New York City Council** and **Mayor Bill de Blasio** passed a bill requiring more transparency in A.I. **Microsoft** hired creative writers and artists to train A.I. in language, while **IBM** is developing a set of independent bias ratings to determine whether A.I. systems are fair.

Conflicting Norms, Standards and Regulations for Scoring

There is no single set of standards nor a unified code of norms for scoring. That's resulted in a piecemeal approach to regulating scoring and scoring agencies. Recently, new laws were proposed in **Latin America** seeking to strengthen privacy law. For example, last year **Argentine President Mauricio Macri** submitted a bill to drastically overhaul the country's data privacy protection law, which hadn't been updated since 2000. It establishes the right to be forgotten, the right to data portability, and it would limit the scope of scoring by third party companies. The **E.U.'s GDPR** regulations restrict what kinds of personal data can be collected and under what circumstances, but even that is enforced differently by local authorities. In 2019, **New York State** lawmakers introduced a consumer privacy law that would give consumers more control over their data. It would require businesses—including news and entertainment companies—to demonstrate they are prioritizing customer privacy over profit. **Illinois** was one of the first states to enact legislation preventing facial recognition

without a consumer's explicit permission. Individual cities are passing their own data privacy laws, too. **Oakland**, **Seattle**, **Portland** and **New York City** also approved guidelines on how personal data can be used. There is no end in sight to scoring regulations, and in the years to come, this kind of data governance will challenge audience insights, risk and compliance, and distribution for entertainment, news and technology companies.

Intentionally Opaque Methodologies

New tools intended to enhance our digital experience instead track us without explicitly showing how or why. The latest version of **reCAPTCHA**, which determines whether we are bots or not, isn't visible. Rather than asking consumers to click a box saying "I'm not a robot" or select which pictures show traffic lights or bananas, this latest version invisibly tracks how someone navigates through a website and assigns them a risk score. Developed by **Google**, reCAPTCHA not only establishes that a computer user is human, it also helps digitize books and improve machine learning programs. While it may be far less annoying than clicking

through the old process, this system looks for other details, such as whether you already have a Google cookie in your browser and whether you're logged into your Google account. Over time, the system learns the patterns of real people—but it also means that Google could gain access to every single page you're accessing. The email program **Superhuman** similarly uses hidden tracking tools. Designer and news entrepreneur **Mike Davidson** researched how consumers were being tracked within Superhuman and revealed numerous opaque surveillance techniques being used—some to power features like email read receipts. (To be fair, Superhuman isn't the only company embedding tracking pixels in emails.) This could be problematic for a journalist working in a country ruled by an authoritarian regime. How to use tracking tools ethically and how to disclose their true reach to consumers should be a discussion had by every entertainment, media and technology company this year.

When the Bathroom at Your Favorite Restaurant Won't Let You In

NEAR-FUTURE CATASTROPHIC SCENARIO

You're out with colleagues at the city's hottest new restaurant, which has amazing Italian food but is in a somewhat dangerous neighborhood. It's a fantastic night. On the menu: Sautéed mussels, shrimp and calamari in a fennel tomato broth over saffron orzo, which you enjoy along with some handmade burrata and a big hunk of fresh baked bread. The group became friendly during your company's LGBTQIA after work happy hour and now shares a bottle of red wine. You opt instead for a nice, hoppy IPA. As you sit together, talking about your projects (and, if we're being totally honest, laughing at that coworker who blathers nonstop and constantly asks everyone else for help), all the water and beer makes its way through you. You take a last swig of your IPA and excuse yourself to the bathroom. You notice cameras outfitted on the doors. Must be because a few weeks ago, there was an "incident." The doors now auto lock and unlock after a quick scan by the camera. You grab a hold of the doorknob, but it won't budge. You try again, shaking it this time. A server comes near, with a sullen, embarrassed expression. "I'm really sorry," she says. "I mean, you look amazing. Really you do. I don't think they intended for this to keep happening, because you're not the only one. It's just that your lipstick and earrings are confusing the camera. We're still stuck with men's and women's bathrooms."

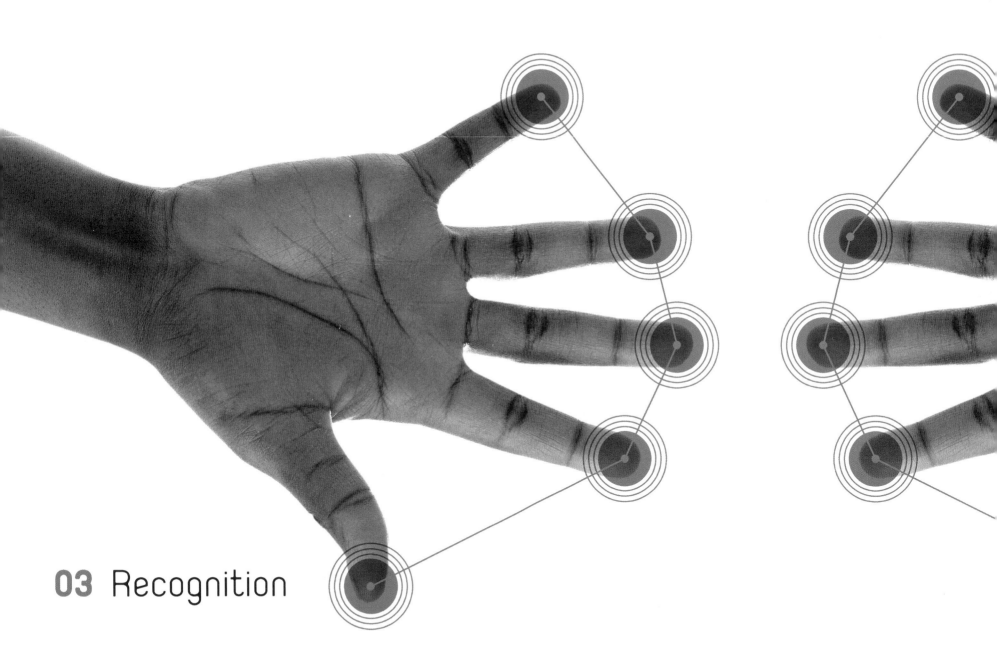

03 Recognition

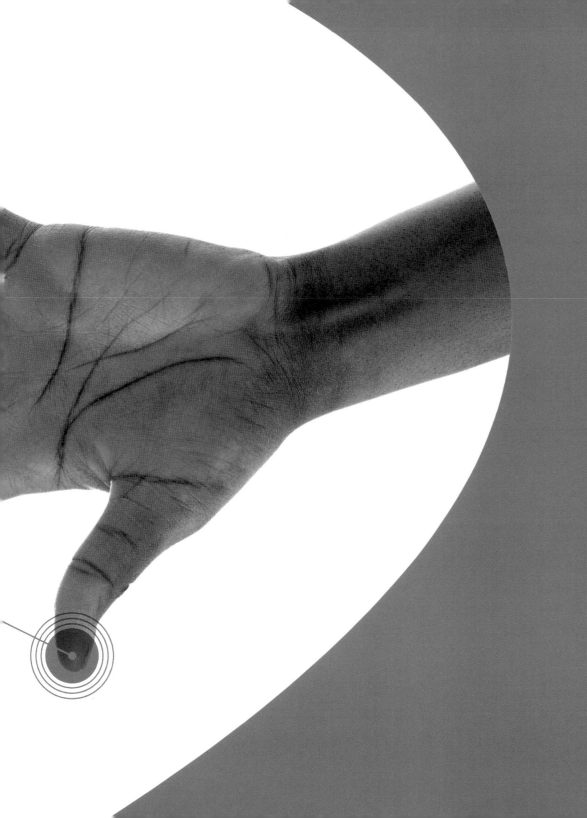

Recognition

HIGH DEGREE OF CERTAINTY

INFORMS STRATEGY	**ACT NOW**
REVISIT LATER	**KEEP VIGILANT WATCH**

LONGER-TERM IMPACT

IMMEDIATE IMPACT

LOW DEGREE OF CERTAINTY

China's Alipay recently added a "beauty filter" to encourage more women to use face recognition payment systems. Users see an enhanced version of themselves reflected back on the screen.

KEY INSIGHT

It is officially the end of anonymity. We are surrounded by cameras, speakers and a host of other smart devices that monitor us in real-time, all the time. Recognition systems use hundreds of different data points to identify and monitor us and to predict our likely future actions both online and in the physical world.

WHAT YOU NEED TO KNOW

Recognition systems, whether they use our voices, faces or fingerprints, are wildly popular for good reason. There is tremendous value in all of this discoverability. Persistent recognition allows companies to learn more about consumers and provide them with a level of personalization that could not possibly be achieved at scale any other way. Predictive recognition systems help law enforcement agencies keep track of criminals and prevent their next offense. Responsive recognition technologies understand context and interact with us accordingly: They're starting to empathize with us when we're sad, and express enthusiasm when we're excited.

WHY IT MATTERS

Our current digital economy is transactional, built on e-commerce, the transfer of data, and automating business processes. What new business models will be needed for our recognition economy?

⊘ DEEPER DIVE

Ethical Concerns

Governments, law enforcement agencies and others are interested in getting access to all of this data for a variety of reasons. The **Federal Bureau of Investigation (FBI)** and **Immigration and Customs Enforcement (ICE)** have each used images from state license databases to build a powerful facial recognition system. While police in the U.S. have access to biometric data (fingerprints and DNA) from people who've been arrested, this image recognition system includes residents who have never been charged with a crime. Whereas someone who has been arrested knows their photo and fingerprints have been taken, U.S. residents are not informed when their driver license photos are being entered into a database and used with machine learning algorithms. Privacy laws differ in every local jurisdiction in the U.S., and they lag behind technology significantly. The cities of Oakland, San Francisco, and Somerville, Massachusetts passed laws banning city departments—including police—from using facial recognition software.

Meanwhile, airports are beginning to test face recognition technology. At JetBlue e-gates, travelers must allow their faces to be scanned before they board planes. In Atlanta, Delta's biometric terminal uses faces—rather than printed or mobile boarding cards—throughout the check-in and boarding process. While technically U.S. citizens have the right to opt out, flying can be a stressful experience, especially when there are complications like delays. As a result, travelers have been trading liberties for conveniences and the opportunity to make air travel less fraught and more efficient.

Data Breaches

Companies and governments are collecting data on the general public, and the data security systems of these organizations have exhibited significant vulnerabilities. In 2019, a line of agencies and firms, including U.S. Customs and Border Protection, Capital One and State Farm, suffered data breaches. In July 2019, the Federal Trade Commission fined Facebook $5 billion after a yearlong investigation into the company's business practices and advertising model. Commissioner Rohit Chopra wrote a stunning dissent: "Facebook's violations were a direct result of the company's behavioral advertising business model. Facebook flagrantly violated the FTC's 2012 order by deceiving its users and allowing pay-for-play data harvesting by developers. The company's behavioral advertising business, which monetizes user behavior through mass surveillance, contributed to these violations. Cambridge Analytica's tactics of profiling and targeting users were a small-scale reflection of Facebook's own

practices... The case against Facebook is about more than just privacy—it is also about the power to control and manipulate. Global regulators and policymakers need to confront the dangers associated with mass surveillance and the resulting ability to control and influence us. The behavioral advertising business incentives of technology platforms spur practices that are dividing our society. The harm from this conduct is immeasurable, and regulators and policymakers must confront it."

There's No Going Back

Smart technology is everywhere: in our cars, homes, offices and pockets—we are literally surrounded by it. Plus, many of our daily activities require some form of biometric recognition. The more commonplace this recognition technology becomes, the harder it will be to regulate it, despite such efforts gaining momentum in the U.S. and Europe. Local city governments can try to ban Face ID on iPhones, but what about all of the other personal data being transmit-

ted? With today's technology, do you really think a company needs a camera to see who we are and what we're doing?

WATCHLIST FOR SECTION

Google's Project Jacquard, Google's Project Soli, Google's Recorder App, JetBlue, Kontakt.io's Bluetooth Card Beacon, LG, Osram, Massachusetts General Hospital, MIT's Computer Science and Artificial Intelligence Laboratory (CSAIL), National Taiwan University of Science and Technology, Nvidia, Road Wise, Samsung, SpotterEDU, State Farm, Tencent, Twitter, U.S. Air Force, U.S. Customs and Border Protection, U.S. Federal Bureau of Investigations, U.S. Federal Trade Commission, U.S. Immigration and Customs Enforcement, University of Arizona's Department of Electrical and Computer Engineering, University of California-Santa Barbara, Vanderbilt University, Waitrose.

Recognition cont.

Google's Recorder app automatically transcribes audio.

Faceprints

Our faces each have unique bone, capillary and muscular construction, in addition to physical characteristics and pigments that are specific to each one of us. Even identical twins aren't truly carbon copies of each other—they have thousands of tiny, potentially even imperceptible differences. Just like we each have unique fingerprints, we also have unique faceprints. When a recognition system scans a human face, it can be used to identify who the person is, based on their biometric features. **Snap's** famous selfie filters use faceprints to map digital overlays and alter them in real time. **China's Alipay** uses faceprints to authenticate people's identities as they make purchases. **Facebook** uses the technology to automatically tag people in the photos uploaded. **Shanghai-based Fudan University** and **Changchun Institute of Optics, Fine Mechanics and Physics** (part of the **Chinese Academy of Sciences**) in **Changchun** developed a 500-megapixel facial recognition camera that is able to capture "thousands of faces at a stadium in perfect detail and generate their facial data for the cloud while locating a particular target in an instant." In practice, this means that a stadium can be scanned and, within seconds, produce a high-resolution image of every single face for recognition algorithms. Researchers in **Japan** and **China** are working on representation models that require only a portion of one's face, even in low light, to accurately predict their identity—even as they change their hairstyles, get plastic surgery or grow a beard. Legal challenges in 2019 resulted in some U.S. cities barring city departments from using facial recognition technology without first going through approved procedures. Individual cities, counties and states now have different regulations stipulating who can use faceprints and under what circumstances.

Voiceprints

Just as each person has a unique set of characteristics that make up their faces, our voices also have a wide array of measurable characteristics that uniquely identify who we are. Our voiceprints are what enable smart Bluetooth speakers like **Amazon's Alexa** to recognize different people within the same space. New machine learning techniques, combined with vast datasets of recorded voices, have now enabled researchers to identify us simply by listening to the micro-signatures produced when we speak. Researchers at **Carnegie Mellon University** discovered a generative technique allowing them to build a 3D version of someone's face using only their voiceprint. This system is being deployed by law enforcement agencies to identify prank callers in a practice known as "swatting," in which they make false claims to local agencies, which then unwittingly deploy emergency crew to false emergencies.

Automatic Voice Transcription

Late in 2019, **Google** debuted a new app called **Recorder**, which uses A.I. to automatically recognize and transcribe voices with near-perfect accuracy. Available on Google's **Pixel 4** phones only, it is able to recognize specific conversations, which means that crosstalk and background noise won't affect the transcription technology. **Amazon's Transcribe Medical** automatically converts speech used in medical settings into text. There are lots of practical applications for automatic voice transcription: recording meeting minutes, taking lecture notes, generating transcriptions for podcasts and

shows and serving medical and pharmacological teams as they work with patients.

Bone Recognition

In 2018, the **U.S. Air Force** applied for a patent that explains how wideband radar can be used to identify people by their bone structure. A transmitting antenna sends a signal to a human, and that person's biometric radar signature is compared against known signatures in a database. For people with screws and metal bars in their bodies, this gives others a new way to identify you in a crowd: Your metal may be invisible to everyday people but turn into clear beacons when scanned. Since 2018, a number of research papers have been published about the technology. In addition, scientists at the **University of Arizona's Department of Electrical and Computer Engineering** have developed a way of measuring skeletal posture using mmWave radar and convolutional neural networks.

Bioacoustic Recognition

Sound is continuously passing through space, even if we can't hear it. As sound waves pass through physical objects, a

unique sound signature is generated. Researchers at the **Electronics Telecommunications Research Institute** in **South Korea** built a system to map the bioacoustic signatures created as sound waves pass through humans. The machine uses a transducer that gently vibrates (and, as a result, generate sound waves even if they're not detectable to human ears). After the sound waves pass through a person's skin, bones and soft tissues, a unique bioacoustic signature is created. Using these signatures, they can now discreetly and non-invasively determine a person's identity.

WiFi Recognition

We are continuously surrounded by radio waves, thanks to the millions of WiFi routers around us. While you can't see, hear or feel them, you're living in a field of 2.4- and 5-gigahertz radio signals. Anytime you move—take a sip of water, or look out your window, wash your hair—you are distorting the waves.

The WiFi transmitter in your home or office is continually sending and receiving information, which it converts into radio waves. The signals aren't very strong, only filling up

the space around you (and possibly spilling just outside to the street). It turns out that, with the right device, it's possible to watch us moving through the signals as they bounce off us and onto other objects. What this means in practice: WiFi signals can be harnessed to recognize us and our movements through our walls. Researchers at the **University of California-Santa Barbara** used ambient wifi signals and a smartphone to look for revealing pattern changes in signal strength. **MIT's Computer Science and Artificial Intelligence Laboratory (CSAIL)** and **Massachusetts General Hospital** developed a device that uses an advanced A.I. algorithm to analyze the radio signals around someone when they're sleeping. The system then translates all of their body movements into the stages of sleep: light, deep or REM (rapid eye movement). Imagine a future in which your WiFi router collects your physical movements, then calculates your health metrics, and automatically adjusts the devices and appliances in your house to help you live a better life—if you're snoring, for example, your pillow could automatically inflate or deflate to adjust the angle of your head and neck. Another CSAIL team built a WiFi device that could read human emotion

Recognition cont.

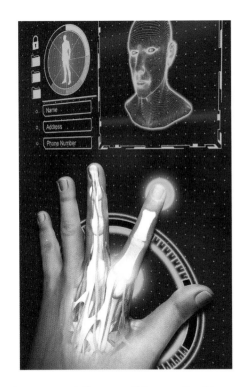

A conceptual diagram of bioacoustics identity authentication from Electronics and Telecommunications Research Institute's Joo Yong Sim.

using a wireless router. Called **EQ-Radio**, it successfully detected emotions without disturbing the person being monitored. In 2018, they were able to generate images of a person's skeleton in motion, showing posture and movements in real time using WiFi. Practical applications of the technology range from motion capture for video gaming to giving law enforcement and military new ways to see through walls.

Proximity Recognition

Instead of GPS coordinates, some offices and schools have deployed Bluetooth beacons and wireless access points to track people as they move around. The technology can collect as many as 6,000 data points per day per person, which suggests that location can be pinpointed down to just a few feet. **Kontakt.io's Bluetooth Card Beacon** is used as a traditional security access card, and it also tracks employee movement throughout an office. Card beacon technology can also be used to automatically recognize when an employee has left their desk and activate a computer's screensaver, or to automatically customize meeting room temperatures. Tracking systems, combined with other A.I. systems, can assign people

scores. For example, **Toronto-based GAO Group** developed a system that monitors location and predicts safety, develops better workflow optimization and monitors employee productivity. On college campuses, **SpotterEDU** has deployed its Bluetooth technology to 40 schools in the U.S., including **Indiana University** and **Columbia University**. Proximity recognition technology might track a student who is habitually late for class and doesn't visit the library enough—they could be labeled as "high risk" for dropping out.

Two-Factor Biometric-Based Authentication

Looking for unique biomarkers beneath the surface of our skin is a clever way of identifying us—you can change your hairstyle or wear colored contacts, but it's really tricky to rewire your vein structure. Using biometrics to recognize and authenticate someone also has an added layer of security in that it requires that they are living, since these systems look for both structure and movement. But for those who are concerned that one bio-identifier isn't secure enough, scientists at the **National Taiwan University of Science and Technology** developed a kind of

two-factor authentication method that first looks at skeleton topologies and then finger vein patterns.

Gesture Recognition

Gesture recognition technologies are now capable of interpreting motion to identify us and make decisions on our behalf. Emerging gesture recognition systems represent natural user interfaces (NUIs), and they will be an important future component of many different technologies. Imagine picking up a digital object with your hand, or controlling a remote robotic arm without being tethered to a bunch of wires. Gesture recognition unlocks the interplay between our physical and digital realms. **Google's Pixel 4 phone** can be controlled without touching the screen. Instead, the phone uses motion sense and radar technology to detect micro-gestures. The technology comes out of **Project Soli**, an early hand-tracking technology developed by **Google's Advanced Technology and Projects group**, which also developed the **Project Jacquard** connected clothing system found in **Levi's** Commuter Trucker jackets. (In early 2019 **Google** won approval from the **Federal Communications Commission** to run its

Project Soli hand-tracking technology on commercial aircraft.) NUIs will soon allow us to control many devices with our body movement alone. We'll also start to see applications in the workplace that record our body movement to predict when we'll be most productive. It could also help security systems and teams learn when we might cause harm to others.

Object Recognition in Computational Photography

Computational photography is the convergence of computer vision, computer graphics, the internet and photography. Rather than relying on optical processes alone, it uses digital capturing and processing techniques to reflect and enhance the visual effects and phenomena of real life in photographic form. Everyone with a smartphone now has access to computational photography tools. In its **iPhones**, **Apple** uses computational photography to achieve a shallow depth of field, while **Facebook** corrects any 360-degree photos you upload. Research from **Nvidia** and the **University of California-Santa Barbara** has revealed a computational zoom technique, which allows photographers to change the composition of their photographs in real time. Photos are taken in a stack, and then rendered with multiple views. This would allow photographers to change perspective and the relative size of objects within a photo after it has been taken. Other use cases of computational photography include seamlessly removing or adding objects to scenes, changing shadows, reflections, and other atmospheric touches. Meanwhile, **MIT's CSAIL** and **Google** developed a technique that now automatically retouches and enhances the photos we take with our mobile phones.

Biometric Camouflage

New compounds are being developed to help people fool recognition algorithms and, somewhat paradoxically, help them be seen more clearly. U.S.-based **Road Wise** developed **Safety Skin**, a reflective lotion that makes your skin incredibly reflective. This is a solution for people who like to run or bike at night—the compound helps motorists see them more easily. But the compound, which includes glass microspheres and plant-based emollients, also confuses recognition algorithms, effectively acting as digital camouflage for those who don't want to be

When There's Truly Nowhere to Hide

MID-FUTURE CATASTROPHIC SCENARIO

All of the cameras and sensors seem futuristic and fantastic at the beginning, promising to optimize your diets and keep intruders at bay. We spend a decade acquiring new technologies that make our lives a little more easy and convenient, and so we silence those nagging voices asking us what we're giving up in exchange for all those new features. Eventually, we realize that while we weren't paying attention, our homes were turned into ventures for marketing, which is now constant and intrusive. We see custom video advertisements everywhere there's a screen: the smart mirrors in your bathroom and closets, the retractable screens we carry in our pockets, even the smart window panes we had to install in our houses to block out extreme solar heat. There is nowhere to hide anymore, because some entity is always watching, always listening, always there. We're uncomfortable in our own homes, the one place we used to feel most safe and relaxed.

Recognition cont.

Roughly 6 in 10 Americans believe it is not possible to go through daily life without having their data collected.

Percentage of U.S. adults who say...

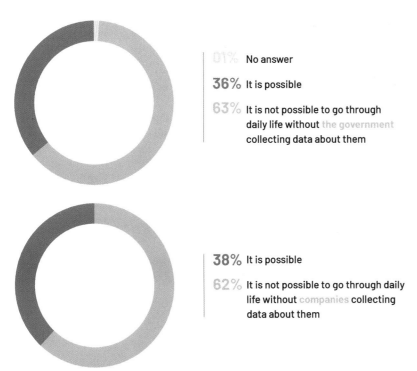

01% No answer

36% It is possible

63% It is not possible to go through daily life without the government collecting data about them

38% It is possible

62% It is not possible to go through daily life without companies collecting data about them

Source: Pew Research Center survey conducted June 3-17, 2019

seen. Meanwhile, **Japanese** company **Real-f** has developed super-realistic face masks made of plastic resin around 1 millimeter thick. It takes two weeks to complete a mask and at the moment, the company is only able to produce 100 a year. Masks can be made to look exactly like you to other humans while simultaneously confusing A.I. systems. Artist **Jing-Cai Liu** invented a wearable face projector that beams different images onto your face, subtly changing your appearance just enough to confuse the machines.

Personality Recognition

Numerous academic studies have used **Twitter** and **Facebook** as sandboxes for computational personality recognition experiments. What they're hoping to understand: Given a set of data, can an A.I. system predict how you're likely to react in just about any situation? This was also a question posed by the now infamous predictive analytics firm **Cambridge Analytica**, which in 2018 used automated personality recognition and targeting to help **Donald Trump** win the election. Political candidates, law firms, marketers, customer service reps and others are beginning to

use new systems that review your online behavior, emails, and conversations you have by phone and in person, to assess your personality in real time. The goal: to predict your specific needs and desires. **ElectronicArts** is working on a system that assesses the personality of its multiplayer video game users to do a better job of matching players, using their play style, conversational style and willingness to spend money as criteria. In the real world, insurance underwriters are attempting to assess your personality—via your magazine and website subscriptions, the photos you post to social media, and more—in order to determine how risky an investment you are. Some lenders have used personality algorithms to predict your future financial transactions. In the field of human resources, hiring managers are using personality recognition systems to decide whether you'll be a good cultural fit for their organization.

Accent Recognition

The problem with voice recognition is that we tend not to speak using standard, perfect language. Depending on where you're from in the U.S., the brown, fizzy, caffeinated beverage you drink from a can might be called soda, soda pop, pop, or "Coke," even if what you're drinking is a Dr. Pepper. And if a common word is used, it might not sound the same. "Caramel" is pronounced "car-ml" in Colorado and "carra-mel" in Maine. Historically, voice recognition systems haven't done well with accents or dialects, but that's finally starting to change. **Tmall Genie**, **Alibaba's** digital assistant, is now being trained to recognize some of China's many regional dialects. **Amazon's Alexa** is similarly being trained to recognize accents and dialects as well as ethnic origin.

Emotional Recognition

Alexa doesn't just know who you are—she now knows how you're feeling. In 2018, **Amazon** filed a patent for a new system that detects the physical and emotional well-being of users based on their previous and current interactions. In 2019, it announced that its **Rekognition** suite (used by outside businesses and organizations) is capable of seeing fear in our faces, while Alexa can sense and understand frustration. It's also working on a voice-activated wearable that can help decode how others are feeling. A real-world use case for the technology: Paired with smart earbuds, Alexa could ad-vise the wearer in real time how to interact more effectively with others.

Responsive Recognition Technology

Alexa is about to sound a lot more human. In 2019, **Amazon** announced some upgrades to the famed digital assistant, giving her emotions like excitement and disappointment. For the time being, Alexa will respond in a low, disappointed tone when you answer a question incorrectly, but she'll perk up and sound excited if you win a game, for example. Soon, Alexa's more humanlike expression will be responsive. If you sound sad, she'll empathize. If you're stoked about a great day at work, she'll match your level of happiness.

Affective Computing

Affective computing is an interdisciplinary field spanning computer science, psychology, neurobiology and cognitive science. It encompasses the emotion recognition research being conducted in A.I. but isn't one and the same. Researchers at **MIT** are using electrodermal activity collected from our wearable computers (smart watches, fitness trackers) with machine learning algorithms that respond to our emotions, but biological data from other sources can be useful, too: our skin, our faces, and our DNA. Analysts speculate that affective computing could become a $25 billion industry by 2023.

Genetic Recognition

Late in 2019, popular **U.K.** grocery store chain **Waitrose** partnered with the DNA discovery platform **DnaNudge**. Inside stores was a popup service offering shoppers genetic testing and an app that, based on their DNA profile, would "nudge" them to make healthier choices. The genetic recognition technology from DnaNudge required only a fast cheek swab. Customers could then use the DnaNudge app in Waitrose stores to scan barcodes and assess whether or not foods matched their genetic profile.

The popularity of consumer DNA testing may help people learn more about their ancestry, but it's also making it easier to recognize people without their express permission or knowledge. It is now possible to find and recognize about 60% of people in the U.S. who are of European descent, even if they've never sent in a sample to **23andMe**, **Color**, **AncestryDNA** or any of the other testing services now available. That's because raw biometric data can be uploaded to open-source databases like **GEDmatch**, which allows users to look for relatives across all of the other DNA platforms, and because of the pervasiveness of other websites (Facebook, government databases) that forensic researchers use to search across many different data points.

23andMe's enormous bank of human genetic data is now one of the largest in the world—and certainly one of the most valuable. Nearly 10 million people have now paid the company to sequence their DNA, and 80% have consented to have their DNA used for drug research. In 2018, 23andMe received $300 million to share its data with pharmaceutical company **GlaxoSmithKline**, and last year 23andMe developed and sold a drug to **Spanish** pharmaceutical company **Almirall** designed to treat inflammatory diseases such as psoriasis.

Universal Genetic Databases

The proliferation of consumer DNA testing services represents significant untapped

Recognition cont.

The DnaNudge wristband shows your genetic predispositions and risk levels (red, yellow, and green) corresponding to products you scan when shopping at the grocery store.

opportunity in myriad industries and fields, including insurance, pharmaceuticals and law enforcement. As a result, there is a new effort underway to collect and structure all of this data so that it is more easily accessed. A team of researchers from **Vanderbilt University** say that developing a universal database with standardized genetic profiles for every person living in or visiting a given country would allow law enforcement to find people who've committed serious crimes. **GEDmatch**, the open-source genetic database that helps compare and match DNA data files from different testing companies, was used to help find the Golden State Killer in 2018. It subsequently sparked renewed interest in developing universal genetic databases for government use. Of course, there are lots of ethical concerns. Under what circumstances should third parties be able to pull and use genetic data housed in private databases? What jurisdiction should law enforcement have over our genetic data, even if we haven't committed a crime? The governments of **Saudi Arabia**, **Kuwait**, the **UK** and **China** have all been researching whether to create universal databases populated with the genetic information of their citizens.

Persistent Workplace and School Surveillance

In the U.S. and many other countries, schools and employers have the legal right to monitor people, and they don't always have to disclose what is being tracked. For years, **China** has deployed cameras and other technology in classrooms to monitor students' attentiveness. In **New York**, the **Lockport City School District** began piloting its **Aegis** facial and object recognition system built by **Canadian** company **SN Technologies**. Meanwhile, **Microsoft** mines chat, email, calendar and meeting data to measure worker productivity within Microsoft itself. Sales team members were given personalized dashboards visualizing how they spend their time, and the system made recommendations for how to optimize their workflows. **Bunch.ai** monitors **Slack** channels to help managers understand their team dynamics and chemistry. **Teramind** offers monitoring software that captures real-time keystrokes, records video of their activity and will send an alert to managers if an employee attempts to print a sensitive document. **Humanyze** uses Bluetooth-enabled badges to track a worker throughout the day and then correlates that information with other data points drawn from email in order to find opportunities for collaboration within teams.

—
Food Recognition Systems

Several years ago, **Amazon** updated its mobile app to allow people to shop for real-world objects by scanning their barcodes. Its latest iteration lets users take and upload a photo. Now you only need to wave your smartphone near a given object to get more information on it, or have the option to directly add it to your shopping cart. For example, **German** lighting manufacturer **Osram** built a tiny chip that can scan a bar of chocolate to determine how much cacao it contains. At the 2020 **Consumer Electronics Show**, **Samsung** and **LG** both unveiled refrigerators with recognition systems that can recognize food. The refrigerators will scan what's inside, let you know what you're out of, and suggest recipes to make the best use of your available groceries.

Humanitarian Surveillance

NEAR-FUTURE CATASTROPHIC SCENARIO

The year is 2023, multiple hurricanes have devastated coastline communities in the southeastern part of the United States. As part of emergency response and recovery efforts, FEMA is giving every affected citizen $500 and a box of foodstuffs and basic necessities. These resources will be distributed at massive Amazon fulfillment centers because those facilities have the physical space and technological infrastructure to support the facial-recognition verification process. Citizens line up, scan their faces and present government documents to collect their emergency packages. To get an additional $25 in aid, individuals have the option to give Amazon full rights to use their faceprints in future research and analytics projects. For a 10% discount on their next order, individuals can opt to credit the money directly to their Amazon account. The average processing time for an individual to pass the verification process and receive aid is 90 minutes. Citizens are welcome to opt-out of the Face-AID program. Should they opt-out, the average time to receive aid is 90 days. This is the first time FEMA has deployed this technology in the United States, however these Face-AID systems are standard for USAID operations around the world in places such as Syria, Haiti, Venezuela and Iran. This Faceprint database, similar to fingerprint databases, is shared with law enforcement agencies to improve security systems and counter-terrorism efforts.

04 Emerging Digital Interfaces

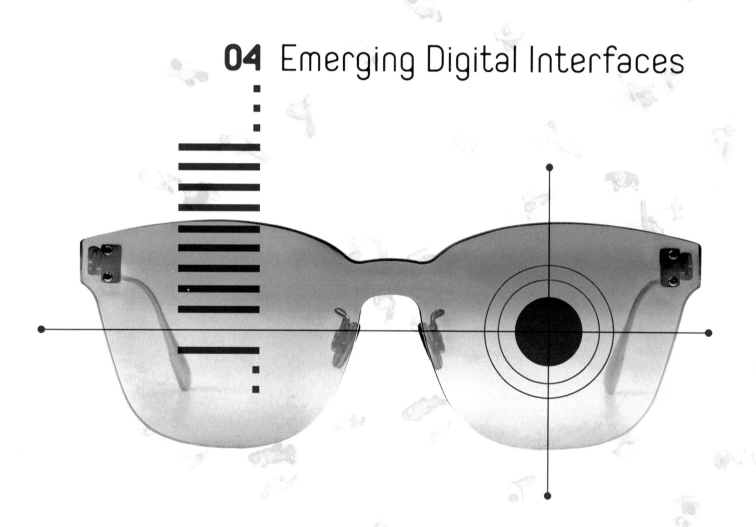

Emerging Digital Interfaces

HIGH DEGREE OF CERTAINTY

LONGER-TERM IMPACT

INFORMS STRATEGY	ACT NOW
REVISIT LATER	KEEP VIGILANT WATCH

IMMEDIATE IMPACT

LOW DEGREE OF CERTAINTY

Informational overlays are an AR functionality that can unlock efficiencies in warehouses and on factory floors.

KEY INSIGHT

There are scores of new devices on the horizon that are designed to alter and enhance the way we interact both with the world around us, and with entirely new digital worlds. These interfaces give us access to new experiences, extending our sensory abilities and overlaying our experiences with layers of illuminating data.

WHAT YOU NEED TO KNOW

From augmented reality workplace training to holographically enhanced surgeries, the future of digital interfaces will impact virtually every aspect of our lives. Most of us today think of digital interfaces as portals to alternate or artificial versions of reality. But over time, these digital realities will begin to play a more constant and primary role in our lives. The interfaces we use to access them will no longer simply be occasionally helpful tools or temporary forms of diversion—they will arguably become our means of existence.

WHY IT MATTERS

Every aspect of our perceived reality is increasingly shaped by devices, platforms, and content that intervene between our senses and the "real-life" physical world. The makers of our digital interfaces will have immeasurable influence on our psyches and behaviors.

THE IMPACT

Consumer market analyst **IDC** determined that total spending on augmented and virtual reality spending will continue to grow, hitting $18.8 billion in 2020, and that the total market size could balloon to $200 billion by 2024.

WATCHLIST

Amazon, Apple, Base Hologram Productions, Crypton Future Media, EchoPixel, Eyellusion, Facebook, Facebook 360, Garmin, GoPro, Hologram USA, Insta360, Kodak, Magic Leap, Microsoft HoloLens, Oculus, OpenSight, Pulse Evolution, Ricoh, Samsung, Vimeo 360, Xiaomi, YouTube.

Mixed Reality

Mixed reality (MR), also referred to as extended reality (XR), combines the physical and digital realms and encompasses a number of technologies—including augmented reality (AR), virtual reality (VR), 360-degree video, and holograms. Each of these technologies requires an interface of some kind: touch or gesture-based, voice-controlled, an eye tracking system, or a combination of various bio-inputs. Nearly every industry can use these technologies, whether it's teaching anatomy to medical students and training remote employees in technical skills, to experiencing virtual prototypes of cars and attending virtual concerts of artists (Tupac, Elvis) who are long dead.

A prominent device in the mixed reality space, **Microsoft's** Hololens 2 relies on eyelined-based user interactions. At the beginning of each use, the headset is calibrated to the unique shape and movement of a user's eye. Eye tracking enables applications to track where the user is looking in real time. For example, following a user's gaze helps the system understand intent. Combined with a voice command, a user can look at a desk and say "put this here" without having to specifically name or describe the desk. There are implicit use cases, too: If someone is reading a screen with a lot of text, the page can automatically scroll to keep pace with her eyes. As mixed reality developers aim to reproduce the nuances of human vision, including depth-of-field, this eye-tracking technology could also prove quite useful in establishing the user's point of focus. **The Food and Drug Administration** has approved multiple surgical planning apps for **Microsoft's** Hololens mixed reality headset. Florida-based **Magic Leap** is expanding its developer program for the Magic Leap One MR headset, which will mean new consumer applications and games in the coming year.

Augmented reality can be used to create shared, interactive digital renderings with creative applications in real estate, architecture, and design.

BASE Hologram launched a 2018 world tour featuring music icons Roy Orbison and Buddy Holly.
Photo: BASE Hologram

Virtual Reality

Virtual Reality (VR) is an immersive computer-simulated environment. VR is typically experienced through a Head Mounted Display, which can create the illusion of being physically present in the scenes being viewed. VR headsets are available from brands including **Google**, **Sony**, **Samsung**, **Facebook's Oculus**, and **HTC**, and they can also be constructed by slipping a mobile phone into a special mask.

"Standing" VR is viewed from a relatively stationary perspective and differs from "room scale" VR, which allows the viewer to walk more freely in a physical space, with their digital environment reflecting their real-life movements. VR arcades are popping up across the globe, offering teens who can't afford to buy their own headsets the chance to experience computer-generated worlds for a couple hours. The VR marketplace is now well established, but not quite mature enough for widespread adoption. The drivers of further popularization will be gradual refinement of the tech, lower costs for consumer products, and greater richness and variety of content.

Augmented Reality

Augmented Reality (AR) doesn't simulate an entirely new environment, but rather overlays digital elements onto your natural field of vision. AR is often experienced with a Head Mounted Display or smart eyewear, with devices in the latter category being introduced this year from many of tech's most dominant firms. (See also: The Decade of Connected Eyewear) Following a $480 million contract with the **U.S. military**, Microsoft is developing the **Integrated Visual Augmentation System (IVAS)**, a custom device based on the company's Hololens 2 mixed reality product. This one is for soldiers to use in training and in combat.

AR has incredible valuable market potential, with applications across the military, healthcare, engineering, and entertainment industries, to name a few. Be on the lookout for significant investment in the space, due to growing demand for its practical applications. We expect AR's adoption and value to eclipse VR over the next few years, especially as smart eyewear grows in popularity among consumers for everyday use.

Holograms

Holograms are light field recordings that, when reproduced, can appear as static or dynamic three-dimensional visuals. The term is also more generally applied to any image that is rendered to appear in 3D. We see potential applications by companies in entertainment, medical, advertising and telecommunications. Looking further ahead, perfecting hologram technology represents a critical step in the future of mixed reality technology, giving depth and detail to volumetric forms and achieving a convincing sense of realism.

In the past few years, hologram technology has been used to create virtual concert performances, using the likenesses of bygone artists. With many of music's highest grossing touring acts nearing the end of their careers and lives, and with encouraging sales data from recent tours featuring holograms of stars like **Roy Orbison** (produced by **Base Hologram**) and **Frank Zappa** (produced by **Eyellusion**), holographic tech looks poised to unlock a new corner of the events market. Elsewhere in entertainment, rapper **Chief Keef** used holograms to perform live in Illinois from a soundstage in

Los Angeles. The **German Circus Roncalli** created digital stand-ins to avoid the costly and controversial use of live animals, and the **Coachella** music festival featured the computer-generated **Japanese** holographic act **Hatsune Miku**.

In the medical field, such 3D mapping could provide doctors with a 360-degree view of a patient's internal organs, vessels, bones, and tissue and could assist with diagnostics and surgeries. The technology also paves the way for "holoporting" when it comes to both personal and professional telecommunications. Facilitated through the use of a head-mounted display, holoporting would let people communicate in person via holographs—your friend's likeness would be projected in dynamic physical form in your physical office space. Think of it like a full-body 3D video chat where the person you're speaking to can appear to interact with objects in your environment. As it evolves, this technology will likely revolutionize web-based social interaction, as well as remote workplace training and collaboration.

Though scalable in certain event contexts, affordable consumer hologram hardware isn't available. The functionality, too, is not yet advanced and accessible enough to

fuel demand. Expect to hear more about holograms, however, as engineers improve resolution, volumetrics, and depth of field, and as 5G enables the high-bandwidth instantaneous data transfer speeds needed for lifelike holographic streaming. To evolve beyond virtual and augmented reality, it will be critical to create dynamic 3D forms, which includes accurate digital reproduction of faces, bodies, and other complex structures. Holograms and hologram-related technology will play an increasingly significant role in our everyday lives, especially as smart eyewear begins to replace the smartphone as our primary personal device.

360-degree Video

360-degree video is created with a special camera rig designed to capture omnidirectional footage. Once the video is rendered, viewers can rotate their point of view using a mouse, touchscreen, or motion-control gesture to explore the recorded scene. The format offers a more immersive and active viewing experience than traditional video for entertainment, documentary, and news, and it can be viewed through standard mediums like laptops and mobile devices. It is a relatively simple and low-cost alternative to

the total immersion you'd find in advanced forms of virtual reality. Online platforms like **YouTube**, **Facebook**, and **Vimeo**, as well as major television networks including **ABC**, **Fox**, and **CNN** use 360-degree video in social media content, entertainment, news, and sports. User-generated 360-degree footage has also flourished, due to portable 360-degree cameras from **GoPro**, **Insta360**, **Ricoh** and **Xiaomi**. Garmin also recently introduced a 360-degree dash cam for more practical applications.

The future of 360-degree video is likely as a rudimentary version of VR. Because 360-degree content can be created with relatively inexpensive and user-friendly hardware, can be shared easily on popular platforms, and can be consumed on a variety of standard devices, it will probably persevere as a significant, if somewhat niche, format for the foreseeable future. With camera companies regularly improving functionality and lowering prices, we can expect an improvement in the caliber of 360-degree video in the coming years, which may coincide with the emergence of more sophisticated genres of content. Ultimately, however, the format may be eclipsed by more advanced forms of VR.

Virtual Human Touch Brings Intimacy

MID-FUTURE OPTIMISTIC SCENARIO

As digital interfaces become less indistinguishable from the real world—with audiovisual elements indistinguishable from their real-world counterparts—developers focus their efforts on a new sensorial challenge: recreating our sense of touch. With a combination of haptic technology and soft robotics, technology convincingly emulates the mutual sensations of touch between humans. It provides simple but significant interactions, whether it's handshakes or hugs that are given—and felt—between multiple remote parties through mixed reality interfaces. This remote physical interaction serves as a welcome antidote to the isolating and intangible aspects of the early internet, and it marks a new era of more realistic digitally-generated environments. Starting with applications in physical therapy, medical diagnostics, enhanced telecommuting and social companionship, the technology represents a monumental step toward merging our physical and digital realities.

Redefining Our Relationships and Personal Identity

MID-FUTURE NEUTRAL SCENARIO

The distinction between online and offline relationships blurs as more people adopt online personas that correspond to their real-life selves. Eventually, people experiment more freely with various identities, creating exponentially more connections between a person's manifestations, whether it's physical, digital or a combination of both. Complex social spheres take on even more dimensions with advanced mixed reality and holograms, as well as the rise of synthetic media. We begin, en masse, to view the world around us primarily through a digital medium and see the dawn of a limitless fragmentation of identity. A person can now feasibly choose a new persona every morning, use an algorithm to generate an entirely artificial character to socialize digitally on their behalf. They can alter their image while maintaining their personality and behaviors, or vice versa. And, presented through near-flawlessly lifelike digital interfaces, every one of these identities could be experienced as genuinely real. This makes us view identity as a far more pliable and transient construct than in past generations, and it redefines what an authentic and meaningful relationship means.

We Abandon Our Physical Bodies

MID-FUTURE CATASTROPHIC SCENARIO

We spend years bracing for the mental health impact of digital and internet addictions but failed to fully see the danger they posed to our physical health. Virtual interfaces and content grow more and more powerfully habit-forming. They become the primary medium for daily life, whether it's work, communication or entertainment. We spend more time in the 3-D virtual world, neglecting fitness, diet and sleep. Mixed reality attempts to recreate some of these activities on a superficial level—immersive VR experiences that give you the bodily reactions of rest or exercise, for example—but it's a false substitute. Our bodies get weaker without the real thing. Cases of severe exhaustion, malnourishment, weakened immune systems, and premature death climb dramatically. Society hits a crisis point, because our digitally-induced disregard for our physical bodies poses an existential risk for the human species.

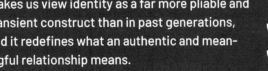

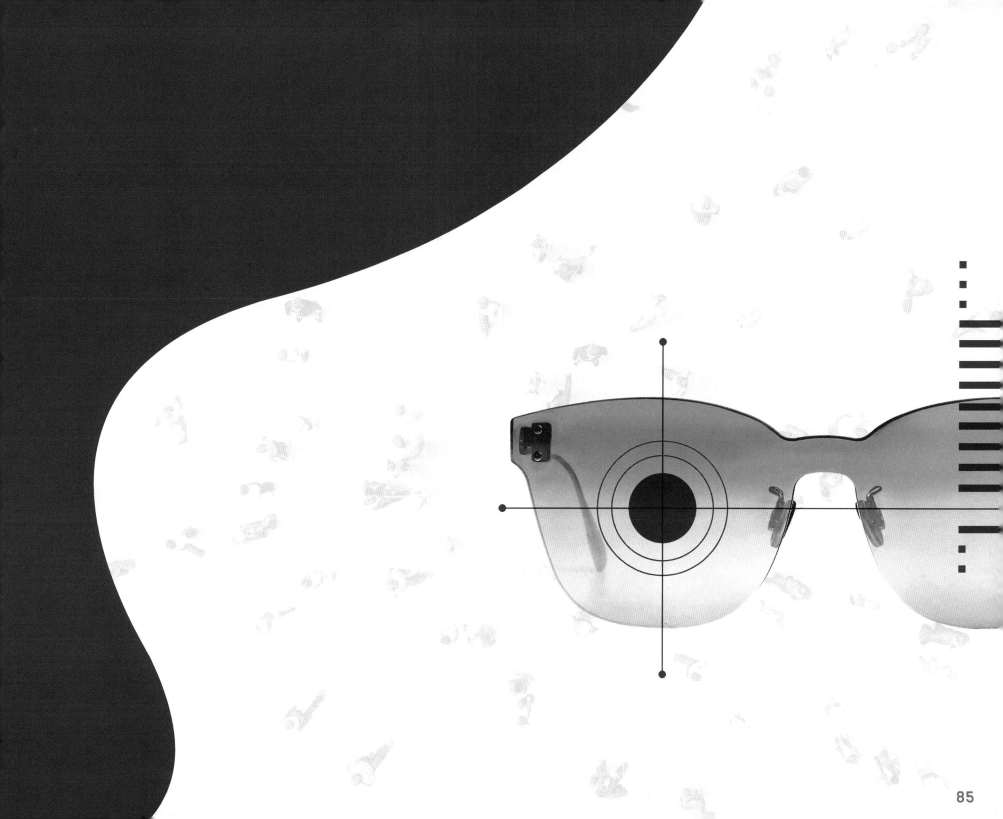

05 Synthetic
Media &
Content

Synthetic Media and Content

HIGH DEGREE OF CERTAINTY

INFORMS STRATEGY	ACT NOW
REVISIT LATER	KEEP VIGILANT WATCH

LONGER-TERM IMPACT · IMMEDIATE IMPACT

LOW DEGREE OF CERTAINTY

Synthetic media stars Lil Miquela, Blawko and Bermuda in a Christmas post on Instagram.

KEY INSIGHT

There are different categories of deepfakes, which include malicious, non-malicious and benign. Last year's malicious deepfakes included **Jon Snow's** public apology for the ending of *Game of Thrones* and **Barack Obama** calling **Donald Trump** a "complete dipshit." We also watched Rasputin offering a convincing rendition of Beyoncé's Halo. That latter, non-malicious category is better known as synthetic media, and you're about to see a lot of it.

WHAT YOU NEED TO KNOW

Synthetic media is created using artificial intelligence. Algorithms use an initial set of data to learn—people, voices, photos, objects, motions, videos, text and other types of media. The end result is realistic-looking and sounding artificial digital content. Voice clones, voice skins, unique gestures, photos and interactive bots are all part of the ecosystem. Synthetic media can be used for practical reasons, such as generating characters in animated movies or acting as a stand-in for live action movies. Synthetic media can automate dubbing in foreign languages on video chats and fill in the banks when video call frames are dropped because of low bandwidth issues. Imagine an entirely new genre of soap opera, where AI systems learn from your digital behavior, biometrics and personal data and use details from your personal life for the storylines of synthetic characters. In an ultimate expression of a "reality show," synthetic characters would play to an audience of exactly one: you.

WHY IT MATTERS

Synthetic media will spark new business opportunities and risks in 2020.

⊘ DEEPER DIVE

Synthetic Media in Pop Culture

You've probably already encountered synthetic media, such as virtual Japanese pop star **Hatsune Miku** (she debuted in 2007) or the **British** virtual band **Gorillaz**, a project by artist Jamie Hewlett and musician Damon Albarn that released its first track in 1998. What's next is algorithmically-created or modified media.

Eugenia Kuyda cofounded the synthetic content company **Replika** after her best friend was killed in a car accident. She built a database of old text messages to preserve his memory and then trained a chatbot to mimic his personality and speaking style. Anyone who wants to build a replica of themselves for others to interact with can use Replika. Another synthetic media example: **Google's Duplex** assistant, which can make calls on a user's behalf to book appointments or order products. Its initial launch provoked questions and concern over whether it would (or needed to) let call recipients know the system was an A.I. agent.

How it's Made

Synthetic media requires a considerable amount of data: photos, videos, audio recordings. That corpus is run through an A.I. algorithm called an encoder, which uses machine learning to discover patterns. Over time, the system parses all of those patterns down to shared features. Then, a decoder is taught to compose new content using the shared features. If you've ever used the face swap filter on **Snap**, the system is identifying the faces, using encoders to find features, then reconstructing those features on the opposite face using decoders. What's tricky—and remarkable, considering we use Snap on our phones—is that the system has to perform and repeat this process on every frame without lag.

More recently, synthetic media has been developed using generative adversarial images (see also: A.I. section). ThisPersonDoesNotExist.com is a website that will produce an infinite number of synthetic people who look perfectly... human. (A similar site, ThisCatDoesNotExist.com, was less successful in producing images of synthetic cats.) There are pages dedicated to algorithmically-generated scenes from the TV shows "Friends" and "The Office." These were accomplished using GANs (or generative adversarial networks, a type of machine learning in A.I.)

Deepfakes vs Deeply Edited

In May 2019, footage of **U.S. Democratic House Speaker Nancy Pelosi** went viral. In the video, she was slurring her words and, it appeared to many viewers that she was either drunk or unwell. Soon, journalists debunked the footage, and many news organizations worldwide referred to it as a "deepfake video." Many people demanded that the video be removed from **Facebook** and **Instagram**, where it was being shared widely. After the platform took no action, a video of F**acebook CEO Mark Zuckerberg** giving a sinister speech was uploaded to Instagram. In it, Zuckerberg appeared to say, "Imagine this for a second: One man, with total control of billions of people's stolen data, all their secrets, their lives, their futures... whoever controls the data, controls the future." The Pelosi video was edited skillfully—but it is not really an example of synthetic content because humans manually manipulated the video using traditional video editing software. The Zuckerberg video, however, was created using an algorithm trained on a real-world videos of him talking. The distinction is important, because not all synthetic content is necessarily fake news—and not all fake news is necessarily synthetic content.

A Business Case for Synthetic Media

Synthetic media isn't just about goofing around to make entertaining videos. There are serious business cases to invest in the synthetic media ecosystem:

• Cost savings and scheduling
Synthesizing voices could cut down on the time needed for busy voice actors. If you have Awkwafina voicing a character in your animated film, you could capture a sample of her voice and then program a system to generate her lines.

• Custom regional accents
Advertisers could generate hundreds (or even thousands) of synthetic characters to appeal to narrow demographic bases.

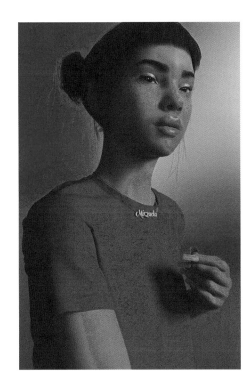

Synthetic media star Lil Miquela.
Photo: Omar Pineiro

Rather than selecting one human actor to extol the virtues of a particular toothpaste, different synthetic characters could speak directly to Southern California trendsetters, stay-at-home-dads living in Chicago, and aspirational Gen Z-ers who are just entering college.

- Reaching people in their own languages
In 2019, a campaign produced by A.I. video synthesis company **Synthesia** and advertising agency **R/GA London** created synthetic versions of **David Beckham** for a public service announcement about malaria. The short film shows Beckham talking about how to fight malaria in nine different languages. (His face moved correctly, but the voices weren't matched to his—though emulating voices is also possible.)

- Archiving ourselves
Advancements in synthetic media will let us preserve ourselves throughout our lifetimes. Imagine being able to ask questions to a 5-year-old version of you or listen to your mother read to you long after she's passed.

Legal and Intellectual Property Challenges

We're just entering a new, and very complicated, field of intellectual property law. For example, if a synthetic version of your likeness is created but borrows only some features, who owns the final product? Can you sue someone for making a digital caricature with infinite modification possibilities? Who gets to earn money from that creation? What about synthetic characters—who owns the right to program, control and decommission them?

This leads to thorny questions about our legal rights to all of the characteristics that make us who we are. Should a corporation own pieces of our human identity? What about a government? What happens if laws are changed to enable us to monetize our faces, voices and expressions?

THE IMPACT

There will be new public debates about the emerging legal and IP landscape as synthetic media gains popularity in 2020. Some will argue that synthetic media should have their own digital rights, permissions and governing structures online—just like we humans do.

WATCHLIST FOR SECTION

Adobe, Alibaba, Alipay, Amazon, Amazon's Scout delivery robot, Apple, ASVspoof Challenge, Baidu, Bermuda, Blawko, D-ID, Facebook, Google's Duplex, Gorillaz, Instagram, Lil Miquela, Lyrebird, MagicLeap, MagicLeap's Mica, MIT's Computer Science and Artificial Intelligence Laboratory, Nvidia, Pindrop, Playhouse, R/GA London, Reddit, Replika, Russia's Main Intelligence Directorate (GRU), Samsung AI Center, Samsung's Technology and Advanced Research Labs (STAR Labs), Samsung's Neon, Skolkovo Institute of Science and Technology, Snap, SoundCloud, Spotify, Synthesia, Talespin, Tencent, TikTok, TwentyBN, University of California-Berkeley, University of Washington, Vimeo, Voicery, Xinhua, YouTube.

Synthetic Media Technologies

At MIT's annual EmTech conference, MIT Technology Review editor-in-chief Gideon Lichfield interviewed a synthetic version Vladimir Putin using real-time adaptive deepfake technology.

❯ TRENDS

Speech Synthesis

Also known as "synthetic speech" or "text-to-speech technology," speech synthesis mimics real human voices and deploys them to various interfaces. With enough data and training, a speech synthesis system can learn the spectral frequency of anyone's voice and produce someone's digital voiceprint. One company, **Synthesia**, uses this technology to dub people through automated facial re-animation. This will be especially useful for movies with wide, international releases. Actors' facial expressions and mouths can be reformatted to ensure local languages are synchronized correctly.

Modulating Custom Voices

Generative algorithms are creating synthetic voices that sound just like the original, and those voices can be modulated to the exact pitch and tone desired. Montreal-based A.I. startup **Lyrebird** built a voice imitation algorithm capable of generating fake speech that sounds indistinguishable from the real thing. It uses a database of voice samples that are either available in public repositories (**YouTube**, **Vimeo**, **SoundCloud**) or samples uploaded by the user. The A.I. learns over time to recognize not only intonation, but also emotional cadences. This technology can be fun to play with. You can fake a conversation between yourself and your favorite celebrity, provided there are enough publicly-available audio files of that celebrity to build a dataset. Soon, the technology will be able to match and rapidly deploy synthetic voices personalized for each individual consumer. **Y Combinator**-backed **Voicery** creates bespoke voices for brands. If you loved Daria as a kid, you might hear Daria Morgendorffer's voice (or Jane Lane's) during a car commercial, while your spouse might instead hear Phil and Lil's mom from Rugrats. We should remember that in this era of misinformation, synthetic voices might also be used to trick unwitting consumers.

Deep Behaviors and Predictive Machine Vision

Researchers at **MIT's Computer Science and Artificial Intelligence Laboratory** trained computers to not only recognize what's in a video, but to predict what humans will do next. Trained on **YouTube** videos and TV

A still from a deepfake video in which Bill Hader slowly transforms into Arnold Schwarzenegger.
Image courtesy of ctrl shift face and YouTube.

shows such as "The Office" and "Desperate Housewives," a computer system can now predict whether two people are likely to hug, kiss, shake hands or slap a high five. This research will someday enable robots to more easily navigate human environments—and to interact with humans by taking cues from our body language. It could also be used in retail environments, while we're operating machinery or while we're in classrooms learning.

Generative Algorithms for Voice, Sound and Video

Researchers at chipmaker **Nvidia** deployed a new generative algorithm in 2018 that created realistic human faces using a GAN (generative adversarial network.) In their system, the algorithm could also tweak various elements, like age and freckle density. A team at **University of California-Berkeley** created software that can transfer the movements of one person in a video to someone in another video automatically. For some time, we've been training computers to watch videos and predict corresponding sounds in our physical world. For example, researchers at **MIT's CSAIL** experimented to learn whether a computer could accurately

predict what sound is generated when a wooden drumstick taps a couch, a pile of leaves or a glass windowpane. The focus of this research is to help systems understand how objects interact with each other in the physical realm. That work led to more sophisticated spoofing: In 2017, researchers at the **University of Washington** developed a model that convincingly showed former **President Barack Obama** giving a speech—one that he never actually gave in real life. In 2018, a **Belgian** political party, **Socialistische Partij Anders**, or **sp.a** for short, published realistic videos of **Donald Trump** all over social media in which he offered advice on climate change: "As you know, I had the balls to withdraw from the Paris climate agreement," he said, looking directly into the camera, "and so should you." This trend is likely to become more problematic as non-malicious deepfakes are used more widely in entertainment, gaming and news media.

Mapped Synthetic Environments

Companies are now mapping the real world to generate synthetic digital twins. **Amazon** has been studying **Snohomish County** in **Washington**, building realistic simulations of the region's roads, buildings and traffic. Its maps are reported to be accurate down to the centimeter, precisely tracking subtle gradients in pavement and noting unique markings on sidewalks. Amazon fused maps and 3D data to build synthetic versions of the county to test delivery drones. These kinds of virtual environments will be necessary as the company moves drones from research labs into the mainstream. In 2019, Amazon tested its **Scout** delivery robot in the real world, having trained it in the synthetic environment.

SCENARIO • AMY WEBB

The Rolling Stones are Dead— But They're Making New Music

MID-FUTURE OPTIMISTIC SCENARIO

The original members of the Rolling Stones die, but thanks to replicating algorithms, they still make new music. That sensation you felt after hearing the opening 30 seconds of "Paint It Black" for the first time—the melancholy guitar melody, followed by eight loud bangs on the drum and a repetitive hook that culminates in Mick Jagger singing "I see a red door and I want it painted black…"—was a singular moment of excitement and satisfaction. It didn't seem possible you might get to feel that way again with a new Stones song, and yet their latest track, which was created entirely by an A.I. trained to emulate their sound, is just as loud, hard and fulfilling.

Synthetic Media and Society

Samsung's Neons are designed to interact with you.

Synth-Pop Makes a Comeback

Synthetic media will give rise to an entirely new kind of celebrity in the 21st century: synthetic pop stars. It also affords a host of opportunities to make and save money. Already there are a number of synthetic pop stars with very large fan bases. **Lil Miquela** is a sort of Beyonce of synthetic stars, with 1.8 million followers on Instagram as of the start of this year. She is a model for brands like **Prada** and **Calvin Klein**, a musician with popular tracks on **Spotify** and a paid brand ambassador for enormous, global companies like **Samsung**. And she has friends: **Bermuda**, a rule-breaking bad girl model/influencer and **Blawko**, an L.A.-based guy who likes fast cars, **Absolut** vodka and is never without his trademark face scarf covering his nose and mouth.

In many ways, these stars are the antidote to teen stars like Lindsay Lohan and Shia LeBeouf who, for one reason or another, stray from their carefully-crafted public images and cause headaches for their agents, managers and the brands or projects they represent. Synthetic stars don't sleep. They don't eat. They never get tired, even if they're pushed 24-hours a day. They don't

drink alcohol or use drugs, would never say anything off-message, and their mug shots would never go viral on the internet. (Unless it was planned, of course. Over the summer, Bermuda posted her own mugshot on Instagram to "get ahead" of the press.)

While Bermuda and Blawko aren't programmable yet, **China's** A.I. news anchors are. Last year, China's state news agency **Xinhua** unveiled A.I. news anchors Xin Xiaomeng, Qui Hao, and Xin Xiaohao, who appear in videos and also write stories for the agency.

Simulating Human Experiences

What if you could interact with a simulated person to learn from them or practice management techniques? Would you invite a synth to a dinner party? **Samsung's Technology and Advanced Research Labs (STAR Labs)** thinks the answer is yes. It developed **Neon**, "a computationally created virtual being that looks and behaves like a real human, with the ability to show emotions and intelligence." Neons aren't intended as a stand-in for the internet. They were built to hang out with you. **U.S.**-based startup **Talespin** built synths in virtual reality to teach people "soft" management skills, including how to encourage team members or how to fire someone with empathy and compassion. Canadian startup **TwentyBN** built a synthetic sales associate to cheerfully interact with customers—and convince them to spend more money.

Synthetic Voice Fraud

Synthesized media has a known problem area: It can be used by malicious actors to mislead people, to trick voice authentication systems and to create forged audio recordings. Voice fraud cost U.S. businesses with call centers $14 billion last year alone, according to a study by call center software maker **Pindrop**. **Google** has been working on a synthetic speech dataset as part of the **ASVspoof 2019 Challenge**, which is an open source, global initiative designed to help develop countermeasures to fight spoofed speech. Researchers hope that the challenge will lead to more secure synthetic voice content. Voice synthesis startup **Lyrebird** keeps its ethics statement in view on its website, and warns that its software "could potentially have dangerous consequences such as misleading diplomats, fraud and more generally any other problem caused by stealing the identity of someone else."

Synthetic Sex Tapes

Natalie Portman, **Emma Watson**, **Taylor Swift** and **Daisy Ridley**—smart, talented artists—began "appearing" in adult videos in late 2018. Convincing short clips were made using deepfake techniques and soon went viral on **Reddit**. Not too long after, another Reddit user published a mobile application allowing anyone to make their own porn deepfakes. This poses a particular problem for public figures, because right now there isn't an easy way for the average person to tell what's real and what's fake. Photos and videos can spread through social networks and online without much protection for those victimized. In the absence of digital tools to spot fakes, we're left relying on critical thinking and common sense.

Synthetic Property Rights and Legal Protections

The video game Call of Duty: Modern Warfare, was designed with brutal realism. Players enter lifelike combat situations and must decide whether to shoot synthetic civilians. Where do we draw the lines between disclosure and pure fantasy? Parody for laughs and deepfakes for harm? What

happens when synthetic content seems so real that the psychological implications are intense and profound? What if someone generates synthetic environments that mirror real-world situations and real people? No existing laws or regulations govern synthetic content, although some people suggest adapting current laws, such as those covering libel, defamation, identity fraud or impersonating a government official.

Using Synthetic Media to Get Around Copyright Laws

In many countries it is illegal to plagiarize someone's original content. You might remember the 1989 pop-rap crossover hit "Ice Ice Baby" by Vanilla Ice. He sampled David Bowie and Queen's collaboration "Under Pressure" (you know the base line hook: da-da-da—-da-da-da-dum) but didn't get permission first. He tried to get around copyright law saying that he added a beat between notes (Ice's version: da-da-da—-da-da-da-dum, _DA_—-da-da-da—-da-da-da-dum) and made it a distinctly different song. The case settled out of court, but it shined a light on how U.S. copyright laws were created to protect the financial—not creative—interests of artists. What if someone created

a slightly altered copy of you for use in promotional commercials? For example if your likeness was edited to include facial hair and a pair of glasses you don't have in real life, and then used without your permission. Would that eliminate the legal requirement for consent? **Israeli startup D-ID** thinks so. It designed software to scrape video from security cameras to study emotion recognition—without first getting the express permission from the people in those videos. Using software like this might not be a technical violation of the **GDPR** in **Europe** or **CCPA** in **California**, but it certainly violates the spirit of those laws.

Synthetic Media Marketplaces

We already got a taste of what our future synth media marketplaces will look like. In 2018 a subreddit dedicated to publishing deepfakes morphed into a makeshift marketplace. Users were volunteering to create deepfake videos of celebrities, coworkers, family members, neighbors and enemies in exchange for cryptocurrency. In the near-future, marketplaces to commission, buy and sell synthetic media, as well as their attributes, will be visible on the dark social web.

Truth Decay in an Era of Synthetic Media

In 2020, we expect to see synthetic media technologies commercialized and made widely available. But without the infrastructure in place to help consumers distinguish between synths and humans, the likelihood of misinformation campaigns will rise. Synthetic media could be weaponized by governments, activist groups and individuals and could be treated the same as all other internet content, showing up in search results, on our smart speakers as audio content, on our connected TVs, in our inboxes and throughout social media. It is possible that ahead of the 2020 elections in the U.S., sacred information channels—public, commercial, and cable news, government agencies, even family members—could become compromised.

AMY WEBB

Finding Truth in Virtual Worlds

Synthetic content is still built by humans, but at some point, it will be completely algorithmically generated. This raises some difficult questions we ought to be addressing today, including:

- ➡ Who "owns" synthetic content? Who is responsible for it?

- ➡ Would a country's speech laws govern humans and synthetic characters in the same way?

- ➡ What responsibility would be required to preserve a synthetic character's actions? Or could they be easily deleted?

- ➡ If the person who created the synthetic character and all their content dies, or if the company goes out of business, who inherits that character?

- ➡ If an A.I. system starts generating synthetic characters, and those characters cause harm to others, who is then responsible?

- ➡ What disclosures should be required to let people know content or characters are synthetic?

- ➡ How do we define "truth" in an era of synthesized media?

AMY WEBB

Project Hermione:
Towards Cognitive Synthetic Media

Mathematician and computer scientist **Alan Turing** once proposed a thesis and a test: If someday, a computer could answer questions in a manner indistinguishable from humans, then it must be "thinking." You've likely heard of the paper by another name: the Turing Test. It's been a guiding force in the development of artificial intelligence ever since.

Tests built on either deception (can a computer fool a human into believing it's human?) or replication (can a computer act exactly as we would?) do not acknowledge A.I. for what it has always been: intelligence gained and expressed in ways that do not resemble our own human experience. Rather than judging an A.I. based on whether it can or cannot "think" exactly like we do, the **Future Today Institute** proposes a new test to measure the meaningful contributions of an A.I. It would judge the value of cognitive and behavioral tasks that we could not perform on our own. A system passes the test when it makes general contributions that are equal to or better than a human's.

Making a valuable contribution in a group is something that most people have had to do themselves, whether it's at work, in a religious setting, at the neighborhood pub with friends or in a high school history class. Simply interjecting with a factoid or to answer a question doesn't add real value to a conversation. Making a valuable contribution involves many different skills:

⊙ **Making educated guesses**
This is also called "abductive reasoning," and it's how most of us get through the day. We use the best information available, make and test hypotheses and come up with an answer even if there's no clear explanation.

⊙ **Correctly extracting meaning from words, pauses and ambient noise**
Just because someone says they're "happy" to take on a new project doesn't mean it literally makes them *happy*. Other cues, like their body language, might tell us that they're fairly *unhappy* with the request but, for whatever reason, they're not able to say no.

⊙ **Using experience, knowledge and historical context for understanding**
When people interact, they bring with them a nuanced worldview, a unique set of personal experiences and, typically, their own expectations. Sometimes logic and facts won't win an argument. Other times, they're all that matter.

⊙ **Reading the room**
There's the explicit interaction—and the tacit one happening beneath the surface. Subtle cues help us figure out when there's an elephant demanding our attention.

Inspired by the *Harry Potter* character Hermione Granger, who always, and in every situation, knows just what to say or do, we propose the Hermione Meaningful Contribution Test. It would be passed when the A.I. can function in a group of diverse humans representing different cultures, personalities and power dynamics. For example, when a synthetic media can push back on a small but growing consensus, tactfully argue for an alternative plan and recruit another member of the group to support that alternative, it would have made a valuable contribution. **The Hermione Meaningful Contribution Test** would be passed.

06 Content

IRL Geography Reshapes the Virtual World

HIGH DEGREE OF CERTAINTY

INFORMS STRATEGY	ACT NOW
REVISIT LATER	KEEP VIGILANT WATCH

LONGER-TERM IMPACT / IMMEDIATE IMPACT

LOW DEGREE OF CERTAINTY

Key Insight

In the internet's first two decades, information crossed borders freely. Now local, state, and national governments are creating a complex patchwork of regulation that assigns internet users (and their data) different rights in different places.

Why It Matters

Anyone producing content—marketers, advertising agencies, brands, news organizations and entertainment companies—will need to adapt to a fragmented landscape of laws and regulations.

Examples

The California Consumer Privacy Act (CCPA) went into effect in January 2020, giving Californians the power to stop businesses from selling their personal information and a GDPR-style right to have information deleted. Even though the first enforcement actions aren't expected before April, businesses that serve Californians—even if they're not based in California—were required to be compliant in January.

Vermont's data broker regulation law went into effect on January 1, 2019. Washington State passed a law strengthening the definition of personally identifiable information in the state and shortening the window companies have to notify consumers and the state attorney general after a data breach. In New York, legislators passed the Stop Hacks and Improve Electronic Data Security Act to increase the types of personal information covered by the state's data breach reporting law. The New York State Senate also considered the New York Privacy Act, a bill that would give companies a fiduciary responsibility to protect data—and establish a right for New Yorkers to sue for damages if their data was compromised.

New laws will give real meaning to the physical geography of where a user accesses the internet, and of where the companies involved are located. The CCPA, for example, protects California residents no matter where they are; the scope of other laws may be different.

What's Next

CCPA and the other state laws on the horizon will impact ad targeting, but watch for major changes in any business that depends on knowing its consumers, like subscription marketing. Expect the debate about regulation of the internet (and its consequences) to continue. Bills that were defeated by lobbyists this past session may be back next year.

The Impact

Without coordinated effort, geographic differences in rights and expectations will continue to proliferate. This could change the economics and operating model for firms that serve customers across international borders (or even across state lines in the U.S.). Established tech platforms and multinational organizations will have the scale to account for that kind of regulatory complexity, but new entrants may find it hard to serve—and monetize—audiences in multiple jurisdictions.

Watchlist

European Union, Federal Communications Commission, tech platforms, news and entertainment media companies and lawmakers around the world.

Local laws now govern how content can be published and shared.

The End of Attention Metrics

HIGH DEGREE OF CERTAINTY

INFORMS STRATEGY	ACT NOW
REVISIT LATER	KEEP VIGILANT WATCH

LONGER-TERM IMPACT — IMMEDIATE IMPACT

LOW DEGREE OF CERTAINTY

Key Insight

The attention economy, which spawned listicles and tweet roundups, isn't as easily measured as previously thought.

Why It Matters

Measuring how consumers allocate their attention depends on how you count—and who is counting.

Examples

Researchers estimate that more than half of web traffic is fake. Fraudulent traffic is generated by bots that can fake clicks and by click farms in which a single user can interact across scores of devices simultaneously. Nevertheless, vast portions of the digital economy are built around quantifying how users consume media online.

One week after the film "The Irishman" was made available for streaming, **Netflix** (who had purchased the rights to the production) reported that 26.4 million households had watched the 3.5 hour-long feature to at least 70 percent completion. Independent measurement firm **Nielsen** calculated that the film drew half that audience (13.2 million viewers) in the first five days it was posted. The vastly different numbers can shape whether we think the film was a success, how we perceive Netflix's future strategy and more.

Beyond different ways of counting, there's also outright fraud online. Schemes to manipulate metrics follow the money: **MadHive**, a digital TV advertising company, estimates that 20% of video ad requests are fake, which accounted for nearly $1.4 billion wasted in 2019. That growth comes as digital advertising budgets are shifting to video to match the growth in ad-supported streaming options.

This is a serious problem for both publishers that rely on ad revenue and for advertisers that need to satisfy client metrics. **Facebook** reached a tentative $40 million settlement with advertisers in 2019 over a miscalculation of video metrics in 2016. A federal judge in California should approve the settlement this year, and an unrelated suit—over allegedly inflated "potential reach" estimates—will move forward, keeping the issue top-of-mind for publishers and advertisers.

What's Next

Newsrooms have relied on real-time analytics platforms for years. **Chartbeat** blinks and nags every editor's station. Broadcasters depend on Nielsen ratings. But if so much internet traffic is fake, why bother with analytics platforms that measure everything rather than only what's verifiably real? Watch for sharper, more discerning real-time analytics platforms, as well as more home-grown engagement metrics that reflect how people value content.

The Impact

As mainstream browsers increasingly block third-party tracking cookies by default, it will be harder to connect individuals to their actions across the web. Digital marketers and advertisers must find new ways to quantify the impact of their work—and to ensure that their partners trust their metrics.

Watchlist

Amazon Connect, Chartbeat, Financial Times, Google Analytics, Interactive Advertising Bureau, streaming platforms.

Calculating how many people streamed The Irishman, and for how long, became a point of contention between Netflix and independent measurement companies.

Digital Frailty

HIGH DEGREE OF CERTAINTY

LONGER-TERM IMPACT | IMMEDIATE IMPACT

| INFORMS STRATEGY | ACT NOW |
| REVISIT LATER | KEEP VIGILANT WATCH |

LOW DEGREE OF CERTAINTY

RO PUBLICA   Politwoops   f y [DONATE]

Politwoops

Explore the Tweets They Didn't Want You to See

Originally published by The Sunlight Foundation. Updated regularly.

litwoops tracks deleted tweets by public officials, including people currently in office and candidates for office. If you think we're missing meone, please email us with their name, state, political party, office they hold or are seeking and, of course, their Twitter handle.

e your deleted tweets displayed here but you think they shouldn't be? Here's how to let us know.

Search Deleted Tweets

Search   See them by state: Pick a state

'or example: Trump, selfie, Obamacare   See all politicians

RepShalala (D-Fla.)
@RepShalala

Got a surprise visit today from #FIU students. I'm honored to be fighting for these students' best interests in Congress, and I'm lucky to have some of their students and alumni working with me to build a better tomorrow for South Florida. #PawsUp
@FIU @FIUdc @FIUSGA https://t.co/WLGawY1e5z
Deleted after 60 seconds 6 minutes ago. y &

DorisMatsui (D-Calif.)
@DorisMatsui

Capping funding for Medicaid is not flexibility – it's taking away people's coverage

Politwoops tracks deleted tweets by public officials, including incumbents and candidates running for office.

Key Insight

Digital Frailty is when digital assets are impermanent or easily compromised by technical glitches.

Why It Matters

Digital frailty is evolving from a flaw into a feature: This trend emerged as media was erased from the web because old sites were no longer maintained. It's still problematic when information with archival value is lost, but more systems are being designed to encode impermanence as users adapt ephemeral tools like **Instagram** stories or messages that expire within a set timeframe.

Examples

MySpace announced in March 2019 that it had accidentally deleted all of the photos, videos and audio files uploaded to the platform before 2015, which included an estimated 50 million songs. **The Internet Archive** found a fraction of those, but the incident remains a cautionary tale for those who assume their uploads are stored forever.

Differentiating material with archival value from digital flotsam isn't always simple. **Twitter** announced that it would delete accounts that had been inactive for an extended time in November 2019. That decision was meant to make unused usernames available to active Tweeters, but it neglected a major reason that accounts go stale: death. After backlash from folks who wanted to preserve their loved ones' tweets, Twitter quickly backed off the policy shift, saying it wouldn't move forward until it created a way to memorialize dormant accounts.

Most material disappears unintentionally, but that's not always the case: Users post stories to **Snapchat** and **Instagram** with the expectation that their posts will expire. Platforms could remove posts that violate their terms of service, even if that information is newsworthy or relevant to a public debate. Twitter has said it will make exceptions to its content regulation rules for certain public figures but other platforms might act differently.

There's also risk when organizations turn to external tools or services to manage their prominent programming. **Storify** was a popular tool for aggregating social media posts around a major news event. A team of journalists working for **Reported.ly**, a now defunct experiment run by **First Look Media**, won a 2015 Online Journalism Award for reporting on the shooting at **Charlie Hebdo magazine** in real-time. All that reporting lived on Storify but was lost when the platform shut down in 2018.

The Environmental and Data Governance Initiative estimates that the **Trump administration** removed one-quarter of all references to climate change on government web pages. This was an effort to support the Trump administration's ideas and policies. The Trump administration also removed LGBTQ content from federal websites, scrubbed a lot of civil rights information off of WhiteHouse.gov and scrubbed the HHS. gov website of healthcare data. While digital deletions can be politically motivated, they

aren't always: An archive of administration-curated news updates (primarily from conservative outlets) was removed from the White House website last year as a matter of housekeeping.

And what about a president's tweets? **The U.S. National Archives** says that posted tweets are considered presidential records and requested that the White House save deleted or altered tweets. **The COVFEFE Act** (a backronym for one of **President Trump's** unexplained and presumably mistyped tweets) sought to reduce confusion by amending the **Presidential Records Act** to include social media posts, but it stalled in the House. Some independent websites, including **ProPublica**'s Politwoops project, are now archiving President Trump's deleted tweets. Other news organizations are following suit and applying the same standard to other officials—**The Intercept**, for example, reported on and preserved racist posts by **Border Patrol** agents to a private **Facebook** group.

What's Next

Sometimes new technology obviates the old before anyone has had a chance to convert files or develop archives. **The Internet Archive** and others try to create snapshots in time, but the services can struggle with dynamic sites that rely heavily on JavaScript. While there's archival value to the files we post online, users are increasingly choosing ephemeral formats to share via Instagram Stories and Snap. How will future societies learn from the past if they cannot study the first draft of our present history? Do we have an obligation to preserve the digital conversations shaping society? Should we be working harder to ensure that digital archives aren't lost?

As we develop expectations for what should be archived, we must consider the risks of creating an indelible record: What should happen to posts shared by minors to social networks or student assignments posted to a school's digital portal? Do young people have the right to a blank slate when they

reach adulthood or should they be held accountable for ideas they try on for size on the way to maturity? (See also: Cancel culture)

The Impact

Future historians might look back at the generations alive today and wish we had done a better job of preserving daily life as it was unfolding.

Watchlist

Messaging platforms.

Trigger Warnings

HIGH DEGREE OF CERTAINTY

LONGER-TERM IMPACT	INFORMS STRATEGY	ACT NOW	IMMEDIATE IMPACT
	REVISIT LATER	KEEP VIGILANT WATCH	

LOW DEGREE OF CERTAINTY

Prefacing content with the term "trigger warning" (sometimes shortened to "TW") is a signal that what's about to be conveyed could be unsettling or offensive.

Key Insight

Trigger warnings now appear in email subject lines, on social media posts and even in conversation. They're a way of signaling that the information about to be conveyed may upset or aggravate certain readers, viewers, or listeners.

Why It Matters

Do trigger warnings protect vulnerable populations or coddle overly sensitive youth and encumber free speech? The longevity of the debate and growing empirical evidence suggest both positions are wrong: trigger warnings don't mitigate trauma, but clearly serve a social function that has led to their propagation.

Examples

The controversy about trigger warnings has cooled since **Slate** declared 2013 "year of the trigger warning," but signposting what a reader might encounter is no less common: Trigger warnings appear on **Twitter** threads and in blogs. Reviewers include spoiler alerts when revealing pivotal details about content that their audience may not yet have consumed. On the new **Disney+** streaming service, movies like "Lady and The Tramp" and "Dumbo" include warnings that the films may contain "outdated cultural depictions."

The first trigger warnings appeared on feminist message boards during the '90s in posts discussing sexual assault. The practice of warning readers about what they might encounter spread to other online communities, but hit the mainstream when the warnings started to appear in syllabi on college campuses: A **NPR** survey of 800 professors in 2015 found that about half reported using a trigger warning before introducing potentially difficult material on a variety of subjects.

Harvard researchers designed an experiment last year to test whether trigger warnings can help trauma survivors engage with potentially distressing literature. The psychologists randomly split 451 survivors into one group that received trigger warnings before being exposed to the content, and one that didn't. There was no evidence that trigger warnings reduced anxiety (even among those with diagnosed PTSD), and in fact there was "substantial evidence that trigger warnings countertherapeutically reinforce survivors' view of their trauma as central to their identity." That study adds to a growing body of literature with similar conclusions.

What's Next

Researchers will continue to investigate how trigger warnings function as a precautionary measure for potential trauma, and some pundits will continue to decry them as hypersensitive. But the practice of warning audiences about what they might encounter while reading or watching is unlikely to disappear: The signposts are a way to build a connection between the creator and consumer and to forge a community among individuals who use and expect certain types of warnings. So far, trigger warnings have widened existing divisions between people who value their usage and those who mock their usage.

The Impact

If we conceptualize the term broadly, perhaps we could imagine a way to bridge our fractured media landscape by enabling individuals to broach controversial subjects without excluding potentially sensitive groups from the conversation.

Watchlist

American Association of University Professors, Modern Language Association, National Coalition Against Censorship.

Abusing the Notification Layer

HIGH DEGREE OF CERTAINTY

INFORMS STRATEGY	ACT NOW
REVISIT LATER	KEEP VIGILANT WATCH

LONGER-TERM IMPACT   IMMEDIATE IMPACT

LOW DEGREE OF CERTAINTY

Wireless users in the U.S. cannot opt out of notifications from the president.

Key Insight

Push notifications can be a powerful tool to deliver time-sensitive information, updates, reminders and messages directly to our phones, wearables or connected devices—and they seize our attention in a way that passive or in-app notifications can't.

Why It Matters

Precisely because they are designed to demand attention, notifications can be used either to inform or to pester users, potentially reshaping their behavior.

Examples

News organizations have been refining their push notification strategies for several years, and consumers are starting to respond: A growing share of consumers around the world reported using a push notification to get a news story in the last week, according to the 2019 **Reuters Institute** Digital News Report.

Publishers commonly see dramatic spikes in app usage when an alert is sent. Users who opt in to push notifications use their apps more frequently, and active users are less likely to drop a subscription.

It's not just news apps that use push notifications: Social networking apps and games use them to command our attention (see digital vices). Wearables, including the **Apple Watch** and **Fitbit**, use them to remind us to stay active. Law enforcement, the national weather service and local governments use them to broadcast emergency information or Amber Alerts. **President Donald Trump** ordered a nationwide test of the **National Wireless Emergency Alert System** in October 2018. That alert, delivered to mobile devices, generated headlines because users cannot opt out of presidential alerts, but the underlying system is a routine tool for emergency managers. **The Federal Communications Commission** said local governments have sent more than 40,000 alerts since 2012.

What's Next

As consumers receive notifications from more sources, it will get harder to be heard through the din. iOS already clusters multiple incoming notifications from a single source, making it easier for users to then dismiss them wholesale.

The Impact

Publishers and app makers must get more sophisticated to ensure their messages don't get lost—and must help users understand what types of notifications will be sent before asking them to opt in, for example, so people can make an informed choice.

Watchlist

Tech platforms, mobile OEMS, emergency management systems, local government agencies, and federal agencies.

Cancel Culture and its Backlash

HIGH DEGREE OF CERTAINTY

INFORMS STRATEGY	ACT NOW
REVISIT LATER	KEEP VIGILANT WATCH

LONGER-TERM IMPACT — IMMEDIATE IMPACT

LOW DEGREE OF CERTAINTY

Key Insight

Shame isn't a new political tactic, but social media has created a supercharged cycle of outrage, boycott and backlash with its own name: "cancel culture."

Why It Matters

The impulse to "cancel" an individual, publicly and collectively labeling them as a pariah in response to perceived bad behavior, raises deep questions about how we hold others—especially those with broad platforms—accountable, but also challenges us to think about how one might seek forgiveness after transgressing communal decorum.

Examples

"Cancelling" can come in many forms: calling out, deplatforming, boycotting. It has happened to celebrities like comedian **Louis C.K.**, who was pilloried and lost lucrative contracts after being exposed for sexual misconduct, and political figures like conservative columnist **Michelle Malkin**, who had a university speaking engagement literally canceled over her views on immigration—plus many, many other individuals who are seen to have acted immorally or unjustly.

Although cancel culture is frequently seen as endemic to the political left, the transgressions that lead to calls for cancellation take many forms:Conservative activists cancel their **Netflix** subscriptions for perceived liberal bias on the streaming service. Students at **Harvard** reject the Harvard Crimson after student journalists ask **U.S. Immigration and Customs Enforcement (ICE)** officials to comment on an immigration-related event on campus. **YouTube** personalities cancel each other for personal slights, and teenagers use the term colloquially to single out social behavior they think is unacceptable.

Former President Barack Obama was one of many voices pushing back against the culture of calling people out online. "The world is messy; there are ambiguities," he said at an Obama Foundation event in October. "People who do really good stuff have flaws. People who you are fighting may love their kids, and share certain things with you."

What's Next

Every day we create a lasting record of our lives thanks to the proliferation of connected devices and the often indelible nature of online data and content. As people evolve, those records will memorialize their choices, messages, and frustrations—including those that are glaringly out of sync with current society. Not only will it be easier to find past actions of individuals that transgress contemporary social norms, but there will inevitably continue to be individuals who actively breach our trust in the present day with unacceptable, illegal or repulsive behavior.

The Impact

As a society, the question is whether cancel culture will leave any room for redemption. Will we have a mechanism for those who transgress to learn from their mistakes? What can someone do to repent for their actions? And who gets to decide when that repentance is complete—the transgressor, or the person or community who feels they were violated?

Watchlist

Political movements on all sides of the spectrum, public figures, social media influencers, technology platforms.

In 2017, a New York Times story revealed allegations of sexual misconduct by Louis CK, who later acknowledged they were true.

107

07 Social Media Platforms

Decentralized Content Platforms

HIGH DEGREE OF CERTAINTY

LONGER-TERM IMPACT · **INFORMS STRATEGY**	**ACT NOW** · IMMEDIATE IMPACT
REVISIT LATER	**KEEP VIGILANT WATCH**

LOW DEGREE OF CERTAINTY

YouTube star **PewDiePie** struck a deal to exclusively livestream all his content on **DLive**, a new decentralized video platform.

Key Insight

Digital influencers will wield far more influence over consumers than big, recognizable brands by using decentralized platforms. How? Blockchains and distributed ledgers now shift the incentive structures for how content gets curated and consumed—from centralized algorithms to vast user bases who vote for content in return for payments, reputation, and access.

Why It Matters

This impacts myriad industries, including online gaming, fashion, retail, tourism, auto manufacturers and even the 2020 political campaigns.

Examples

In July 2019, **Jack Dorsey** announced plans to "decentralize" **Twitter** by making it an open-source protocol—a move that underscores a larger trend in decentralizing content platforms. Platforms like **Gab** and **Mastodon** give content creators and community administrators more flexibility, ownership, and rewards for the content they produce and curate. In April 2019, one of **YouTube**'s most popular content creators, **PewDiePie**, struck a deal to exclusively livestream all his content on **DLive**, a new decentralized video platform. These kinds of decentralized systems allow audiences of any size to coordinate and self-organize, reducing the need for intermediaries and diminishing the role of distributors and curators. This could create a proving ground for an alternate form of editorial curation—one that gives more control to content creators, whether it's a social media or posting a public speech. These kinds of networks also make it harder to censor or limit access to information, and creators can be guaranteed that what they produce doesn't get altered, filtered, or blocked by a third party. Gab, a decentralized social media alternative to Twitter, has grown by providing an alternative to larger platforms, which have banned such users as **Alex Jones**, and which have strict content moderation policies restricting inappropriate content and cyberbullying.

What's Next

Centralized content platforms must make concessions in the form of revenue splits, content moderation, or managing audiences. By making parts of their platforms decentralized, companies like Twitter and **Facebook** will also be able to shirk the responsibility of moderating offensive content.

The Impact

Expect users to demand that platforms place greater importance on trust and credibility.

Watchlist

DLive, Facebook, Gab, Mastodon, Mixer, Reddit, Twitter, YouTube.

Platform Ownership

HIGH DEGREE OF CERTAINTY

INFORMS STRATEGY	ACT NOW
REVISIT LATER	KEEP VIGILANT WATCH

LONGER-TERM IMPACT · IMMEDIATE IMPACT

LOW DEGREE OF CERTAINTY

Key Insight

The platforms that shaped the last decade came out of Silicon Valley; that won't necessarily be true in the future. Popular apps are now emerging from countries like **China** and **Russia**, where censorship is commonplace. As a result, we must grapple with the values and features that define social networking.

Why it Matters

A leaked version of **TikTok's** moderation policy suggests the platform takes steps to reduce the reach of political posts, even if the original video isn't deleted outright. How will we respond to platforms with a very different understanding of free speech than our own?

Examples

A makeup tutorial went viral on TikTok in November 2019—not noteworthy on its own, except that the video was actually a plea for viewers to inform themselves about China's treatment of **Uighurs**. The video was designed to entice the creator's audience to keep watching past the first few seconds while also evading notice by TikTok's moderators, who could have removed or curtailed the reach of the video. The creator claims she was suspended from the platform for a month, but TikTok said the video was accidentally removed and the suspension was due to a video posted to a different account. The **Committee on Foreign Investment in the United States**, a government entity that reviews transactions involving foreign companies, launched an investigation into TikTok and its parent company **ByteDance** after it acquired the app **Musical.ly** for $1 billion. That review will draw additional scrutiny of TikTok, specifically around how it treats **American** user data and whether the app is being used to further Chinese political interests.

Earlier in the year, selfies from **FaceApp** were all over social media. The **Russian**-based app uses neural networks to make users look older or younger. To use the photo filters, however, users had to agree to the privacy policy, which gave FaceApp permission to upload the images to its cloud servers—and potentially to transfer to the data to any location where the company operates. The company's founder said no data was transferred to Russia, and the firm added an option to let users delete their data. But the uproar that preceded those announcements foreshadowed a fear that a seemingly silly game could become a tool for capturing data to be used as fodder in a geopolitical conflict.

What's Next

App designers encode their values and political attitudes into every choice they make. As a result, we will increasingly grapple with technology that challenges deeply held assumptions about the world. Should we download apps that transfer data into regions with different privacy laws? Should we post to platforms that actively censor controversial ideas? When should we act on suspicion about a tech company's practices—only when we can prove wrongdoing completely? Or do we do it preemptively?

The Impact

The growth of TikTok offers an opportunity to consider the implications of platforms built without American notions of free speech at their core.

Watchlist

ByteDance, Committee on Foreign Investment in the United States, FaceApp, People's Republic of China, TikTok, social media tools and apps everywhere.

This viral TikTok video disguised itself as a makeup tutorial but really implored viewers to learn about China's treatment of Uighurs. TikTok removed the video.

Platform Switching and Demographic Shifts Threaten Established Social Networks

HIGH DEGREE OF CERTAINTY

INFORMS STRATEGY	**ACT NOW**
REVISIT LATER	**KEEP VIGILANT WATCH**

LONGER-TERM IMPACT — IMMEDIATE IMPACT

LOW DEGREE OF CERTAINTY

Seventy-three percent of adults aged 18-24 now use Snapchat.

Key Insight

As **Facebook**, **Twitter**, and **Instagram** grew, it seemed inevitable that they couldn't be replaced, so long as they had enough users and successfully worked their way into the fabric of those user's lives. That assumption is proving false as consumer behavior evolves and Gen Z displays a willingness to jump between social networks.

Why it Matters

The most used social networks today—Facebook and **YouTube**—started more than a decade ago. Their relative popularity has remained consistent over the last several years, but that could drop as other platforms come into favor: Only 24% of American adults report using **Snapchat**, compared to 73% of 18-24 year olds, according to the **Pew Research Center**.

Examples

While public sharing on Facebook fell in almost every country in 2018, total engagement stayed steady. Why? Because users were creating Stories, a feature adapted from other platforms. To preserve its dominance, Facebook also formed a team in July of 2019 to develop experimental apps that could win over new audiences. The New Product Experimentation (NPE) team launched its first apps just months later—one a chat app for introducing new people, and another devoted to streaming music with friends.

What's Next

Beyond keeping up with the changing preferences of Gen-Z, will today's most popular platforms evolve to fit into the world they've shaped? The children of millenials will come of age with memories and experiences shaped by starring roles in their parents' posts, stories, and memes. A strong user base today won't be enough to guarantee a social platform's future; instead, successful players will wrestle constantly with privacy, interpersonal connections and evolving consumption patterns.

The Impact

If platform switching is more common than previously thought, it raises the stakes for incumbents trying to defend their market position, and opens new opportunities for startups trying to win market share.

Watchlist

ByteDance, Facebook, Instagram, NPE team, Twitter, Snap, YouTube.

Platforms Forced to Pick a Side

HIGH DEGREE OF CERTAINTY

INFORMS STRATEGY	ACT NOW
REVISIT LATER	KEEP VIGILANT WATCH

LONGER-TERM IMPACT   IMMEDIATE IMPACT

LOW DEGREE OF CERTAINTY

Key Insight

As hate speech, fake news, and rampant harassment escalate, online platforms and social media sites are increasingly investing in moderation of their platforms. Each platform takes a different tack to enforce its own policies, including blending human moderators and algorithms to detect hate or problematic speech, and other features like muting or blocking users.

Why it Matters

Moderation requires making choices about what is acceptable—and what isn't. Platforms must think carefully about what they optimize for and whose needs they consider, because any decision could be politicized and the platform's interests may not align with society's.

Examples

YouTube rolled out new terms of service at the end of 2019, adding the phrase, "YouTube is under no obligation to host or serve content." Facebook is wading into preemptive moderation with a policy to ban misinformation about the 2020 census and a ban on videos manipulated with A.I. systems. But the company has generally taken a more hands-off approach—in particular when it comes to fact-checking political ads. Twitter, meanwhile, decided it would ban political advertising entirely.

Classifying political speech is difficult because the process inevitably becomes, well, political—and moderation policies sometimes have unexpected consequences. When Tumblr announced in 2018 it would ban pornography, it disrupted communities of queer and gender non-conforming adults who were drawn to the site's formerly permissive rules. When Twitter announced it would ban political advertising, some labor groups and activists worried it would be harder to share their messages. An energy company, for instance, could post a brand campaign painting a rosy picture of fossil fuels, while environmental activists couldn't post ads for legislation to cut back on emissions.

What's Next

As platforms take a more active stance, they must balance their principles with possible backlash from users: When Reddit quarantined the controversial President Trump-focused subreddit r/The_Donald, users started a campaign to move the conversations to other platforms that might be more welcoming to conservatives.

Decisions about all kinds of content, from user posts to political advertising, will be highly scrutinized and possibly politicized. The proliferation of policies to regulate speech could push meaningful conversations about what should be allowed in the public forum; if not, it could further polarize debate, pushing users deeper into channels with narrower audiences.

The Impact

As the 2020 election cycle kicks into full swing, each major social platform has a different posture toward political advertising, misleading posts and more. Those stances will be politicized and exploited with far reaching consequences for our political climate.

Watchlist

The Coral Project, Facebook, Perspective API by Google, Reddit, Tumblr, Twitter, YouTube, political parties and candidates on both sides.

Facebook, Twitter, YouTube, and Instagram are investing in moderation of content on their platforms.

Forcing Difficult Conversations

NEAR-FUTURE OPTIMISTIC SCENARIO

Social networks and publishers aren't excited to define standards for acceptable behavior, but they recognize that doing so is their responsibility. Because there are as many rules as platforms, designers and developers explain how users should act (not just how they shouldn't). The result: meaningful conversations about how we engage digitally. Some people migrate to platforms based on what posts are allowed, just as newspapers see subscribers cancel after a controversial editorial or investigation. But because policies are revised and enforced transparently, most people make those decisions without losing overall trust in the media.

Perfectly Passable Platforms

NEAR-FUTURE NEUTRAL SCENARIO

Platforms are largely reactive. While A.I.-powered and human moderators at Facebook, Twitter, YouTube, and others make countless decisions every day, they function largely behind the curtain. While posts are sometimes removed, more often they are just made less discoverable. Because moderation largely happens out of view, platforms make headlines when they take decisive action, such as banning prominent users or removing controversial posts. These key players don't coordinate explicitly, but they tend to act in lock step, hoping to fend off criticism. As a result, users increasingly believe that there's political bias baked into social products.

Treating the Symptom, Not the Problem

NEAR-FUTURE CATASTROPHIC SCENARIO

Stung by public relations crises and aware of regulations on acceptable speech around the world, platform companies know they need to take bigger steps to moderate what they post. But development is slow: Each time they introduce a new tool to curb extreme posts, engagement drops among a small but measurable segment of the audience. Engagement is the lifeblood of a digital platform, and key product managers know they can't exacerbate user declines while solving the toxic speech problem. They thread the needle by making it harder to know whether a post was removed or seen by other users. Users notice fewer posts that "cross the line," but mostly because they've stopped seeing opinions they disagree with.

Censorship in the Digital Age

Following the February 2019 terrorist attacks in Kashmir, India, fake stories, photos and videos spread at unprecedented levels.

Key Insight

As fake news spreads across the globe on the internet and social platforms, censorship and free speech play instrumental roles in terms of design, development, and the legal protections afforded to creators and users of technology.

Why It Matters

If **Facebook** or **Twitter** decided to block all politically related posts because they could not sufficiently weed out "fake" posts, they would be making a business decision, but not one that would raise **First Amendment** issues. So, though we expect to see platforms tighten the rules on what they deem permissible, they are fully entitled to do so. In the **United States**, the larger First Amendment issues as they relate to media involve questions of what (if any) rights are afforded to A.I. and what liability (if any) can be imposed on the creators of technology, algorithms, and code.

Examples

The term "fake news" is relatively new, but worries about misinformation aren't. Just look at the 1938 "War of the Worlds" radio broadcast—**Orson Welles'** fictional story about an alien invasion that sent real-life **New Yorkers** into mass hysteria. The same kind of hysteria takes place today on various levels, thanks to the viral nature of fake news, conspiracy theories, and misinformation spread on the internet. It's causing damage outside the **United States**, too: Following the February 2019 terrorist attacks in **Kashmir, India**, fake stories, photos, and videos spread at unprecedented levels—ultimately fueling calls for military retaliation against Pakistan and nearly leading the two countries into war. In **Egypt**, fake news laws are being used to silence dissent. For instance, Egyptian activist **Amal Fathy** posted a video in which she claimed police officers had sexually harassed her. Two days later, her house was raided, and she and her son were jailed for "spreading false news."

Egyptian activist Amal Fathy posted a video in which she claimed police officers sexually harassed her. She was soon jailed for violating the country's "fake news" laws.

What's Next

Moving forward, there are numerous scenarios for how the U.S. government chooses to protect speech created by A.I. or automated devices. The most restrictive scenario would involve deciding that First Amendment protections do not extend beyond human produced speech. This scenario is unlikely due to the fact that some human programming does go into bot creation, and would mean that a string of different technological advances (such as voice recognition and generation) could be afforded fewer protections.

A second possibility involves deciding that the human programmer would be protected under the First Amendment, while A.I.-created speech would not be afforded protections. This attempt to compromise makes sense at some level but could fall short when it comes to being able to fully give credit (or blame) to content created by a human vs A.I. technology.

Yet another option would be deciding that all A.I.-produced content is considered free speech. Supporters of this view contend that the First Amendment does not limit speech to that created by humans, hence any content produced by a voice interface or bot should be protected. While on one hand this opens the possibility to all content being considered speech, if A.I.-created content is protected as speech, the legal entities producing such content could be held liable if appropriate.

We are likely to see some hybrids of these stances come about as legal questions arise. Look for media and journalism to be at the epicenter of numerous technology-related legal questions moving forward everywhere around the world.

The Impact

Americans say fake news is a more pressing problem than climate change, terrorism, or racism, according to a 2019 study by the **Pew Research Center**. Social media companies, governments, and citizens across the globe must balance the need for free speech with the need for truth. Fake news threatens democracy globally, causing confusion, spreading misinformation and seeding distrust of the news media.

Watchlist

European Union, Federal Communications Commission, Google, Facebook, Microsoft, Apple, Amazon, Snap, Instagram, YouTube, Twitch, broadcasters, newspapers, radio stations, digital media organizations, Jack Balkin (Knight Professor of Constitutional Law and the First Amendment at Yale Law School), Margot Kaminski (Associate Professor, University of Colorado Law).

Detecting Authentic Activity

HIGH DEGREE OF CERTAINTY

	INFORMS STRATEGY	ACT NOW	
LONGER-TERM IMPACT	REVISIT LATER	KEEP VIGILANT WATCH	IMMEDIATE IMPACT

LOW DEGREE OF CERTAINTY

Key Insight

Social networks including **Facebook** and **Twitter** have promised to tweak their algorithms to curb the spread of bot-generated content and engagement—but the bots are becoming more human and difficult to detect.

Why It Matters

Some bots may be harmless, helpful, or funny, but others manipulate people by spreading misinformation, artificially inflating the popularity of people, ideas, or products. There's also the risk of fraud, suppressing speech, spam, malware, cyberbullying, and trolling. The result: a social media landscape in which the public increasingly struggles to distinguish reality from lies.

Examples

Russian-linked Facebook and Twitter bot accounts spread disinformation during the 2016 U.S. presidential election. This is concerning when two-thirds of Americans get their news online, according to the **Pew Research Center**. In some cases, conspiracy theories spread by bots inspired real-world violence.

In December 2019, Facebook and Twitter shut down a system of fake accounts pretending to be real Americans that were photos of A.I.-generated faces and disseminating pro-Trump messages. All told, in 2019, Facebook removed 3.2 billion fake accounts between April and September—double that of the same time period in 2018—while Twitter suspended 88,000 accounts. **The University of Indiana** created a bot tool called **Botometer** that checks Twitter activity on accounts and scores them on the likelihood they are a bot.

However, researchers at the **NATO Strategic Command Centre of Excellence** in **Latvia** found it's simple to buy tens of thousands of comments, likes, and views on Facebook, **YouTube**, **Instagram**, and Twitter. Countries across the globe—including **India** following the aforementioned terrorist attack—have warned social media companies that they must reel in fake news, and special working groups within the **United Nations** have explored the topic of regulation, questioning what responsibilities and standards social media companies should have when it comes to international law.

What's Next

The challenge going forward: Algorithm changes tend to happen in real-time, with live audiences. Not all scenarios have been mapped and tested. This became apparent when a fake story about a Muslim man, warning others about a planned terrorist attack in **Slovakia**, went viral. Local police issued a statement correcting the story, but since it came from the official police station's account, tweaks to the News Feed algorithm prevented Facebook users from seeing it. As social media companies experiment with better ways to curb the spread of fake and misleading information, we will see glitches and potentially even more fake news stories being spread in the foreseeable future.

Impact

Labeling of bots will continue to be problematic. Algorithms, for instance, could cast a too-wide net, wrongfully flagging innocent content, such as voice-to-text posts from those with disabilities. If not carefully handled by tech companies and regulators, the labeling could also undermine freedom of expression in democracies.

Watchlist

Facebook, Google, Instagram, Snap, Twitter, the United Nations, regulators, digital advertisers, digital marketers.

Fake accounts and bots spread misinformation and artificially inflate the popularity of people, ideas, or products.

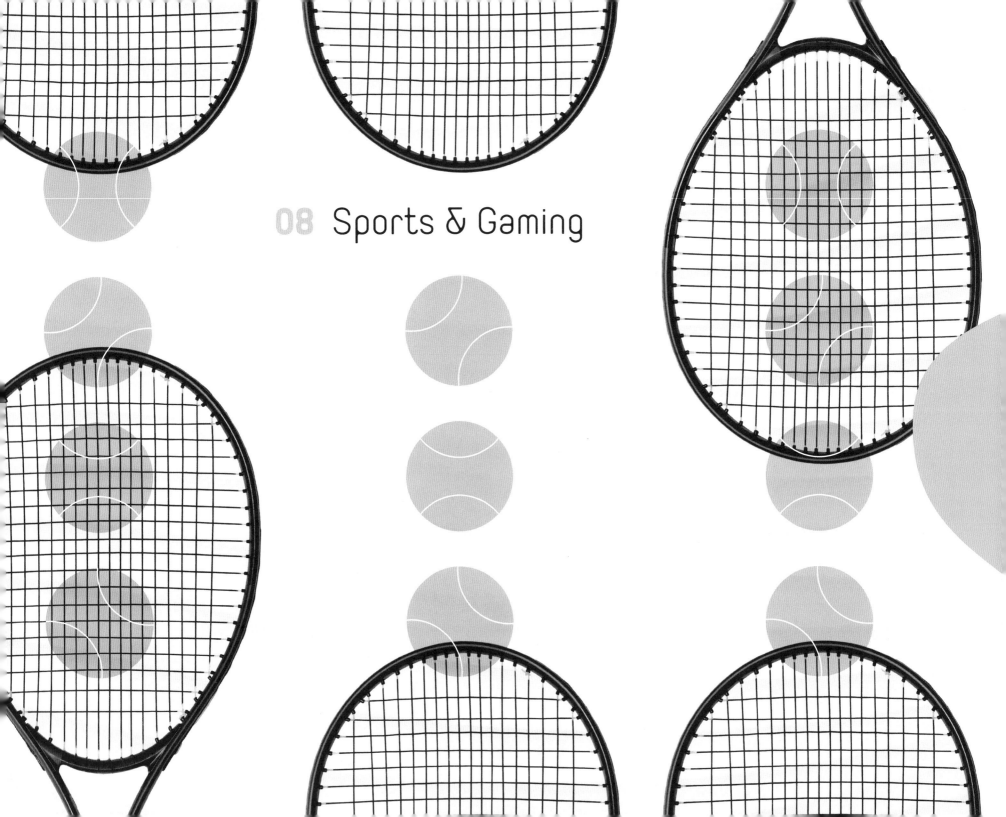

08 Sports & Gaming

eSports

HIGH DEGREE OF CERTAINTY

	INFORMS STRATEGY	ACT NOW
	REVISIT LATER	KEEP VIGILANT WATCH

LONGER-TERM IMPACT

IMMEDIATE IMPACT

LOW DEGREE OF CERTAINTY

FunPlus Phoenix, the League of Legends world champions, took home over $2.5 million in prize money and a massive trophy.

Image credit: Joao Ferreira / ESPAT Media

Key Insight

eSports is the rapidly growing industry of competitive digital gaming, specifically when performed professionally and for a live streaming, broadcast, or in-person audience. While organized competitive gaming has arguably existed for decades, advancements in gaming technology, accessibility, streaming capabilities, and popularity have led to an astronomical rise in its commercial potential and perceived legitimacy in recent years.

Why It Matters

In 2019, the top four gaming platforms had a combined 12.7 billion hours of streaming content. Players endure 14-hour day marathon gaming sessions seven days a week in pursuit of huge cash prizes. Millions of dollars are at stake, and millions of fans are watching.

Examples

The 2019 **League of Legends World Championships** had more than 100 million unique viewers. For comparison, the **Super Bowl** had 103 million unique viewers that year. **Twitch**, the primary streaming portal for eSports in the Western world, logged a staggering 800,000 years worth of content viewed in 2018 alone. (Twitch was acquired by **Amazon** in 2014.) One game that entered the global zeitgeist since its launch in 2017 is **Fortnite**, with a reported 250 million registered accounts and monthly active users in the tens of millions. In 2019, Fornite pushed boundaries on in-game content with events such as the **DJ Marshmello** concert, with more than 10 million unique views, and the black hole blackout, where millions of viewers logged in to watch essentially a looped video of a black hole while the game was offline for maintenance for 48 hours. Parent company **Epic Games** quickly capitalized on Fortnite's success, pledging a record $100 million in prize money for the game's tournament season last year. Non-gaming content also does well on eSports platforms. The "Just Chatting" chatroom channel on Twitch has been the third most popular channel for the past two years. Platforms like **Facebook**, **YouTube** and **Microsoft's Mixer** now lure top gamers away from Twitch with exclusivity contracts, but it will take more than that to chip away at Twitch's dominance.

What's Next

Leading up to this year's **2020 Olympic Games in Tokyo**, **Intel** will host its **Intel World Open eSports** tournament featuring **Street Fighter V** and **Rocket League** with a total prize pool of $500,000. The **2024 Olympics**, held in **Paris**, will include demonstration eSports events.

As audience numbers for eSports continue to climb, platforms will compete to outbid each other for media and streaming rights for events like League of Legends World Championships and Fortnite concerts. eSports may one day rival television as a form of mainstream entertainment because of its interactive and immersive nature. Advertisers are taking notice. **Louis Vuitton** partnered with **Riot Games** to design custom avatar skins and player accessories. **Nike** sponsors several professional teams. As the sport matures, so will concerns about fair play. E-doping is already an issue in professional eSports leagues, where Adderall and Ritalin are banned substances and using a cheat-code can get you banned for life.

The Impact

eSports is primed to continue its growth as a major cultural phenomenon in the near future, with significant impact expected in the gaming, sports, streaming, entertainment and tech sectors. eSports is also viewed as one of the first truly global entertainment mediums in its reach and influence, which has investors salivating.

Watchlist

100 Thieves, Activision Blizzard, Alienware, AppGameKit, Apple, ARCore, Bethesda Game Studios, Buildbox, Caffeine, Call of Duty, Call of Duty World League, Capcom, Catalyst Sports & Media, Cloud9, Complexity, Corona, Counter Logic Gaming, Crunchyroll, Dogo Madness, Douyu.com, Dreamhack, EA, EA's Origin, Echo Fox, ECS, Epic Games, ESEA, ESP Gaming, ESPN+, eSports Arena, eSports One, eSports Stadium, Evolved, Facebook Gaming, Fifa, Fnatic, Fortnight, Galibelum, Game Coach, Gamer Sensei, GamerHours, GameWorks, Godot, Google Play, Google's Stadia, HTC eSports, Huya, HyperX, iBuyPower, Immortals, Intel, Intel Extreme Masters, League of Legends, League of Legends Championship Series, Logitech, MagicLeap, Minecraft, Microsoft Studios, Microsoft's Hololens, Microsoft's Mixer, MLG, Nintendo, Nvidia, Oculus, Overwatch, Overwatch League, PandaScore, Playvs, PressX, Red Dead Redemption, Rocket League, RTSmunity, Sega, Sillz, Smashcast, Smite, Sony, StarLadder, StarCraft, Street Fighter V, Steam Fluence, Super League Gaming, TeamLiquid, Tencent, Turtle Beach, Twitch, Ubisoft, Unity, Upfluence, Vive, Y Media Labs, YouTube.

Infinite Gameplay

HIGH DEGREE OF CERTAINTY

INFORMS STRATEGY	ACT NOW
REVISIT LATER	KEEP VIGILANT WATCH

LONGER-TERM IMPACT

IMMEDIATE IMPACT

LOW DEGREE OF CERTAINTY

Fortnight launched in 2017 and quickly became one of the world's most popular games.

Key Insight

The most popular video games today have one thing in common: They never end. Rather than traditional games with a beginning, middle and end, many of these video games are more like online worlds, where players can participate whenever and for however long they like, with success measured in achievements instead of a single, finite objective. Infinite gameplay means you never have to log off, and you'll never defeat the final boss. In these never-ending games, players can also take part in hybrid real-world experiences like going to a concert or even buying real estate.

Why It Matters

Infinite gameplay sheds light on the hardware and software needs we might encounter as our lives shift more and more online, and the increasingly immersive and durational experience of online gaming.

Examples

Never-ending games are nothing new. Virtual world **Second Life** was launched all the way back in 2003, and **The Sims** and **Minecraft** are examples of longstanding games that allow players to build their own realities. More recent titles like **Fortnight** and **League of Legends** are universes that players can log into at any time for a fully immersive and interactive break from the real world. Classic games like **Super Mario**, **Pokemon** and **Grand Theft Auto** are being redesigned and re-released in this unrestricted format to the delight of gamers everywhere.

What's Next

How do you "win" a game if it has no end? Newer game design elements perfect addiction triggers and dopamine rewards to shape and alter our psychological state and behavior. Our lives will be increasingly gamified, as never-ending games merge with the activities that already form part of our lives. Connected exercise platforms, such as **Peloton** bikes, use built-in game elements (badges, contests and leaderboards). Meditation apps like **Headspace** nudge and reward us (somewhat paradoxically) to engage with them. Workplace optimization tools also encourage us to strive for new achievements, with progress and rewards being symbolized in digital form.

The Impact

In the future, never-ending games will blur the line between the multiple digital spaces we inhabit, be they personal, professional or social.

Watchlist

Android, EA, EVE Online, The Elder Scrolls, Fortnight, Google Play, Google's Stadia, Grand Theft Auto, HTC, iOS, LittleBigPlanet, Minecraft, Microsoft, Nintendo, Nintendo Switch, PlayStation, Red Dead Redemption, Ring Fit Adventure for Nintendo Switch, SimCity, Sony, Tencent, Tetris, The Sims, Twitch, Xbox, Youtube.

Sports Tech

HIGH DEGREE OF CERTAINTY

INFORMS STRATEGY	ACT NOW
REVISIT LATER	KEEP VIGILANT WATCH

LONGER-TERM IMPACT · IMMEDIATE IMPACT

LOW DEGREE OF CERTAINTY

Key Insight

Elite athletes are using more and more sophisticated tech tools to improve training and performance. Stadiums now use audience analysis and drones to improve the live and televised experience. Much of this sport technology could eventually end up in the hands of consumers looking to improve their health and well-being.

Why It Matters

Professional **NFL** players are retiring early, citing a history of concussions and the risks of chronic traumatic encephalopathy, or CTE. In January of 2020, seven-time Pro Bowl linebacker **Luke Kuechly** retired from the NFL at just 28 years old, and he wasn't the first to hang up his helmet before 30. **Rob Gronkowski** and **Andrew Luck** both retired last year at age 29. As competitive sports become more intense, data-tracking tools could help prevent the kinds of injuries that have led to these early retirements. But

this has significance beyond concussions in the NFL. In 2015, **the Fédération Internationale de Football Association** (Europe's governing body for professional soccer, or **FIFA**) approved the use of "wearable technology" in games. Since then, athletes have started using increasingly complex performance tracking systems such as smart gloves and smart helmets.

Examples

Football equipment manufacturer **Riddell** now makes smart helmets outfitted with tiny sensors that transmit impact data in real time. Coaches on the sidelines can see the effects of single and multiple impacts sustained during a game, and they receive alerts if the numbers get too high. The **Wilson X Connected** basketball is embedded with sensors and tracks patterns in shooting. **Adidas** makes a smart soccer ball with integrated sensors that can detect speed, spin, strike, and trajectory when the ball is

kicked. Meanwhile stadiums employ drones and video for everything from audience sentiment analysis to cleaning up garbage after games.

What's Next

Italian equipment manufacturer **TechnoGym** is developing next-generation machines that incorporate a user's biometric data, which can be tracked before, during and after exercise. Emerging research in reduced-gravity activity is helping athletes re-acclimate after injury. **AlterG's** anti-gravity treadmill automatically unweights athletes to as little as 20% of body weight in precise 1% increments for low-impact, pain-free movement.

The Impact

Smart sports equipment could reach a market size of $12 billion over the next five years. The use of advanced technology in both analytics and performance is likely to alter the state of many contemporary sports.

Watchlist

Adidas, AHL, AlterG, ASICS, Babolat, Black Diamond, Bundesliga, Campeonato Brasileiro, Chinese Super League, CWHL, ESPN, FIBA, FIFA, Formula One, J1 League, La Liga, Ligue 1, Major League Soccer, MLB, National Pro Fastpitch, NBA, NFL, NHL, Nike, Nippon Professional Baseball, NWHL, NWSL, Peloton, Premier League, Puma, Reebok, Riddell, TechnoGym, UEFA Champions League, Under Armour, Wilson, WNBA.

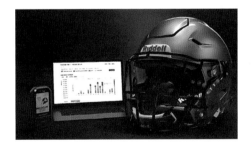

Riddell's InSite training helmet collects and analyzes on-field head impacts.

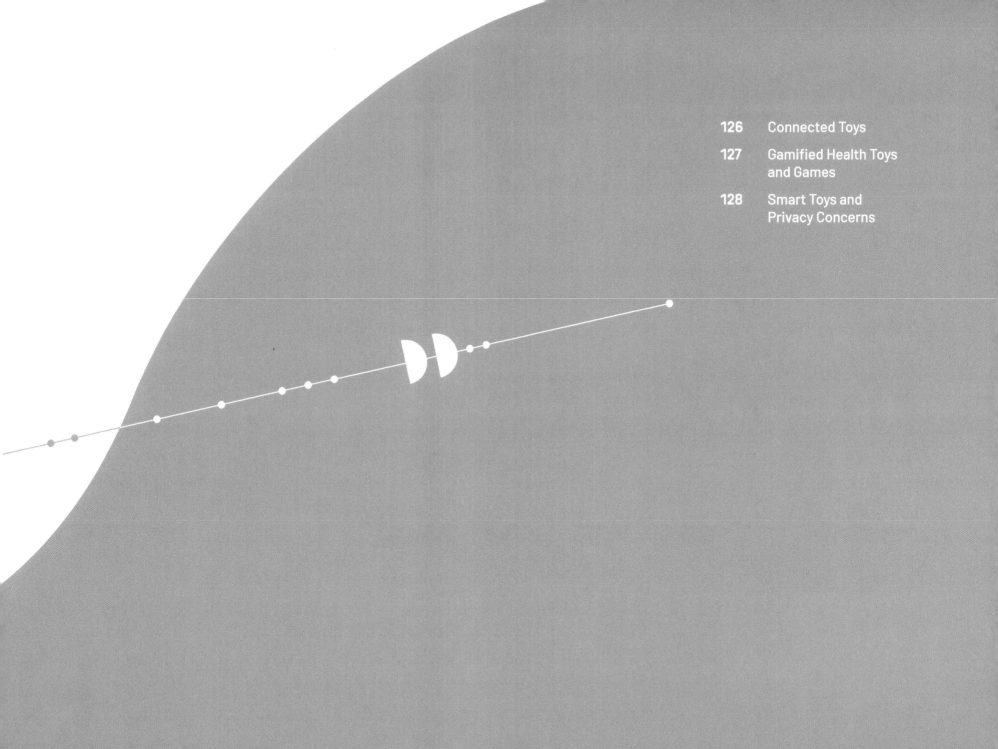

Connected Toys

Sony's connected toy dog Aibo doubles as a smart home assistant.

Key Insight

Connected toys collect and use data for interactive experiences. While they're fun for kids, lawmakers and academic researchers have raised questions about privacy.

Why It Matters

Some of the most coveted toys from the 2019 holiday season were connected dolls, robots and coding kits.

Context

Twenty-five years ago, animatronic Teddy Ruxpin bears sang, told stories and even blinked. Priced at $69.99 (roughly $167.00 in 2020 dollars), the dolls had audio cassette decks built into their backs; specially-formatted tapes controlled the servo motors for Teddy's eyes and mouth, and also played audio recordings. For about the same price today, Cozmo is a small, self-aware, A.I.-powered robot with a base personality, and the more you play with him, the more that personality evolves. Made by San Francisco-based company Anki, the toy expresses anger when he loses a contest, and his eyes turn into upside-down U's to show joy. Facial recognition allows it to remember faces and call people by their names. Sony's Aibo is a lifelike robotic dog that responds to touch—scratch his neck and his tail will start wagging. You can teach him tricks, like fetching a ball and giving a high-five. Aibo also recognizes his owners using computer vision technology.

What's Next

The upcoming generation of connected toys will use more data and will include even more personalization. Advancements in computer vision, voice and sound recognition, and spatial computing will result in richer, more interactive experiences. As connected toys evolve, they will rely less on mobile devices and will instead connect to the cloud. This means increased bandwidth needs—and, very likely, new privacy concerns.

The Impact

As connected toys become more affordable, kids might prefer to play with devices rather than simply watch content on them. This could start to negatively impact the use of tablets and apps.

Watchlist

Anki, Bandai Namco Holdings, Fisher-Price, Kano, Lego, Mattel, Meccano, Mibro, Soap-Box Labs, Sony, Spin Master, Sphero, Toymail, UBTECH, WowWee, Wonder Workshop.

Gamified Health Toys and Games

HIGH DEGREE OF CERTAINTY

INFORMS STRATEGY	ACT NOW
REVISIT LATER	KEEP VIGILANT WATCH

LONGER-TERM IMPACT

IMMEDIATE IMPACT

LOW DEGREE OF CERTAINTY

Nintendo's Ring Fit Adventure teaches kids how to do basic exercises.

Key Insight

Parents, increasingly concerned that their children aren't getting enough exercise, are looking to toys and games that nudge kids into more active lifestyles. They're also borrowing from the quantified-self movement to monitor kids' health and wellness.

Why It Matters

Approximately one in three children in the U.S. are now considered to be overweight or obese, according to the **U.S. Centers for Disease Control and Prevention**. That number has tripled since the 1970s. Researchers point to a lack of physical activity as a contributing factor. As a result, games and toys that encourage healthy behaviors are an attractive market for toy developers, fitness trackers and game designers.

Context

The **Gululu** interactive smart water bottle and health tracker for kids encourages them to drink more water. The bottle includes an LED screen with a preloaded game. The more water kids drink, the further their character will get in the game. Parents can monitor their children's hydration in real-time using a mobile app. **Garmin's** Vivofit Jr. is a fitness tracker that logs steps and activity, and its companion app works alongside an adventure game. Parents set daily targets and rewards. When an activity goal has been reached, kids can redeem their activity for the prizes their parents have created. (Playdates and sleepovers are popular.)

What's Next

Nintendo's Ring Fit Adventure, which debuted in October 2019, highlights a new era of gamified health toys and games built for kids. As an add-on for the Nintendo Switch console, the game takes the player on an athletic adventure through worlds, villages and gyms. Cute monsters, dispatched by arch-nemesis Drageaux, challenge players to battles: simple yoga poses, squats, crunches and planks. During the quest, players jog or run in place. Kids who play the game spend an average of 30 minutes in active movement. On the horizon: massively multiplayer online fitness games, in which kids can connect with each other and go on active adventures together.

The Impact

Apps, games and toys to quantify kids' health are becoming widely available, and they will have a spill-over effect into other sectors like consumer electronics, home automation and network connectivity.

Watchlist

Bandai Namco Holdings, Garmin, Google's Stadia, Gululu, Microsoft, Nintendo, Sony, toy retailers everywhere.

Smart Toys and Privacy Concerns

HIGH DEGREE OF CERTAINTY

INFORMS STRATEGY	ACT NOW
REVISIT LATER	KEEP VIGILANT WATCH

LONGER-TERM IMPACT · IMMEDIATE IMPACT

LOW DEGREE OF CERTAINTY

Parents and privacy advocates are increasingly concerned about the data being collected as children play with connected toys and games.

Key Insight

Connected toys and games require data to work properly, and privacy experts are concerned about how children's data are being collected, used and safeguarded.

Why It Matters

The smart toy industry is growing rapidly. Some estimate the market could be worth more than $18 billion by 2023, but privacy regulation is lagging behind technological innovation. The biggest market for toys is **China**, and the world's largest toy retailer is now **Amazon**.

Context

In 2018, **Mozilla** discovered that the Dash robot, which is a popular coding toy used in schools, was sharing children's data with third parties. So was Amazon's Fire HD Kids' Edition, although the company has repeatedly said that parents have the ability to view their children's activity and to delete their data. In the U.S., the **Children's Online Privacy Protection Act** (COPPA) makes it illegal to collect data from children under the age of 13 without first obtaining a parent's consent, and in 2017 the **Federal Trade Commission** updated COPPA guidelines to specifically include toy manufacturers. For connected toys, the terms of service are shown during set up, but most people don't read the fine print. As a result, they are agreeing to data sharing, whether they realize it or not.

What's Next

The privacy risks posed by connected toys mirror those adults face whenever using phones, smart cameras and speakers, and other connected devices. But our tolerance for data exposure shifts when children are involved. In the U.S., we expect to see heightened privacy concerns ahead of the 2020 holiday season and increased scrutiny by the FTC.

The Impact

Toy manufacturers could find their products pulled from shelves if their toys are found to be in violation of local guidelines and recommendations.

Watchlist

Amazon, China, Federal Trade Commission, Mozilla, U.S. Public Interest Research Group.

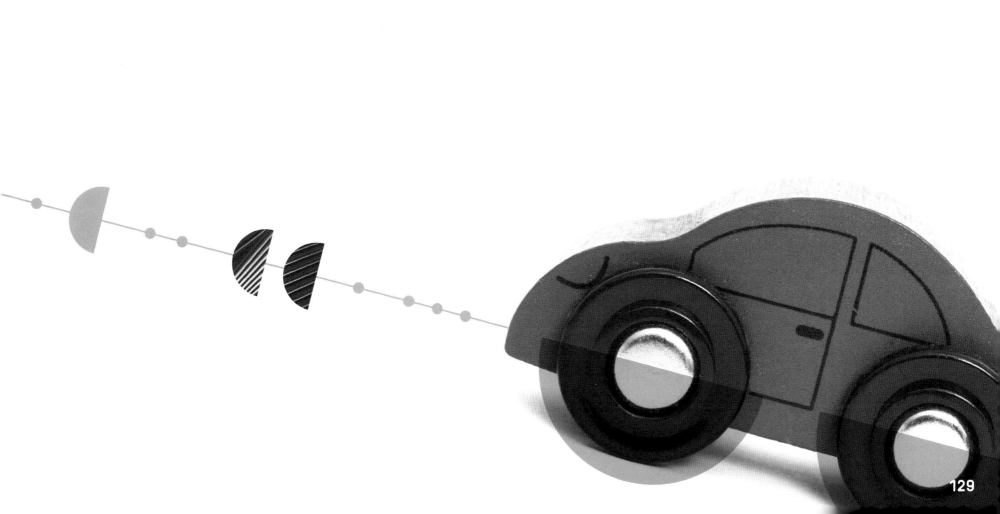

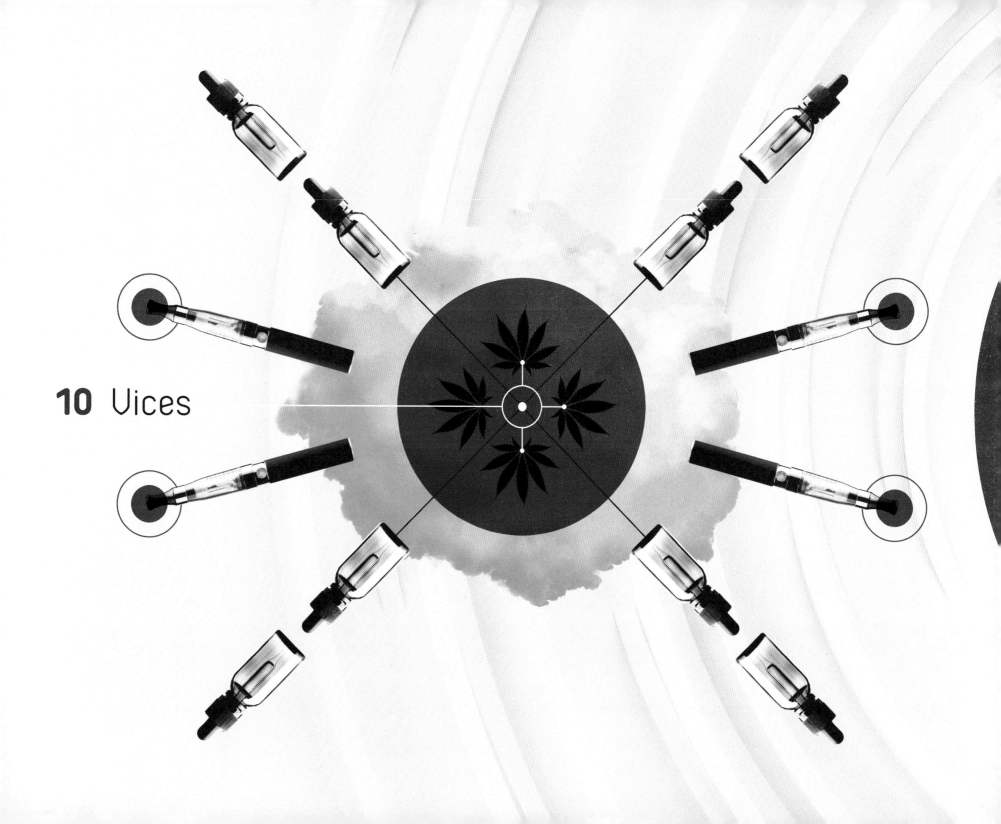

10 Vices

Vices

HIGH DEGREE OF CERTAINTY

INFORMS STRATEGY	**ACT NOW**
REVISIT LATER	**KEEP VIGILANT WATCH**

LONGER-TERM IMPACT / IMMEDIATE IMPACT

LOW DEGREE OF CERTAINTY

General Washington's Secret Stash beer is infused with cannabinoids.

JUUL
SMOKING EVOLVED

The Juul vape device is so popular that "juuling" is now commonly used as a verb to describe use of the device or other e-cigarettes.

KEY INSIGHT

In our increasingly stressful society, people are seeking new forms of escape from reality and mood alteration. This isn't necessarily bad. In fact, many emerging digital vices can actually strengthen our mental performance and agility, help us relax, and afford us moments of pleasure.

WHAT YOU NEED TO KNOW

From audio stimulants to digital beauty filters, the unique market for digital and high-tech vices is growing.

WHY IT MATTERS

According to a global survey of 150,000 by **Gallop**, **Americans** are now the most stressed people in the world. More than half of adults report experiencing stress during "a lot of the day," while 22% say they feel "a lot" of anger daily. More Americans than ever are now practicing yoga and meditation, in addition to seeking out new ways to relax and unwind.

WATCHLIST FOR SECTION

Alibaba, Alipay, Amazon, Baker, Bulletproof, Centers for Disease Control and Prevention, Constellation Brands, Doppel, Eaze, Emotiv, Fedex, Food and Drug Administration, GreenRush, Heineken, Juul, MakeLoveNot-Porn, MasterCard, Muse, New Frontier Data, Sina Technology, SmartCap, State Grid Zhejiang Electric Power, Thync Kit, U.S. House of Representatives, U.S. Senate Banking Committee, UPS, Visa, Wayv.

⊘ TRENDS

CBD-Infused Products

You can now get CBD in your post-workout smoothie, hand lotion, and even your morning coffee. Cannabidiol, otherwise known as CBD, is a chemical compound found in the resinous flower of cannabis. While it's a component of marijuana—one of hundreds, actually—it is far less psychoactive than the better-known THC, if at all. In other words, it doesn't really get you high. In the **U.S.**, the federal government's stance on CBD is murky. It depends on whether the CBD came from hemp or marijuana, and every state follows different local laws. CBD has been touted for a variety of health benefits and has been shown in many studies to reduce seizures, especially in children with epilepsy syndromes. It's commonly used in adults for anxiety and insomnia. Because the **Food and Drug Administration** doesn't regulate CBD, there aren't yet studies that determine the most effective doses. Most of what's commercially available in infused products like drinks and snacks is very low, but the market is huge. In 2019, sales of CBD-infused products tripled from the year earlier, and some analysts say that the market could reach $20 billion by 2024.

Scaling Cannabis Infusion Techniques

One of the new business verticals within the cannabis industry is cannabis you can drink. As restrictions loosen on recreational marijuana use, we will start to see big commercial beverage companies launching new sparkling waters and non-alcoholic drinks infused with CBD, the non-(or less) psychoactive component of marijuana that is allegedly capable of reducing pain without getting you high. There is also plenty of research into cannabis-infused alcoholic beverages, teas to help you relax and to sleep, and sports drinks to aid athletes in faster post-workout recovery. **Constellation Brands**, which makes **Corona** beer, and **Lagunitas** (a subsidiary of **Heineken**), are both investing in new techniques to infuse their products with CBD.

Cannabis Supply Chains

Cannabis supply chain logistics is challenging. Because of federal laws, the largest logistics companies—**Amazon**, **Fedex**, and **UPS**—cannot legally service vendors. It's complicated: Cannabis brands must become their own first party distributor and must own all of their own logistics

systems (vehicles, warehouses, packaging) or else use specially-licensed third-party vendors. That latter category is catalyzing new business growth. Local dispensaries are supporting startups that can take orders, authenticate users, and ensure safe and legal delivery to consumers. **Eaze** and **GreenRush** are the biggest players in medical marijuana delivery. In 2019, **Wayv**, a B2B cannabis logistics firm, launched its Dynamic Distribution platform, which helps companies list themselves as third-party distributors for other brands, and automatically runs compliance checks. This will enable cannabis brands to move products within their states more easily.

Cannabis Compliance Systems

With the industry heavily regulated, it can be difficult for dispensary companies with business units located in different states to keep track of compliance. New A.I.-powered platforms are helping dispensaries meet these sometimes complex compliance regulations.

Specialized Cannabis CRM Platforms

Unlike traditional CRM or customer databases, marketers in the cannabis space have additional regulations to contend with. **Baker** is an automation platform that caters to dispensaries, combining e-commerce, distribution, inventory management, texting, and loyalty programs.

Banking for Cannabis Dispensaries

Banking is a big hurdle for dispensaries and their parent companies in the U.S. **Visa** and **MasterCard** can't work with the cannabis industry because that would expose the financial institutions to the risk of federal prosecution. However the **SAFT Banking Act**, which would make banking more available to the cannabis industry, passed the **House of Representatives** in October 2019—but the bill was then held up by **Senate Banking Committee Chairman Mike Crapo** (R-Idaho), who as of February 3, 2020 hadn't yet advanced the Senate version of the bill.

As the cannabis industry grows, its shortage of financial services is causing a strain. The legal cannabis market could be worth $29 billion by 2025, according to research firm **New Frontier Data**. Some in the cryptocurrency market think that blockchain technology could provide the industry with an alternative commerce system. The hope would be for customers to pay for cannabis products at a kiosk using cryptocurrency rather than cash.

Digital Makeup

Beauty, science, and technology have always been intertwined. Hundreds of years ago in **Japan**, geisha formulated a makeup base using wax from local trees. (To be fair, it was also made from harmful lead.) Chalk-white faces, necks and forearms were in vogue. In the 1920s, makeup artist **Helena Rubinstein** experimented with kohl to invent mascara for the silver screen, which set off a new trend in long, jet-black eyelashes. Today, artificial intelligence, augmented reality, and smart cameras are converging at an interesting moment in time: We are under

Vices cont.

continual surveillance and many of us are striving to look our best. In **China**, many people now use facial recognition to pay for everything from groceries to taxi cabs. It isn't privacy that has many Chinese people concerned, but rather how they look in all of the next-gen pay-by-face apps. A poll by Chinese news organization **Sina Technology** revealed that 60% of those who use facial recognition for payments feel self-conscious about how they look and would prefer a system of payment that is more flattering. In response, payment giants like **Alipay**— that's **Alibaba's** e-wallet subsidiary, which counts more than a billion monthly active users—are building in beauty filters to their systems. This could have a reverberating effect as more digital payment companies enter the marketplace and competition for market share heats up. Consumers might be willing to pay higher transaction fees in exchange for looking great (or at least avoiding looking bad) while they make purchases.

Vaping and E-cigarettes

Last year was terrible for the electronic cigarette industry, and worse for the hundreds of people who became very ill after using the devices. **The Centers for Disease Con-** **trol and Prevention** confirmed 64 deaths in the **U.S.** from vaping-related illnesses. The majority of people who got sick were using black market or modified e-liquids or products that contained tetrahydrocannabinol (THC). A new federal law raised the legal age to buy tobacco products in the U.S. from 18 to 21, and the **Food and Drug Administration** banned most flavored e-cigs. **Juul Labs**, which dominates the e-cig market and is largely blamed for America's vaping epidemic, voluntarily discontinued its flavored products, with the exception of tobacco and menthol flavors. Many competing brands including **Puff, blu, Posh, and Stig**, now produce pre-charged, pre-filled vaping devices, and they're cheaper than Juul pods.

Nootropics

If you need to manage stress or focus, you might look to "nootropics," cognitive enhancement drugs that promise to help keep you calm and attentive. These dietary supplements have been shown to improve cognitive function—even if they're not officially regulated or approved by the **FDA**. You may already be taking a few: caffeine, red reishi mushrooms, ginseng, turmeric, ginkgo biloba, and **Bulletproof** coffee are all popular, while natural supplements like creatine, L-theanine and Bacopa monnieri are also being marketed to help promote mental clarity, focus, and information retention. Synthetic compounds, like Adrafinil and Noopept, last longer and take effect within minutes. By some analyst estimates, the nootropic market could reach $11 billion in America alone by 2024.

Neuroenhancers

Neuroenhancer devices aim to record brain waves and send feedback. Some promise to help you become more productive, while others are meant to boost your mood. **Australia**-based **SmartCap** uses a tracking system with voice warnings and vibrations to keep you alert while on the job. The **Muse** headband uses neurofeedback to help manage stress and improve athletic performance. The **Emotiv** Epoc+ and Emotiv Insight and mobile EEG devices monitor your brain activity and analyze cognitive performance. **Doppel**, which is worn on the wrist, uses electric pulses to augment your energy. The pulsations, which you dial in based on your needs, are supposed to have an effect on your brain similar to that of music. **The Thync Kit** is a series of electrodes and a triangular device that you stick on to your head—as well as a mobile app synced you to your smartphone. It delivers low-grade electric pulses to influence either your sympathetic (fight or flight) or your parasympathetic (rest and digest) nervous system. Of course, this same technology can be used for nefarious purposes. In **China**, the military and some businesses now use connected headbands and hats to monitor employee brain activity. This emotional surveillance technology is said to optimize productivity— **State Grid Zhejiang Electric Power**, based in **Hangzhou**, reported its profits spiked $315 million since using neuroenhancer devices and software to mine, refine, and analyze employee brain data.

Bulletproof makes neuroenhancing supplements.

Digital Addiction

HIGH DEGREE OF CERTAINTY

INFORMS STRATEGY	ACT NOW
REVISIT LATER	KEEP VIGILANT WATCH

LONGER-TERM IMPACT

IMMEDIATE IMPACT

LOW DEGREE OF CERTAINTY

In 2019, digital addiction became a classified disorder.

Key Insight

The notion that gaming, apps, and other digital products can interfere with a person's day-to-day life used to be a punchline. Now the idea is broadly accepted—even **Facebook**'s internal research team has acknowledged that passively consuming information can be linked to feeling badly.

Why it Matters

Digital products rely on habit-forming features for success, but a growing body of research highlights the negative impacts that those sticky features can have on mental health and well-being. Some new products aim to find a technical solution to digital addiction.

Examples

The **World Health Organization** added gaming disorder to the next edition of the **International Classification of Diseases** in May 2019, making it one of the few behavioral health addictions to gain formal recognition. In the tech realm, companies are responding with design changes to reinforce healthy device use. **Instagram** experimented with removing public like counts to discourage users from comparing themselves to others. Several startups are pursuing mini-smartphones designed with smaller screens and stripped down interfaces to encourage users to look at their devices less often. **Google** and **Apple** continue to develop features that help users monitor their digital well-being and "screen time."

What's Next

As concern about digital addiction increases, consumers will become less tolerant of so-called "dark patterns" that use psychological cues to induce greater consumption. Before launching habit-forming features, teams should stop and consider how the product could cause harm or be purposefully abused.

The Impact

Every business model for media hinges on commanding the attention of an audience. As social attitudes toward technology shift, product designers should be mindful that they're not perceived as eliciting detrimental behavior or harming the physical and mental health of their users.

Watchlist

Amazon, Apple, Common Sense, Center for Humane Technology, Facebook, Instagram, Google, Palm, TikTok, Twitch, Twitter, World Health Organization, gaming consoles and systems.

Sextech Trends

❯ Q&A ON SEXTECH

It's been an interesting few years for the sex tech industry. In 2019, the **Consumer Electronics Show** awarded its prestigious CES Innovation Prize in the robotics and drone category to Ose, a prototype of a robotic, hands-free vibrator developed in part by **Oregon State University's** robotics and engineering lab. But when lead designer **Lora Haddock DiCarlo** showed up to her booth at CES, she learned that the Ose had suddenly been disqualified for being "profane," "obscene," and "immoral." There was backlash, boycotting, public outcry, a media blitz, and, eventually, some measure of redemption. In January 2020, CES devoted an exhibition area to sex tech, and a dozen companies showed up to display their innovations.

The sex tech industry still has walls to break down—we're not comfortable as a society talking about sex and sexuality. But **Cindy Gallop**, a longtime advertising executive and famed former U.S. president of the global creative agency **Bartle Bogle Hegarty**, thinks it's a mistake to ignore the market potential of sex tech. In 2009, she shared her idea for the future of sex on the main TED stage, originally as a public service website called "Porn World vs Real World." A positive global response led to the founding of MakeLoveNotPorn, the first user-generated, human-curated video sharing platform designed to promote consent, communication, good sexual values and healthy sexual behavior. She also started the world's first sex tech venture fund, **AllTheSkyHoldings**. As Cindy explains, despite our squeamishness talking about sex, the market is worth an estimated $30 billion. And Statistics, a market research firm, thinks that number is about to skyrocket—it estimates the industry could be worth $123 billion by 2026.

So why aren't we hearing more about sextech? Blame the algorithms. Some people would be embarrassed to see a sextech ad show up in their Facebook feed or on a website at work, which is why **Google** and **Facebook**, the world's largest digital advertising platforms, restrict such advertising. But we are at the beginning of a shift, which some think will bring inclusivity, awareness, and acceptance. The future of sex tech will help shape adjacent tech trend areas, including home automation, health technologies, artificial intelligence, recognition, security, and privacy.

The **Future Today Institute** invited Cindy to share some of the emerging sex tech trends on her radar, and to describe how the future of the market and industry will be shaped.

Cindy Gallop: As I regularly point out, the three huge disruption opportunities in tech today are sex, cannabis and the blockchain - yet ironically, investors are flocking to the other two categories more than the first. This is a world that has operated through a patriarchal lens for far too long, which is why sex toys have been phallic shaped. We as women have never been permitted to bring our lens to bear on human sexuality, and the world is a poorer place for it. Female sextech founders are changing that. Ti Chang founded Crave, which makes gorgeous vibrators that can be worn around your neck. They're jewelry—pendants that can be charged via USB. They also now make rings. The real innovation is in female-lens vision, which goes far beyond the staid male-lens belief that sex toys have to be humanoid or robots. Female-founded sextech doesn't need to depend on the male anatomy to bring disruptive approaches to pleasure.

Nobody is building or funding the Comscore of sex, yet data is a huge trend. And not just in the areas of teledicdonics and virtual reality sex. Yes, there are toys and vibrators that can be remotely controlled by long-distance partners using mobile apps, and artificial intelligence comes into play too. For example, the Lioness tracks data in order to improve orgasm over time. In that arena, MLNP is an utterly unique data resource, because we capture no personal data, and we are able to provide aggregated, de-identified insights into the overall full spectrum of human sexuality.

Sextech is becoming more complicated to use. LELO once sent a special black and gold TIANI couples massager, and I opened the box, looked at the beautiful object and found myself asking how I was supposed to use it. There were no instructions in the box beyond a one-pager that explained how to charge it. So I went to YouTube and found a video desperate to be safe for work featuring a "Stepford Woman" describing how to use the massager, which was impossible to understand. You can design the most cutting-edge sex toy in the universe, but if a couple can't bring themselves to talk to each other about their sex life, they'll never buy and use it.

Which brings me to the most important, if overlooked trend: Socially acceptable sex is an area of big growth. The money to be made out of socially acceptable sex! Normalizing sex makes it easier for everyone to openly promote consent, communication, good sexual lives and good sexual behavior. A million people visited MakeLoveNotPorn.tv last year, which tells you something about the market potential for socially acceptable sex.

CINDY GALLOP, FOUNDER AND CEO OF IfWeRanTheWorld AND MakeLoveNotPorn AND FOUNDER OF AllTheSkyHoldings

makelovenotporn.com

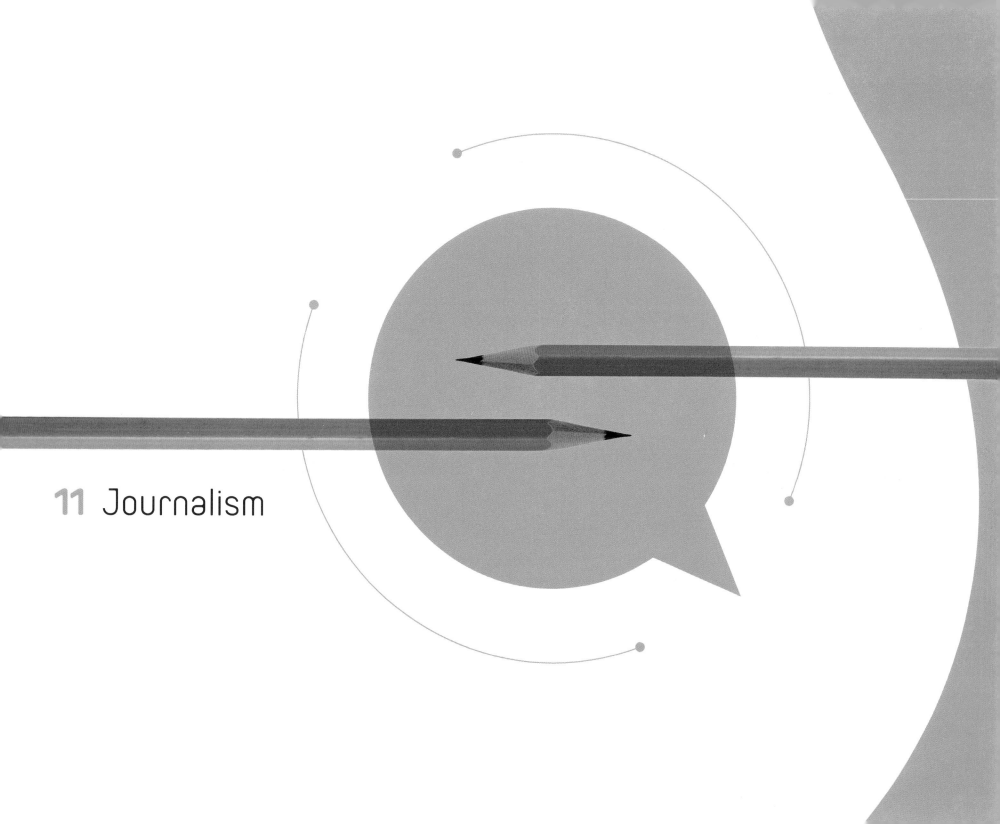

11 Journalism

Continued Media Consolidation

HIGH DEGREE OF CERTAINTY

INFORMS STRATEGY	ACT NOW
REVISIT LATER	KEEP VIGILANT WATCH

LONGER-TERM IMPACT — IMMEDIATE IMPACT

LOW DEGREE OF CERTAINTY

Key Insight

Consolidation continues as regulations shift in the U.S. and margins shrink for traditional media companies. As ownership concentrates into a handful of conglomerates, historic norms about diversity in the press and on the airwaves are challenged.

Why It Matters

Legacy news publishers will continue to face intense merger pressure this year.

Examples

Last year saw the completion of mega deals that were years in the making: CBS and Viacom spent much of the year flirting before coming to terms and finalizing their reunion in December. Disney and Fox completed their merger in March, a deal so large it shifted control of Hulu. An appeals court gave final clearance for AT&T's acquisition of Warner Media in February, rejecting the Justice Department's argument that the deal was anti-competitive.

Just weeks after Gannett defended itself from a hostile takeover bid from Digital First Media, Gannett and Gatehouse Media—the two biggest newspaper publishers in the United States—announced plans to merge. Alden Global Capital, a hedge fund that owns a chain of newspapers under the name Media News Group, became the largest shareholder in Tribune Publishing, an American newspaper publisher, in September.

U.S. telecommunications firm Nexstar acquired Tribune Local Media in September, creating the largest operator of local television stations in the country. That deal required Nexstar to divest from 21 stations in order to comply with Federal Communication Commission regulations about media ownership.

The extent of media concentration means those FCC regulations have started to produce counter-intuitive outcomes: In Ohio, three daily newspapers owned by Cox Media Group changed their publication schedule to three days per week after Apollo Global Management acquired a controlling share. (FCC rules on cross-ownership only apply to newspapers that publish four or more times per week).

What's Next

FCC Chair Ajit Pai's push to deregulate has accelerated the pace—and the corporate benefits—of consolidation. More recent FCC votes may have a more immediate impact on the local news landscape and corporate profits: At the FCC's August meeting, the Republican-appointed majority voted to limit the ability of municipalities to assess "franchise fees" that support local access TV stations and other community services. The new rule will likely boost profits for internet service providers and reduce the capacity for publicly-funded media to compete.

The Impact

Media consolidation affects governments, businesses and citizens everywhere.

Watchlist

Asahi Shimbun Company, AT&T, CBS, Center for Innovation and Sustainability In Local Media at the University of North Carolina at Chapel Hill, Comcast, Cox Media Group, Digital First Media, Disney, FCC, Gannett, Grupo Globo, Hearst, Hubert Burda Media, ITU, local access channels, Meredith Corp, Microsoft, News Corp, Nexstar, Sinclair Broadcast Group, Univision, news organizations everywhere.

In January 2020, Warren Buffet's Berkshire Hathaway sold its newspaper holdings for $140 million to Lee Enterprises.

The Subscription Economy Matures

HIGH DEGREE OF CERTAINTY

| LONGER-TERM IMPACT | INFORMS STRATEGY | ACT NOW | IMMEDIATE IMPACT |
| | REVISIT LATER | KEEP VIGILANT WATCH | |

LOW DEGREE OF CERTAINTY

News Corp launched its Knewz aggregation platform in January 2020.

Key Insight

Whether you call it a subscription, a membership or a donation, we're living in the age of audience revenue. For media companies—news outlets especially—that means business incentives may soon align what consumers want.

Why It Matters

The risk is that the propagation of subscriptions will overwhelm audiences' willingness (or ability) to pay.

Examples

Everywhere you look, a new subscription product is launching: **Disney+** and **Apple TV** joined the crowded streaming subscription landscape last year. **Conde Nast** announced in January 2019 that it was putting all of its magazine websites—historically ad supported—behind a paywall. Local newspapers are pushing to launch new subscriptions or to refine existing offerings. And it's not just in media: There are subscription services for toothbrushes (**Quip**), "ugly" discount vegetables (**Misfits Market**) and probiotics (**Seed**).

Launching a subscription or membership program is relatively easy. Keeping your subscribers is harder: A report from subscription service platform **Zuora** estimated an average annualized churn rate of nearly 34% for media business, the highest of any sector studied. Churn isn't just a legacy media problem, though: on-demand streaming services suffer higher churn rates than news media, according to estimates cited by **The Information**.

July marked the first time that **Netflix** reported a loss in domestic subscribers, and the streaming service has reported flat numbers in the U.S. since then. The platform is still expected to grow internationally, but the lesson about saturation is important for anyone pursuing a subscription model, especially niche and local publishers. **The Los Angeles Times** sought to double its digital subscriber base to 300,000 in 2019, according to a memo leaked in July. While the Times was able to add more than 50,000 new subscribers, its net growth was only 13,000 because of churn.

What's Next

Look for more services that monitor—and cancel—unused subscriptions or free trials, such as **True Bill** and **Free Trial Card**. In **California**, companies selling subscriptions must now offer a clear way to cancel them online, thanks to **California Senate Bill No. 313**, which went into effect in July 2019.

The Impact

Watch for consumers to become more discriminating in their choice of subscriptions as more companies compete for a fixed share of wallet. For publishers, that means a focus on improving subscriber retention, not just recruiting lots of new users.

Watchlist

Apple TV, Conde Nast, Disney+, Bean, Do Not Pay, Free Trial Card, Knewz, Netflix, Membership Puzzle Project, Scroll, True Bill, news organizations and media worldwide.

Optimizing for New Types of Search

HIGH DEGREE OF CERTAINTY

	INFORMS STRATEGY	ACT NOW	
LONGER-TERM IMPACT	REVISIT LATER	KEEP VIGILANT WATCH	IMMEDIATE IMPACT

LOW DEGREE OF CERTAINTY

Key Insight

As voice interfaces proliferate in people's lives, publishers and other organizations face a new strategic consideration: Is our content optimized for voice search? And, looking further into the future, how should we index our content for future forms of interaction?

Why It Matters

Most people still find the majority of information they consume through search.

Examples

A number of companies are racing to index podcasts, radio shows and music, just as Google has done so for traditional, text-based web content. Companies like Trint help publishers transcribe audio to make it more searchable by traditional crawlers, while other startups like Audioburst are trying to use technology to actually "listen" to data previously locked into a waveform and make these units of audio more navigable. Audioburst's technology ingests and analyzes audio and uses natural language processing to understand its contents, contextualize it and make it all searchable.

At the same time, the line between old-fashioned web pages and audio content is blurring. New markup tools let publishers help machines (like voice assistant A.I.s) "read" written content and translate it into spoken audio. Google recently released a structured data markup called Speakable that publishers can use to optimize their content by marking up sections of news articles and optimize them to be read aloud by Google's smart assistant. (The specifications are listed on Schema.org.)

The ultimate goal is to deliver a seamless experience when a user asks their digital assistant: "Tell me the news." For now, a cottage industry of new formats and distributors is growing to bridge the gap between what newsrooms produce today and native programming that fits the syntax of spoken interaction. The startup Spoken Layer and pilot partnerships between Google and select news organizations are taking on this challenge.

What's Next

Voice Search Optimization (VSO) is the new Search Engine Optimization (SEO). Companies will need to consider how their content is delivered via conversational interfaces. As VSO catches on, we may see marketers and publishers attempt to outsmart voice search algorithms with black hat trickery. The algorithms will need to adapt accordingly, deterring manipulation of search optimization without docking legitimate content sources (a challenge we've seen play out before on the pre-voice web).

Spatial computing is in its infancy today, but it will raise similarly complex questions for creators. In the future, consumers might expect to be served stories that are relevant to what they are looking at through smart glasses. Do today's content management systems support the kinds of indexing that anticipate that technology?

The Impact

Searches based on conversation or what a user is looking at will be highly contextual, requiring sophisticated algorithms to anticipate the intent of a query and the relevancy of results.

Watchlist

Amazon, Apple, Audioburst, Facebook, Google, Listen Notes, Spoken Layer, Trint, and marketing and news organizations everywhere.

The more we interact with computers, the more companies will need to optimize for new types of searches.

Investigating the Algorithms

HIGH DEGREE OF CERTAINTY

INFORMS STRATEGY	**ACT NOW**
REVISIT LATER	**KEEP VIGILANT WATCH**

LONGER-TERM IMPACT / IMMEDIATE IMPACT

LOW DEGREE OF CERTAINTY

Journalists are starting to investigate the algorithms and sources of data that companies are using.

Key Insight

News organizations must do better at explaining how algorithms and big data shape our world. To hold artificial intelligence-powered systems accountable, reporters will need the technical skills to unpack how algorithms function and explain that process to a non-technical audience.

Why It Matters

With the increased use of data and algorithms powering our everyday lives, new teams are being deployed to investigate algorithms and the companies using them.

Examples

The Washington Post and The Wall Street Journal both launched teams of reporters with computer science skills last year. The Markup, a startup funded by Craig Newmark Philanthropies and populated with alumni from ProPublica and other newsrooms, is set to start publishing this year. The Markup aims to explore the societal impacts of big tech and algorithms and plans to release tools to help others investigate how data is being used by third parties.

Last year, the New York Times opinion team launched the Privacy Project, a series that explains how firms amass incredibly precise location data from nearly every smart phone. (The series culminated in December.) That analysis would not have been possible without blending multiple disciplines: processing geospatial information, tracing internet traffic, explaining technical concepts and, of course, developing a source willing to leak an incredibly valuable dataset.

What's Next

News organizations must train their reporters to broaden their techniques. As technology advances, it is harder for laypeople to understand how systems function—even as those systems become more deeply embedded in the fabric of our society. Understanding where information comes from, how it spreads and the impact it has—not to mention explaining the outcomes of algorithmic decision-making—are central responsibilities for journalists who wish to hold powerful systems accountable.

The Impact

Dedicating resources to investigating algorithms has never been more important than it is right now, as we all seek to gain a better understanding of new technological systems with immense influential power.

Watchlist

Computational Journalism Lab at Northwestern University, The New York Times, The Markup, ProPublica, Tow Center for Digital Journalism at Columbia University, The Wall Street Journal, Washington Post computational journalism team (led by Jeremy Bowers).

Journalism as a Service

ProPublica offers APIs and other services to developers who want to build apps.

Key Insight

"Software as a Service" is a licensing and delivery model, in which users pay for on-demand access. "Journalism as a Service" lets news organizations sell on-demand access to the components of their reporting, rather than just the finished product.

Why It Matters

On the fringes, news organizations are beginning to provide journalism as a service in addition to traditional news products, allowing outside parties to avail themselves of the organization's functional resources and assets—for a price.

Examples

ProPublica's data store launched as an experiment in 2014. Two years later, the idea had generated more than $200,000 for the non-profit newsroom. The store includes free, open source data products (like Pro-Publica's API for accessing information about **Congress**) and paid products that have been organized and processed (like a regularly updated database of payments by pharmaceutical providers to doctors). Transitioning to "Journalism as a Service" enables news organizations to fully realize their value to everyone working in the knowledge economy—universities, legal startups, data science companies, businesses, hospitals, and even big tech. News organizations that archive their content sit on an enormous corpus—data that can be structured, cleaned and used by numerous other groups.

What's Next

News deployed as a service includes different kinds of parcels: news stories; APIs; databases that can be used by both the newsroom and paying third parties; calendar plug-ins for upcoming news events; systems that can automatically generate reports using the news org's archives and databases, and so on. Services work outside of the social media landscape, relieving news organizations of revenue sharing and allowing them to fully monetize their services.

The Impact

Journalism as a Service models are providing much-needed revenue to cash-strapped news organizations.

Watchlist

The Coral Project, The Information, MIT Media Lab, ProPublica, PRX, REDEF Group, Twilio.

One-To-Few Publishing

INFORMS STRATEGY | ACT NOW | REVISIT LATER | KEEP VIGILANT WATCH

HIGH DEGREE OF CERTAINTY
LONGER-TERM IMPACT / IMMEDIATE IMPACT
LOW DEGREE OF CERTAINTY

Judd Legum publishes a popular paid newsletter on Substack.

Key Insight

Newsletters, podcasts and niche networks can captivate and connect with small, loyal audiences. Those products thrive on their authenticity, helping them to fundraise or to deliver a curated cohort to advertisers.

Why It Matters

Small networks can be uniquely valuable because of their dedicated fanbase—but they can also be dangerous: trusted networks can spread misinformation that goes unchecked.

Examples

It's easier than ever to start a newsletter or a podcast and get paid for your work. Services like **Substack** and **Revue** offer tools to launch a subscription newsletter, while platforms like **Patreon** make it easy to collect recurring payments for various forms of creation. There's evidence that people are willing to pay for highly specialized media, whether it's paying gamers for **Twitch** streams or contributing to a **Kickstarter** campaign for a new idea. Venture capital firm **Andreessen Horowitz** announced in July that it would invest in Substack, suggesting we may see accelerated investment in the space.

Not all niche networks are high-tech: In June, **Wired** reported about the role of conference calls in spreading anti-vax propaganda in ultra-Orthodox Jewish communities in **Brooklyn**. In a community that generally distrusts outside influences and the internet, the recorded conference calls had credibility because they were facilitated by a member of the community. That's a similar challenge to the one faced by **WhatsApp** in 2018, when rumors about child kidnapping spread quickly in rural India via the messaging service, leading to a series of mob lynchings. Despite efforts by WhatsApp to limit the number of times a message can be forwarded, the proliferation of viral rumors on the platform persist: WhatsApp was a major source for disinformation during the 2019 **Nigerian** general election.

What's Next

Tight-knit communities will become stronger as **Facebook** emphasizes private groups and as micro-influencers gain credibility. Informal networks like WhatsApp groups satisfy a basic human need to connect, but risk further isolating niche communities by amplifying a group's beliefs whether or not they are accurate.

The Impact

Major media companies have an opportunity to develop audiences around specific columnists or reporters, but it's uncertain how that might successfully scale.

Watchlist

Auphonic, Garage Band, Iterable, Kickstarter, Libsyn, Mailchimp, Patreon, PRI, PRX, RadioPublic, Revue, Signal, Skype, SoundCloud, Sounderfm, SpeakPipe, Square, Stitcher, Substack, Telegram, TinyLetter, Twilio, WhatsApp.

Popup Newsrooms and Limited-Edition News Products

HIGH DEGREE OF CERTAINTY

INFORMS STRATEGY	ACT NOW
REVISIT LATER	KEEP VIGILANT WATCH

LONGER-TERM IMPACT   IMMEDIATE IMPACT

LOW DEGREE OF CERTAINTY

Electionland is a coalition of newsrooms around the country that are covering misinformation, cybersecurity, and problems that prevent eligible voters from casting their ballots during the 2020 elections.

Key Insight

News organizations are using pop-up newsrooms and limited-edition products to achieve strategic goals. Collaborative newsrooms can focus on a single topic or project, boosting reach and helping uncover deeper stories.

Why It Matters

Limited-run podcasts, newsletters and event series identify engaged readers and help test new ideas.

Examples

During the 2016 and 2018 elections, the **Electionland** coalition brought together more than 1,000 journalists across the **United States** to cover problems that prevent eligible voters from casting a ballot. The project provided a structure for seeking out stories on social media and ensuring those stories were covered. More regularly, groups like the **International Consortium of Investigative Journalists** work together to build scoops across borders.

In March 2019, **BuzzFeed** distributed a single day print edition in **New York**. The move was a stunt, but it generated a stream of engagement online. At subscription-driven publications, limited-run projects can be an opportunity to deliver additional subscriber benefits or to develop a new audience. **The New York Times Magazine's 1619 Project** was a collaboration with the **Smithsonian Institute** that included a limited-run podcast, special issue of the magazine, reader interaction and live events on the history and legacy of slavery in the United States.

What's Next

We expect to see a flurry of collaboration surrounding the 2020 presidential primary and general election, building on initiatives like the Electionland coalition.

The Impact

News organizations that launch limited-run news products will increasingly have specific subscriber engagement goals; these tools could also be used to collect first-party data for targeted ad sales.

Watchlist

News organizations everywhere.

Funding a Vibrant Media Landscape

Meet the New Business Model, Same as the Old Business Model

The Audience Can't Afford to Pay

NEAR-FUTURE OPTIMISTIC SCENARIO

Local news is on a growth trajectory. Audience revenue funds much of the news operation, but it's only one of multiple revenue streams for most publishers. The most successful outlets are thriving because they invested not only in their newsrooms but also in experimental projects that opened up new lines of business. Those ventures were fueled by close collaboration between newsroom and business teams; most often, they relied on input from across the organizational structure, not just leadership.

NEAR-FUTURE PRAGMATIC SCENARIO

Yesterday you were a subscriber to your local newspaper; today you are a member. Not much has changed, though: You get regular, personal email updates from reporters and editors (and sometimes you even read them!). There's a "Local Deals" section in the newspaper's online "Member Center," but you've only visited the page once. Even though you don't read a full article every day (or even every week), you feel like you get value from the push notifications sent directly to your phone. Most of your friends aren't members—they hear the news from you or visit the paper's website once or twice a year. There are enough people like you, however, that the paper is stable. The newsroom isn't as big as it once was, but its leadership has successfully struck a delicate balance: Asking for more money from members, but still maintaining an audience large enough to be valuable to advertisers.

NEAR-FUTURE CATASTROPHIC SCENARIO

As subscriptions become the default format for consuming news, entertainment and daily essentials, consumers must make hard choices about how to spend their money and time. Churn increases for all subscription products, but local news outlets are hit particularly hard because their potential subscriber base is geographically limited. The decision to go "all in" on audience revenue seems like a great idea on paper, but pushes outlets with few options to pivot as the competitive landscape shifts. Publishers fail to anticipate the extent that non-media subscriptions eat up consumers' budgets. Newspapers and websites in large cities and dense suburbs have a critical mass of folks willing to pay, but constantly fight to maintain their revenue, because a substantial portion of their audience is enticed with introductory offers and sales. Rural areas and small cities increasingly become news deserts because they lack the population density to raise enough subscription revenue to support a newsroom.

Demands for Accountability and Trust

HIGH DEGREE OF CERTAINTY

INFORMS STRATEGY	**ACT NOW**
REVISIT LATER	**KEEP VIGILANT WATCH**

LONGER-TERM IMPACT · IMMEDIATE IMPACT

LOW DEGREE OF CERTAINTY

In 2019, doctored videos of Representative Nancy Pelosi spread virally on Facebook and Twitter.

Key Insight

The spread of misinformation will continue until platforms and news organizations adopt norms and standards for accountability and trust.

Why It Matters

Last year, American trust in media declined. According to a **Pew Research Center** poll, roughly 30% of Republicans and Republican-leaning independents said that journalists have "very low" ethical standards.

Examples

A healthy dose of skepticism makes for a strong electorate. But deepfakes, intentionally misleading stories, and salacious content posted by political operatives, hackers, and foreign governments have led to increased calls for new methods to rebuild our trust in the media.

In August 2019, **Twitter** finally published a blog post exposing a series of **Chinese** Twitter bots that were intentionally spreading misinformation on the platform. Along with this transparency about the presence of these bots, Twitter removed them and also promised not to accept sponsored posts from known rogue actors (state or otherwise).

What's Next

There is no clear financial incentive for platforms or news organizations to use a standardized system to prove a piece of content's authenticity. Lawmakers have hesitated to propose legislation that would curb speech, however it's an election year and we're likely to be flooded with malicious content. As platforms come under increased scrutiny this year for issues related to antitrust, we expect to see demands for transparency and traceability. Just as supply chains are inspected to ensure they're secure, in the future we could see new blockchain-powered supply chains for information.

The Impact

Fake or misleading news itself is a problem. But it's also making people less likely to seek out quality information.

Watchlist

Platforms and news organizations everywhere.

The First Amendment in a Digital Age

HIGH DEGREE OF CERTAINTY

INFORMS STRATEGY	**ACT NOW**
REVISIT LATER	**KEEP VIGILANT WATCH**

LONGER-TERM IMPACT · IMMEDIATE IMPACT

LOW DEGREE OF CERTAINTY

Key Insight

The First Amendment shapes how Silicon Valley thinks about the design, development and implications of technology. Its legal protections are broad in scope but limited in geography; they only apply in the United States.

Why It Matters

Publishers and platforms will increasingly need to consider how different expectations of free speech inform their operations.

Examples

Constitutional law often lags behind technology, taking time to adapt and evolve as historic concepts are applied to new situations. Although social media has been a central part of our political conversation, courts are only now starting to specifically consider how our rights apply online. State courts in **New Jersey** recognize that speech cannot be abridged by "restrictive and oppressive conduct by private entities"—like social media platforms—but other states only prevent the government from regulating speech, allowing private entities to do as they please.

A significant case in July 2019 clarified **Twitter's** status as a public forum—and how the First Amendment applies on the platform. **The Second Circuit Court of Appeals** affirmed a lower court ruling in July that **President Donald Trump** could not block followers on Twitter. The three-judge panel held that "the First Amendment does not permit a public official...to exclude persons from an otherwise-open online dialogue because they expressed views with which the official disagrees."

The ruling is a major step toward defining the rules of engagement for free speech on the internet. But there are still deep, unresolved questions. For example, does the First Amendment protect bots or other synthetic media? A **California** law went into effect in July requiring that any bot that tries to influence purchasing or voting behavior identify itself. **The Electronic Frontier Foundation** and others worried that an earlier version of the bill would have gone too far in stifling speech because of careless definitions of the technology.

While the First Amendment's protections in the U.S. are generally broad, its scope is limited in an interconnected world: **Facebook** has little legal exposure in the U.S. because of the intersection of First Amendment rights and protections from Section 230 of the **Communication Decency Act**, but it could be liable under **Germany's** hate speech laws. Even in the offline world there is no global understanding of how to protect "free speech," and that makes defining online rights even harder.

What's Next

Debates about the First Amendment boil down to what "can" be said. Expect more decisions that wrestle with clarifying what is a public forum in the public sphere and whether A.I.-generated text, video and images are legally protected speech. And there will be much murkier debates about what "should" be published.

The Impact

Paying customers will naturally be more invested in decisions made by the organization, and those choices — whether it's sharing or withholding a fact, opinion or photo — may only fuel the debate.

Watchlist

American Civil Liberties Union, Electronic Frontier Foundation, European Union, Federal Communications Commission, Federal Trade Commission, Knight First Amendment Institute at Columbia University, U.S. Supreme Court.

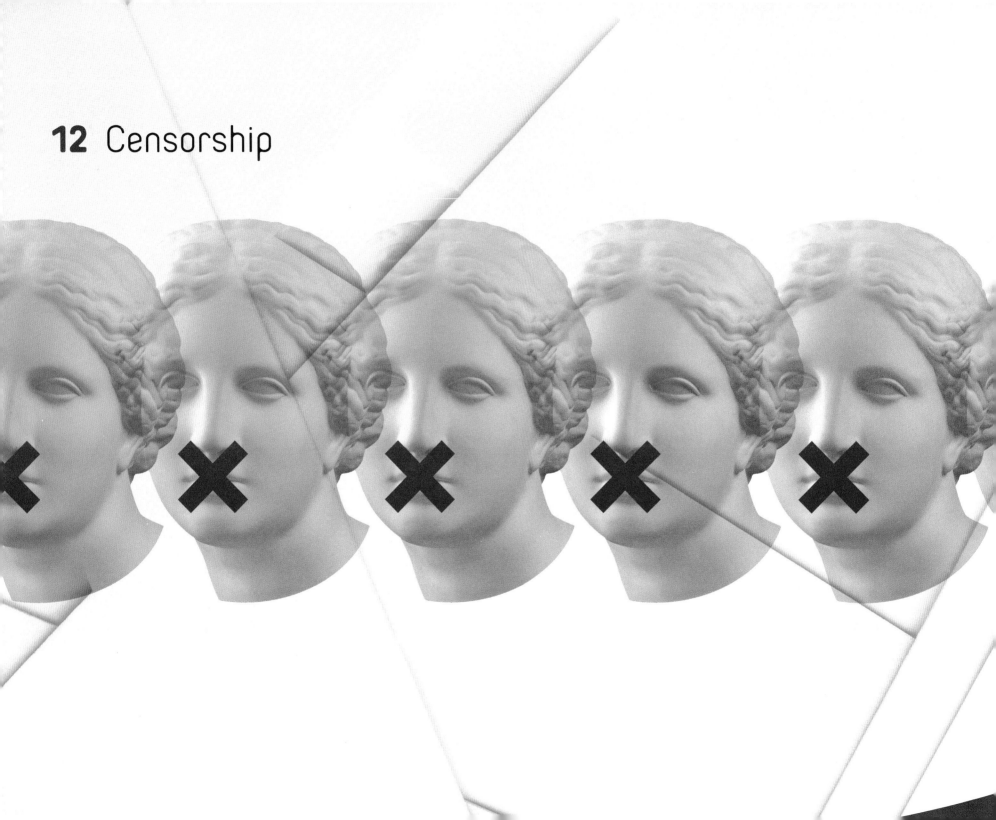

12 Censorship

The Proliferation of Splinternets

HIGH DEGREE OF CERTAINTY

INFORMS STRATEGY	ACT NOW
REVISIT LATER	KEEP VIGILANT WATCH

LONGER-TERM IMPACT

IMMEDIATE IMPACT

LOW DEGREE OF CERTAINTY

The future of the internet is fractured.

Key Insight

The founding promise of the digital world was broad connectivity where information could flow freely. But as some governments take steps to filter (or completely block) access to the internet, and paid subscription models make access to reliable information a luxury, we now have a splintered internet rather than a single world wide web.

Why It Matters

Twenty years ago, the internet emerged as a global space where information was shared freely. Now, everyone has a different idea of how our global information superhighway ought to be regulated, and by whom.

Examples

Nation-scale internet censorship is most closely associated with **China's** "great firewall." The **Chinese government** aggressively monitors the internet and removes information that doesn't meet its political standards. At times of political unrest, as during widespread riots in **Xinjiang** in 2009, China has completely shut down access to the internet. China's leadership believes its restrictive model contributes to stability— and is open to exporting that approach to the rest of the world. "We should respect the right of individual countries to independently choose their own path of cyber-development," said **Chinese President Xi Jinping** at China's second **World Internet Conference** in 2015.

In 2019, we saw ample signs of nations learning from the Chinese playbook: There were nearly 130 documented internet shutdowns in 29 countries between January and July 2019, according to the advocacy group **Access Now**. Those include a shutdown in the **Democratic Republic of the Congo** after an alleged election hijacking effort, and **India's** internet blackout in **Kashmir**—the longest ever in a democracy.

Splinternets—the various versions of a now fractured internet—aren't just the product of blocking free access to the internet;

sometimes it's enough to simply increase the barriers to finding reliable information. Those can be technical roadblocks—as in a censorship regime that doesn't remove websites, but knows the average user won't have the knowledge or time to connect through a VPN to reach unfiltered information—or they can be financial ones.

Even in nations with unrestricted internet access, the business model for many online creators is shifting to paid subscriptions. Creators deserve to be paid for their work, but we haven't begun to wrestle with the implications of a media ecosystem in which the wealthy can afford to consume the news and entertainment they wish, and others cannot. We're already starting to see evidence of this classist dynamic in online gaming: "Children are scorned in games such as **Fortnite** if they are seen to wear the 'default skin' (the free avatar they receive at the start of the game)," a report by the **Children's Commissioner of the U.K.** found. "Children say they feel embarrassed if they cannot afford new 'skins,' because then their friends see them as poor."

What's Next

For governments dealing with social unrest, the playbook increasingly includes trying to disrupt the digital tools activists use to organize. If it becomes clear that leaders can follow that playbook with impunity, expect it to be increasingly adopted by democratic governments.

Mitigating the impacts of political and financial splinternets will require coming to a broad, international consensus about how human rights apply in a digital age: Is there a fundamental human right to connect freely? Is blocking access to the internet a war crime? If a video, meme, or report is illegal in one country but protected in another, how should ISPs respond?

The Impact

As nations start to implement 5G infrastructure, questions of network interoperability will become increasingly relevant. If tensions between the **U.S.** and China continue, there's a risk that components built with American technology will not be compatible with those built by Chinese firms. That could embed the fracturing of the web at a hardware level, making it more difficult to combat in the future.

Watchlist

Access Now, China's government, Freedom House, Software Freedom Law Centre (India).

Content Moderation in the name of national Security

Gab raised more than $1 million in crowdfunding.

Key Insight

It may seem counterintuitive, given that there is so much talk of regulating big tech, but government agencies worldwide expect tech companies to help fight against the spread of misinformation, propaganda and terrorism.

Why It Matters

Content moderation and policing efforts are being met with resistance from free speech advocates from across the political spectrum. Content surveillance and moderation will be ever important battlegrounds around the world for states, companies and individuals.

Examples

Content moderation is a critical consideration in the design and development of online platforms, and requires decisions about the legal protections afforded to creators and users of technology. Throughout history, governments have restricted content and its distribution in the name of security and morality. After the advent of the printing press, the **Catholic Church** started publishing a list of prohibited books in 1559. This practice continued until 1966. With the internet age, content moderation has become a larger technical challenge not just for governments and institutions, but for media and tech companies as well.

Throughout 2018 and 2019, both the **U.S.** and **European governments** held several heated public hearings with representatives from **Twitter**, **Google** and **Facebook** in the wake of controversial elections and increasingly polarized public discourse. Tech companies are inconsistent at best when it comes to enforcing "community standards" of content moderation and of free or acceptable speech. Tech companies are struggling to design algorithms that identify and censor offensive and dangerous content such as pornography and misinformation while protecting the right to personal expression.

Gab, a social network that champions free speech, launched in 2017 mostly in response to the suspension of the high-profile accounts of controversial personalities such as **Milo Yiannopoulos** and **Alex Jones** on Twitter and Facebook. While Gab doesn't have the network effect of mainstream players, expect to see more services like it as content moderation policies become more strictly enforced.

What's Next

Lawmakers and tech companies alike struggle with balancing tensions between censorship, free enterprise, and national security. The questions—and answers—are complicated, and they involve all of us.

Google, Twitter and **Spotify** have all announced restrictions or complete bans on political advertisements in 2020. Facebook is the notable exception here, allowing political ads without fact-checking for accuracy.

Moving forward, there are numerous scenarios for how governments choose to protect and police content, regardless of whether it was created by a human or a bot. One scenario could be that governments decide freedom of speech protections don't extend beyond human-produced speech. Down the road, certain content produced via future technological advances wouldn't be protected either. But it's unlikely this would happen, because humans are involved in programming bots. Another potential outcome: human programmers are protected under the **First Amendment**, but A.I.-created speech is not. This makes sense at some level, but it could fall short when giving credit or blame to content created by a human, versus A.I. technology. Or, ultimately, the government could decide that A.I.-produced content is considered free speech, including any content produced by a voice interface or a bot. In the end, it could open up the liability to legal entities responsible for the content.

The Impact

Complex legal questions will arise, and we're likely to see various hybrids of these scenarios in the future. The media and journalism will be at the center of these legal questions around the world.

Watchlist

Amazon, Apple, Electronic Frontier Foundation, European Union, Facebook, Federal Communications Commission, Google, Instagram, Gab, law enforcement, legal scholars, media organizations, Microsoft, Moritz College of Law, technology and privacy advocates, technology company leaders, Ohio State University, Twitch, YouTube.

Digitally Retouching History

HIGH DEGREE OF CERTAINTY

INFORMS STRATEGY	ACT NOW
REVISIT LATER	KEEP VIGILANT WATCH

LONGER-TERM IMPACT — IMMEDIATE IMPACT

LOW DEGREE OF CERTAINTY

The National Archives removed disparaging messages about President Donald Trump from photos like this one in a 2020 exhibition.

Key Insight

Digital tools now give government agencies the ability to edit, distort, or outright censor content made by citizens.

Why It Matters

Digitally altering archival content—for example, photos taken of a historic event—can lead to misunderstanding and public confusion in the future.

Examples

Throughout history, governments have manipulated photos—in 2008, when it was thought that **North Korean** dictator **Kim Jong-il** was critically ill or had died, the North Korean government released a photo of Jong-il standing with his **People's Army**. Forensic experts suspected that his image had been digitally inserted.

What's Next

Early in 2020, an exhibit at the **U.S. National Archives** celebrated the 100th anniversary of women's suffrage and included a series of photographs taken at the first Women's March, held a day after **President Donald Trump's** inauguration. One of the photographs had been altered to blur placards and signs that disparaged Trump. Signs that depicted or referenced women's anatomy were also digitally edited. In the photo, a sign that had originally read "Trump & GOP-Hands Off Women" was digitally altered so that the word "Trump" could not be seen. Other signs where Trump's name could be read clearly were digitally blurred. The museum said that it had altered images to protect student groups touring the exhibit, but historians balked at the explanation. It was an unusual move in a democratic nation—and yet there are currently no regulations governing the digital alteration of archival content.

The Impact

With deepfake technologies, automatic dubbing, and other automated editing tools more widely available, there is growing concern that autocratic leaders will start digitally manipulating content for use in propaganda and real-time disinformation.

Watchlist

Adobe, Amazon, DataGrid, Facebook, Google, National Archives, MIT's CSAIL, Meo, Microsoft, Modulate, Twitter, governments worldwide.

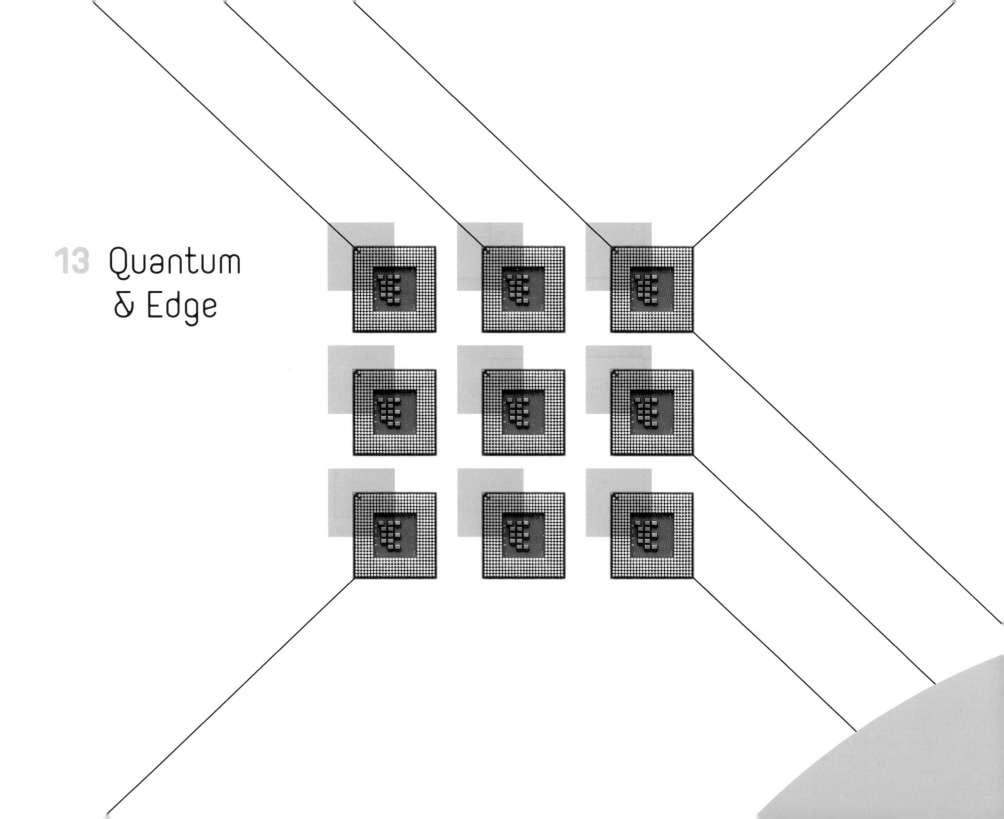

13 Quantum & Edge

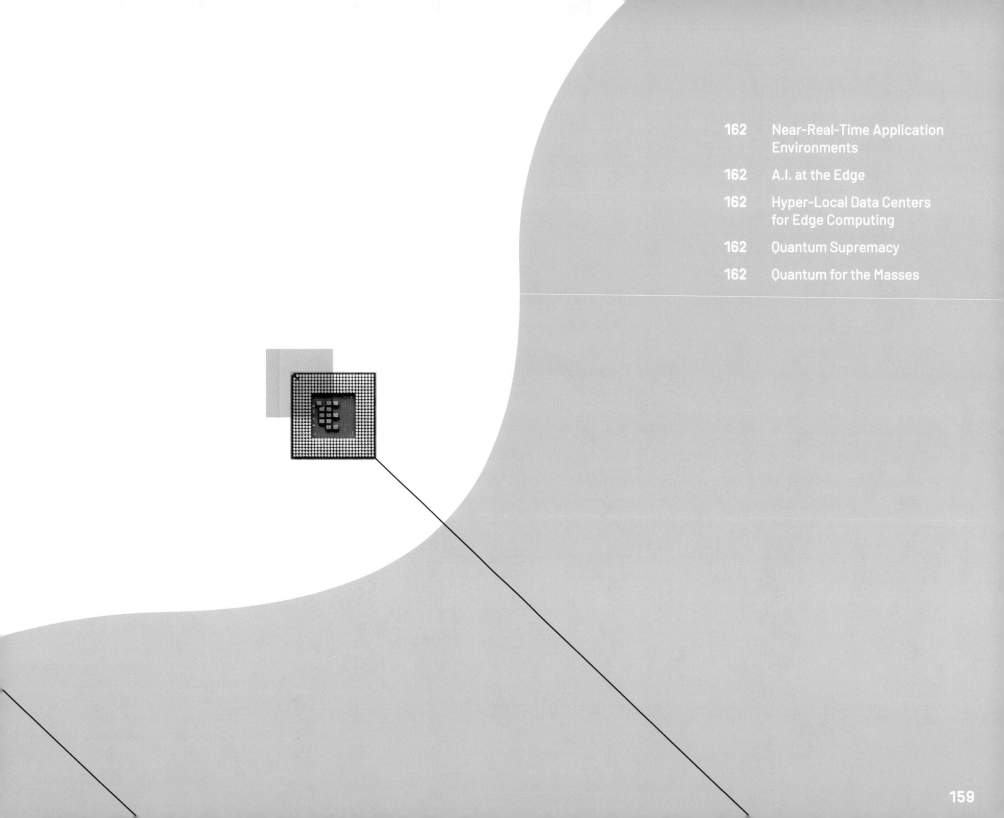

Quantum and Edge

HIGH DEGREE OF CERTAINTY

INFORMS STRATEGY	ACT NOW
REVISIT LATER	KEEP VIGILANT WATCH

LONGER-TERM IMPACT

IMMEDIATE IMPACT

LOW DEGREE OF CERTAINTY

Photograph of the Sycamore processor. Courtesy of Erik Lucero, research scientist and lead production quantum hardware at Google.

KEY INSIGHT

We are at the beginning of a new era of computing, one that will bring powerful new computers and will eventually enable more processing at or near the source of our data.

◯ DEEPER DIVE

What You Need To Know About Quantum Computing

In short, quantum computers can solve problems that are computationally too difficult for a classical computer, which can only process information in 1s or 0s. In the quantum universe, those 1 and 0 bytes can exist in two states (qubits) at once, allowing computations to be performed in parallel. Therefore, if you build two qubits, they are able to hold four values at the same time: 00, 01, 10, 11. Quantum computers require special algorithms capable of doing new things, making them more powerful than anything built to date. Scientists have been researching quantum computing for decades. The challenge, however, has been proving that a quantum machine is actually carrying out quantum computations. That's because in a quantum system, the very act of observing information in transit changes the nature of that data.

What You Need To Know About Edge Computing

Edge computing performs computations near or at the source of data. This differs from the current norm, as today much of our computing takes place in the cloud, with distributed data centers handling the processing work. The challenge for our existing cloud-based computing environments is the potential for delay, which is also known as latency. In the near-future, more of the computational work could be done locally—for example, a car's computer vision system would process and recognize images immediately rather than sending that information to the cloud for verification. Edge computing requires custom chips and hardware and will work alongside the cloud rather than replace its functionality.

WHY IT MATTERS

Recent advancements have spurred interest in quantum and edge computing. In 2019, Google published a paper in the journal Nature saying that it had reached a new benchmark for speed on a new kind of processor. Verizon and Amazon Web Services announced a new 5G edge cloud computing partnership in December 2019 to give developers tools to launch IoT devices and applications at the edge.

WATCHLIST FOR SECTION

Amazon, Amazon Web Services, Alibaba, AT&T, Baidu, Ben-Gurion University of the Negev's Center for Quantum Science & Technology Bleximo, California Institute of Technology's Institute for Quantum Information and Matter (IQIM), Chapman University's Institute for Quantum Studies, Cisco, Crown Castle, D-Wave Systems, Dartmouth University's Quantum and Condensed Matter Physics Group, Duke University, Georgia Tech Research Institute's Quantum Systems Group, Google, Harvard University's Quantum Initiative, Hebrew University of Jerusalem's Quantum Information Science Center, IBM, Intel, Keio University Quantum Computing Center, Massachusetts Institute of Technology's Engineering Quantum Systems Group, Michigan State University's Laboratory for Hybrid Quantum Systems, Microsoft, MIT Center for Quantum Engineering (MIT-CQE), MIT Lincoln Laboratory's Quantum Information and Integrated Nanosystems, Rigetti Computing, Stanford University's Yamamoto Group, University of California-Berkeley's Quantum Information & Computation Center, University of British Columbia's Advanced Materials and Process Engineering Laboratory, University of California-Los Angeles's Center for Quantum Science & Engineering, University of California-Santa Barbara's Center for Spintronics and Quantum Computation, University of Chicago's Chicago Quantum Exchange, University of Maryland's Center for Accelerated Real Time Analytics and UMD's Joint Center for Quantum Information and Computer Science, University of Science and Technology of China's Division of Quantum Physics and Quantum Information, University of Washington's Trapped Ion Quantum Computing Group, Verizon, Zapata Computing.

Quantum and Edge cont.

⊘ TRENDS

Near-Real-Time Application Environments

Within the next decade, there could be as many as 50 billion devices online generating enormous amounts of data. Edge computing is closely tied to the Internet of Things and 5G connectivity. As virtual reality and extended reality become popular, more processes will be pushed onto headsets. For example, Amazon IoT Greengrass, the company's platform for extending Amazon Web Services to edge devices, was created to more easily deploy applications. In October 2019 at Microsoft's Government Leaders Summit, CEO Satya Nadella said that future application environments would exist at the edge first, then be transferred to the cloud for machine learning.

A.I. at the Edge

With the proliferation of smart cameras and speakers, developers are building edge systems that can recognize natural language, people, pets and objects. Nvidia's EGX platform for edge computing features an extensive range of GPU (graphics processing unit)-accelerated software, including Helm charts (collections of files) for deployment on Kubernetes, or portable, open-source systems for managing "containerized" work and services. It also gives users access to third-party domain-specific, pre-trained models and Kubernetes-ready Helm charts that make it easy to deploy software or build customized solutions.

Hyper-Local Data Centers for Edge Computing

All of the new streaming services—Apple TV+, Peacock, Disney, HBO Max, Quibi—are entering a crowded field dominated by Netflix, Amazon, Hulu and YouTube. But there's a problem looming: compression and bandwidth. As a result, we will need lots of hyper-local data centers that are located closer to consumers. In December 2019, Amazon Web Services announced that it would be building "local zones" close to major cities, with the goal of managing latency-sensitive workloads.

Quantum Supremacy

In October 2019, Google researchers published a paper in the journal Nature as well as a blog post on the company's website explaining that they had achieved "quantum supremacy" for the first time. It was a significant revelation. Physicists said that their 53-bit quantum computer, named Sycamore, calculated something that an ordinary computer—even a very powerful one—simply could not have completed. Sycamore performed a challenging calculation in 200 seconds. On the world's current fastest traditional computer, that same calculation would have taken 10,000 years. Google achieved quantum supremacy because a computer running on the laws of quantum physics completed a process that no conventional computer could have completed in any reasonable amount of time. It will be some time before functioning quantum computers can solve practical problems, in addition to test problems run in a lab. But the era of quantum computing has dawned.

Quantum for the Masses

New kinds of processors are being designed to add-on to existing equipment, to give classic computers a quantum boost. The end result isn't a complete quantum computing system, but more of a hybrid. Rigetti Computing is building small quantum processors that integrate with the cloud. Pharmaceutical company Merck is experimenting with the processors for faster drug development and production.

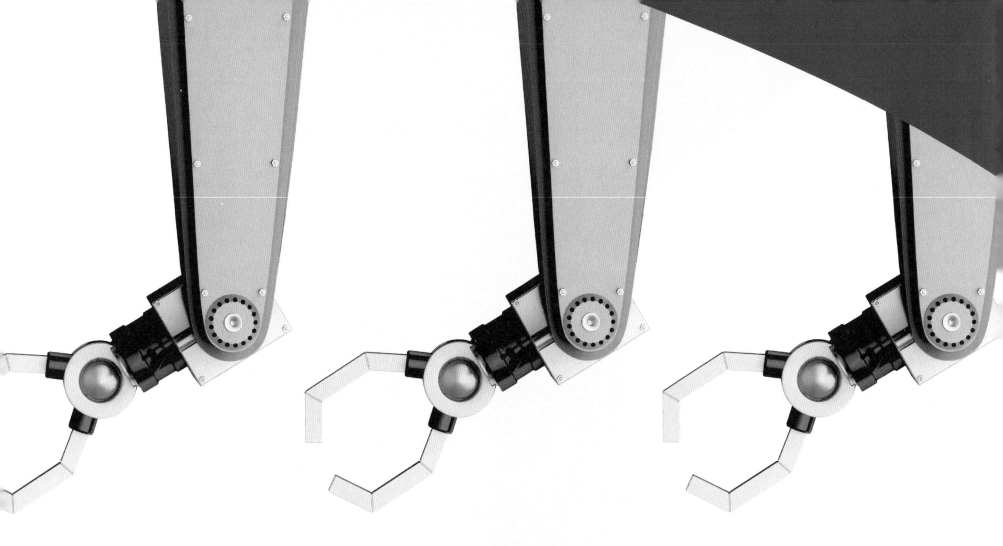

14 5G, Robotics & the Industrial Internet of Things

5G Triggers a Surge of New Businesses

HIGH DEGREE OF CERTAINTY

INFORMS STRATEGY	ACT NOW
REVISIT LATER	KEEP VIGILANT WATCH

LONGER-TERM IMPACT / IMMEDIATE IMPACT

LOW DEGREE OF CERTAINTY

The next generation of wireless infrastructure will require hundreds of thousands of small cells and towers.

Key Insight

The latest (or fifth) generation of mobile networks, 5G is an upgrade from today's 4G (or LTE) networks and will offer higher speeds, low or even no latency in data transfer, and the ability for billions of devices to connect to each other.

Why It Matters

5G will reshape our economies by transforming transportation, education, financial services, entertainment and healthcare, and it will catalyze new businesses and applications we haven't yet imagined.

Examples

5G advances today's networks using a more responsive kind of radio technology that not only moves data faster, but also requires less power to do so. 5G will shorten transmission latency from 30 milliseconds to just a single millisecond, allowing essentially instantaneous connectivity between devices on a network. This means big opportunities for telemedicine and robotic-assisted surgery, autonomous vehicles, and streaming. Unlike WiFi, a 5G network can be built to prioritize certain data transmissions over others. For example, heavy manufacturing companies and utilities will be able to automate more of their core processes using advanced robotics systems, which will in turn create a new market for all of the components, devices and consulting services for that network.

What's Next

There's a geopolitical fight underway, pitting the U.S. against China and South Korea. As developed economies shift to the next generation of wireless technology, some questions loom about which country's technology will power our new networks. The U.S. will not allow Chinese companies ZTE and Huawei to supply gear to American network operators in the states, which is a problem—Qualcomm, a chipmaker, is the only U.S. company making components necessary for a widescale 5G rollout. In 2019, American security experts urged the U.S. to build a 5G network with and for our allies that excludes Chinese equipment entirely. But in January 2020, the U.K. government approved a measure to allow Huawei to build parts of its 5G network. Meanwhile, Chinese President Xi Jinping has made it clear that he intends to wean China and its allies off of Western-made technology.

The Impact

Geopolitical tensions notwithstanding, the business cases for investing in 5G are becoming clearer across a number of industries. It might take longer to find value in consumer applications.

Watchlist

AT&T, China Mobile, China Telecom, China Unicom, Cisco Systems, Ericsson, Huawei, KT, LG, LG Uplus, Nokia, Qualcomm, Samsung, SK Telecom, Sprint, T-Mobile, Verizon, ZTE.

Capturing IIoT Metadata

HIGH DEGREE OF CERTAINTY

INFORMS STRATEGY	**ACT NOW**
REVISIT LATER	**KEEP VIGILANT WATCH**

LONGER-TERM IMPACT · IMMEDIATE IMPACT

LOW DEGREE OF CERTAINTY

Metadata captured from machines will advance IIoT systems.

Key Insight

The industrial internet of things (or IIoT) refers to all of the hardware that's collecting, sharing and using data within industrial settings. Some of what's being collected is metadata, which describes the data that's being generated.

Why It Matters

Metadata is important because it lets us take a deeper dive into what's happening, allowing us to see relationships, keywords, associations, descriptions and other factors used in algorithms and indexes.

Examples

In an industrial setting, there is a tremendous amount of data generated by sensors, switches, and connected devices. Those data can be mined, refined and analyzed for cost savings, greater efficiencies and even new product development. For example, Palo Alto-based **Maana** extracts metadata to optimize a company's processes by revealing previously unknown relationships.

Austin-based **SparkCognition** uses metadata for predictive maintenance applications in energy, gas and utilities.

What's Next

There is no unified approach for how to handle metadata in manufacturing and other IIoT settings—and at the moment, not all systems and devices are interoperable. The metadata itself could help solve that problem, by identifying communication protocols that would facilitate the exchange of data throughout a network.

The Impact

Metadata will make it easier for businesses to organize the data generated from all of their connected machinery within the IIoT. Advancements in artificial intelligence will offer deeper levels of insight into process automation.

Watchlist

Augury, Axzon, Bayshore Networks, Foghorn Systems, KMC Controls, Maana, Plataine, SparkCognition, Tenna, Thetaray, Valarm.

Robots as a Service (RaaS)

HIGH DEGREE OF CERTAINTY

INFORMS STRATEGY	ACT NOW
REVISIT LATER	KEEP VIGILANT WATCH

LONGER-TERM IMPACT / IMMEDIATE IMPACT

LOW DEGREE OF CERTAINTY

Robots as a service will transform business.

Key Insight

Cloud robotics and automation is a field in which physical robots share data and code and perform computations remotely via networks, rather than within their containers alone.

Examples

Autonomous vehicles are robots that use a network to access maps, index data, understand spatial information and more in order to make decisions. That data is shared on a network for optimization and later used by researchers and other vehicles. This is an example of cloud robotics, which is used within autonomous driving as well as in warehouse automation and logistics. **Amazon's AWS RoboMaker** is a cloud robotics service created to develop, test and deploy intelligent robotics applications at scale. Its partners include **Nvidia**, **Qualcomm**, and **UP Squared**, and it supports the most widely-used open-source robotics software framework, Robot Operating System (ROS). **Google's Cloud Robotics Core** is an open

source platform that provides digital infrastructure essential to building and running robotics solutions for business automation.

What's Next

Using the cloud certainly offers advantages: greater efficiencies and opportunities for data sharing and insights, as well as collective learning across robotic networks and shared platforms. Soon, businesses will be able to take advantage of cloud-based robotics for a variety of uses, including strategic warehouse selection in anticipation of seasonal retail spikes, security in large buildings, and factory automation.

The Impact

There will be millions of implementations of RaaS over the next five years, which could generate billions of dollars of revenue.

Watchlist

Amazon AWS Robomaker, Anki, Carnegie Mellon's Robotics Institute Cobalt Robotics, Fetch Robotics, Google Cloud Robotics, Honda RaaS, InVia Robotics, Kuka, Microsoft, NASA's Robotics Alliance Project, Tesla.

Collaborative Robots

HIGH DEGREE OF CERTAINTY

INFORMS STRATEGY	ACT NOW
REVISIT LATER	KEEP VIGILANT WATCH

LONGER-TERM IMPACT — IMMEDIATE IMPACT

LOW DEGREE OF CERTAINTY

The next generation of robots will work cooperatively.

Key Insight

Collaborative robots—or cobots—work alongside humans or together with other machines. Teams of robots can communicate with each other, on their own, about when to wait, when to move, when to carry out an activity, or even to ask what to do next.

Why It Matters

In the past, installing and maintaining collaborative robots had been cost-prohibitive for smaller companies, especially compared to human workforces—but now that's starting to change.

Examples

Collaborative robots are finding more widespread use in industrial settings, which can often prove challenging for humans alone. Under the European Union's Horizon2020 project, researchers at the Karlsruhe Institute of Technology, EPFL, Sapienza Università di Roma, and University College London developed an autonomous humanoid robot assistant for engineers that interacts with other robots and can learn from its human coworkers. Tesla uses robots to assemble its cars, while Amazon uses robots throughout its vast warehouses. German company KUKA and Japan's FANUC both offer collaborative solutions to implement more automation within factories.

What's Next

Researchers are developing cobots with computer vision, faster processors, and A.I. systems. As 5G comes online and reduces latency, cobots will process spatial data at fast enough speeds to adapt to environmental changes. In the near future, collaborative robots will play a key role in warehouses and distribution centers, automating the tasks previously performed by humans. Some other use cases: Collaborative robots will help on construction sites, in factories, and during military operations. In the further future, collaborative robots will underpin fully-automated supply chains, logistics services and delivery networks.

The Impact

Today, collaborative robots make up just 3% of the current installed robot base around the world, but that's going to change. According to the International Federation of Robotics, collaborative robots are the fastest growing segment of new robot sales.

Watchlist

ABB Robotics, Aethon Inc., Amazon, Autonomous Solutions, Boston Dynamics, Carnegie Mellon University, DARPA, Denso, Energid Technologies, EPFL, EPSON Robotics, FANUC, Festo, Hitachi, Honda, iRobot, Johns Hopkins Applied Physics Laboratory, Karlsruhe Institute of Technology, Kawasaki Heavy Industries, KUKA, Lockheed Martin, Mitsubishi Electric, MIT's Interactive Robotics Group, Northrop Grumman, Ocado Technology, Raytheon, Robotshop, Sapienza Università di Roma, Seegrid, SoftBank Group, SoftBank Robotics Corporation, SpaceX, Tesla, Toyota, ULC Robotics, University College London, University of Tokyo, VEX Robotics, Yamaha.

Autonomous, Programmable Robot Swarms

HIGH DEGREE OF CERTAINTY

	INFORMS STRATEGY	ACT NOW
	REVISIT LATER	KEEP VIGILANT WATCH

LONGER-TERM IMPACT

IMMEDIATE IMPACT

LOW DEGREE OF CERTAINTY

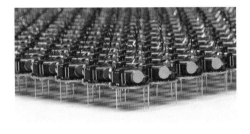

A thousand Kilobots self-assemble and work as a team.

Key Insight

Autonomous robot swarms are coordinated and distributed to perform complex tasks in a more efficient way than a single robot or non-networked group of robots.

Why it matters

Most robots are designed to work independently or on a factory line, not as part of a team, leaving massive untapped opportunities for the emerging field of swarm robotics.

Examples

Researchers at **Harvard's Wyss Institute** are experimenting with different form factors drawn from nature. Last year, they developed robots that can autonomously drive interlocking steel sheet piles into soil. The end result: structures that could be someday be used as retaining walls or check dams for erosion control. Another project, called Kilobots, involves 1,024 tiny robots working collectively to self-assemble and perform a programmed task. In 2018,

Walmart filed a patent for robot bees, which would work collaboratively in teams to pollinate crops autonomously. If the project works at scale, it could potentially counterbalance the effects of the world's honey bee population decline.

What's Next

They'll fly, crawl, self-assemble, and even swim. With enough swarm robotics projects now in the works, researchers are developing next-generation hive operating systems, which would communicate between robots working together on a mission and their human programmers.

The Impact

The possibilities for this technology are staggering: autonomous robot teams could be used to inspect dams and bridges, build complicated 3D structures, and lay protective barriers in the case of toxic chemical spills—freeing up their human counterparts and keeping them out of harm's way.

Watchlist

Carnegie Mellon's Robotics Institute, DARPA, MIT, NASA's Robotics Alliance Project, the Academy of Optoelectronics at the Chinese Academy of Sciences in Beijing, University of California-Berkeley, University of Notre Dame, Walmart, Wyss Institute at Harvard.

Robotic Process Automation

HIGH DEGREE OF CERTAINTY

INFORMS STRATEGY	ACT NOW
REVISIT LATER	KEEP VIGILANT WATCH

LONGER-TERM IMPACT   IMMEDIATE IMPACT

LOW DEGREE OF CERTAINTY

RPA will help automate tasks to increase efficiencies.

Key Insight

Robotic Process Automation (RPA) enables businesses to automate certain tasks and processes within offices, allowing employees to spend time on higher-value work.

Why It Matters

Despite fears that bots are congesting the internet and causing mayhem on social media, they can also automate tasks and applications to save businesses' resources and drive better efficiencies. RPA can be installed in just about any kind of device and can work independently or as part of a company's cloud environment.

Examples

Amazon uses RPA to sift through resumes before prioritizing top candidates for review. Hospitals use RPA such as UiPath, which automates the process of copying patient data between files and electronic patient records. In banking, Blue Prism and Automation Anywhere help staff process re-

petitive data entry work. The availability of artificial intelligence tools and frameworks now let companies digitally automate even more of their functions.

What's Next

RPA has the potential to transform the future of work, which is why so many organizations are researching how to integrate it into their workflows and systems. In January 2020, the U.S. government published a playbook for federal agencies that provides guidance on how to initiate a new RPA program. If the government deployed RPA at scale and was able to eliminate 20 hours of workload per employee, the capacity would be worth $3 billion, according to government estimates.

The Impact

RPA will eventually augment staff and shift their productivity into higher gear, especially as adjacent fields like natural language processing advance. Companies could then make better real-time predictive decisions in a host of different areas, from customer service to cost savings.

Watchlist

Amazon, Automation Anywhere, Blue Prism, Google, IBM, Kofax, Kryon, Microsoft, Nice Robotic Automation, Salesforce, UiPath, WorkFusion.

Self-Assembling Robots

HIGH DEGREE OF CERTAINTY

LONGER-TERM IMPACT

INFORMS STRATEGY	ACT NOW
REVISIT LATER	KEEP VIGILANT WATCH

IMMEDIATE IMPACT

LOW DEGREE OF CERTAINTY

M-Blocks 2.0 self-assemble like Transformers.

Key Insight

A new generation of robots can now self-assemble, merge, split and repair themselves.

Why It Matters

These self-assembling robots will create greater efficiencies in factories and offer new methods to deliver emergency services.

Examples

The **Massachusetts Institute of Technology** developed a set of robots called M-Blocks 2.0 that use a barcode system to communicate. They can identify each other and move as needed to perform designated tasks, which at the moment include forming a straight line and moving down a pathway. **The University of Pennsylvania** developed SMORES-EP robots—tiny, cube-shaped wheeled robots with sensors and cameras. Moving independently and docking with nearby modules, they can form different structures—and even self-assemble to lift objects and drop them off.

What's Next

Self-assembling robots offer a host of possibilities for medicine, manufacturing, construction and the military. The **MIT Computer Science and Artificial Intelligence Laboratory (CSAIL)** built a self-assembling robot called Primer that is controlled by magnetic fields. It can put on exoskeleton parts to help it walk, roll, sail or glide better, depending on the environment. Researchers at the **Georgia Institute of Technology** and at **Peking University (China)** discovered a new technique that mimics automatic origami—in initial testing, structures could fold and unfold on their own using inexpensive liquid polymers and LED projector bulbs.

The Impact

Self-assembling robots will be tremendous assets in emergency response situations. Imagine a set of robots forming a temporary staircase to rescue someone from a burning building, or a set of bots that can lock together to form a bridge over flooded roads.

Watchlist

Georgia Institute of Technology, MIT Computer Science and Artificial Intelligence Laboratory, Peking University, University of Pennsylvania.

Robot Compilers

HIGH DEGREE OF CERTAINTY

INFORMS STRATEGY	ACT NOW
REVISIT LATER	KEEP VIGILANT WATCH

LONGER-TERM IMPACT / IMMEDIATE IMPACT

LOW DEGREE OF CERTAINTY

A robot compiler from CSAIL.

Key Insight

Today, the process of designing, programming and building robots is time-intensive—and the robot's capabilities are limited by its original specifications. In the future, advanced compilers will enable much faster conceptualization and fabrication for a host of different tasks.

Why It Matters

We will soon tell computer systems what tasks we need completed, and they will automatically fabricate new robots for the job.

Examples

Researchers from the **Laboratory for Embedded Machines and Ubiquitous Robots** at **University of California-Los Angeles**, **MIT Computer Science and Artificial Intelligence Laboratory (CSAIL)**, **University of Pennsylvania** and **Harvard University** have been working to develop new methods for rapid robot fabrication. 3D robotic systems can now be produced using basic software and programmed using natural language commands.

What's Next

Fabricating programmable robots may not exactly be a simple, DIY weekend project, but promising research indicates that robot compilers could soon enable people with limited technical knowledge to sketch, design, fabricate and control a robot drawn straight from their imagination.

The Impact

There are tangible applications for businesses: Robot compilers would offer greater efficiencies, big cost savings and increased production for manufacturers in every industry.

Watchlist

Alliance Project, Harvard University, MIT Computer Science and Artificial Intelligence Laboratory (CSAIL), University of Pennsylvania, Laboratory for Embedded Machines and Ubiquitous Robots at University of California-Los Angeles, Walmart.

Soft Robotics

HIGH DEGREE OF CERTAINTY

INFORMS STRATEGY	ACT NOW
REVISIT LATER	KEEP VIGILANT WATCH

LONGER-TERM IMPACT

IMMEDIATE IMPACT

LOW DEGREE OF CERTAINTY

A tissue-based soft robot that mimics the biomechanics of a stingray.

Key Insight

Imagine robots that are pliable and soft to the touch, more like certain biological forms, and can operate in unpredictable environments.

Examples

There are now a variety of soft robots available. Some look like fat, squishy human fingers while others resemble gelatinous cephalopods. Bioengineering researchers at the **University of California-Los Angeles** developed a tissue-based soft robot that mimics the biomechanics of a stingray. Scientists at the **BioRobotics Institute at the Scuola Superiore Sant'Anna** in **Pisa, Italy**, created a robot octopus, capable of emulating the animal's agile motions. To replicate the biology of an octopus, they built computer models using exact measurements and then experimented with a number of soft actuators to develop artificial muscles.

Researchers at **Worcester Polytechnic Institute** have been working on a robotic snake that could navigate through rubble or confined spaces.

MIT engineers created soft and compact 3-D printed structures that can be controlled using magnets. The hope is that they can someday help control biomedical devices, take images within the body, clear arterial blockages, deliver targeted drugs to specific body parts, or even extract tissue samples.

What's Next

Soft robots face a big problem when it comes to heat control, because they're made of flexible synthetic materials rather than metals, which are better at dissipating heat. Researchers at **Cornell's School of Engineering** developed a robot capable of "sweating." They built a soft robotic muscle that can autonomously regulate its internal temperature, just like living organisms do.

The Impact

Someday soon, soft robotics will let us enter and explore environments previously unreachable by conventional methods: deep ocean waters, the terrain of Mars, and perhaps even the gushing rivers of blood inside our own bodies.

Watchlist

Defense Advanced Research Projects Agency (DARPA), Harvard Biodesign Lab, Johns Hopkins Applied Physics Laboratory, MIT Media Lab, MIT Computer Science and Artificial Intelligence Laboratory's Soft Contact Modeling Group, MIT Department of Civil and Environmental Engineering, Scuola Superiore Sant'Anna, Soft Robotics, University of California-Los Angeles School of Engineering, Worcester Polytechnic Institute.

Commercial Quadrupedal Robots

HIGH DEGREE OF CERTAINTY

INFORMS STRATEGY	ACT NOW
REVISIT LATER	KEEP VIGILANT WATCH

LONGER-TERM IMPACT / IMMEDIATE IMPACT

LOW DEGREE OF CERTAINTY

Spot is the first commercially available advanced quadrupedal robot.

Key Insight

Quadrupedal robots have four articulated legs and can move around difficult terrain, making them useful tools for inspections and security applications.

Why It Matters

By emulating the form and mobility of four-legged animals, these robots can be deployed in situations that wheeled or tread-equipped robots cannot navigate, and that may be too dangerous or physically inaccessible for human intervention.

Examples

In October 2019, a quadruped from **Boston Dynamics** went on sale. The robot, named Spot, looks like a headless dog and moves with the agility and athleticism of a border collie. Spot can map environments, move around difficult terrain and interact with a range of different objects.

What's Next

The ecosystem is still forming, but as developers build applications across different industries we expect to see new use cases emerge, particularly in safety, security, maintenance, emergency response, military, and even consumer contexts.

The Impact

For now, Boston Dynamics is the only company selling advanced robots like Spot for commercial, non-military purposes. Still, we believe this is a trend worth following closely for its potential effect across industries.

Watchlist

Amazon Robotics, Boston Dynamics, Fetch Robotics, Genesis Robotics, Google, Honda, Microsoft, NVIDIA, SoftBank, Sony, UBTech, Universal Robots.

Personal Robots and Robot Butlers

HIGH DEGREE OF CERTAINTY

INFORMS STRATEGY	ACT NOW
REVISIT LATER	KEEP VIGILANT WATCH

LONGER-TERM IMPACT — IMMEDIATE IMPACT

LOW DEGREE OF CERTAINTY

Key Insight

Personal robots and robot butlers, capable of carrying out multiple tasks in domestic and everyday environments, have entered the market.

Why It Matters

These assistive robots will soon include APIs, which will allow developers to make more applications for them, and should generate increased demand.

Examples

At the 2020 CES, **Samsung** introduced "Ballie," a small A.I.-powered robo-ball that functions as a security robot, fitness assistant, smart speaker and friend. While there's no word on when Ballie will be available to customers, **Sony** has a robot dog in the market already. Aibo is a cute robot puppy that can play fetch—it responds to reinforcement learning, so the more its owners offer feedback (in the form of neck scratches and pats on the head), the better it gets at interacting. **Panasonic** and **Japan**'s largest homebuilder **Daiwa House** created an A.I.-powered robot that can sort and fold your laundry. **Honda** and **Sony** launched a fleet of personal robots in the past year, offering both companionship and some help with the housework. (Whether there's a **Marie Kondo**-bot on the horizon, we still don't know.)

What's Next

Many countries, including **Japan**, **Italy**, and **Germany**, are facing rapid demographic shifts. Population numbers in certain age groups are changing, and within a generation some of these countries and others will no longer have the demographic makeup needed to make their societies function as they do today. Science and technology will eventually compensate for the lack of people: robots will assist with everything from eldercare, to medical assistance, to everyday companionship. In Japan, the population is inverting: There aren't enough people working to support retirees (one in four people in the country are now age 65 or older), and there aren't enough new babies being born. It's no surprise, then, that the first crop of companion robots is being built in Japan. Anyone interested in the future of robotics would be wise to look beyond **Silicon Valley** to the universities and R&D labs of Japan, where extensive research on the next generation of robot companions is already underway. Out of necessity, robots—mechanical systems, artificial intelligence, and automated services—will act as productive, emotionally-intelligent stand-ins for younger generations that were simply too small in numbers.

Impact

For now, personal robots are out of the price range of average consumers. That will change as the device ecosystem matures in the very near future.

Watchlist

AMY Robotics, ARP, Bioinspired Intelligent Mechatronics Lab, Buddy, Fujitsu, Groove X, Honda, Johns Hopkins Applied Physics Laboratory, LG, MIT Media Lab, Mitsubishi Heavy Industries, Nanyang Technological University, Panasonic, Ritsumeikan University, Samsung, Sharp, Shinpo Electronics, SoftBank Robotics, Sony, Tokyo University, Toyota.

Sony's newest Aibo plays fetch.

Ethical Manufacturing

HIGH DEGREE OF CERTAINTY

INFORMS STRATEGY	ACT NOW
REVISIT LATER	KEEP VIGILANT WATCH

LONGER-TERM IMPACT

IMMEDIATE IMPACT

LOW DEGREE OF CERTAINTY

A garment factory in Southeast Asia.

Key Insight

Robots could bring an end to forced labor and lead a new era of ethical manufacturing.

Why It Matters

Millions of people are victims of forced labor around the world.

Examples

Advancements in robotics will further reduce the need for human labor. While this certainly means that people will be out of certain kinds of work, it could also mean the end of bonded, forced and child labor—not to mention outright slavery—which unfortunately has become commonplace in places like **Uzbekistan**, **China** and **Bangladesh**. In September 2018, the **Associated Press** published a devastating account of foreign fishing workers, confined and forced to work on U.S. fishing boats. The AP's investigation revealed a disturbing present-day reality: Fishermen who were forced to use buckets instead of toilets, suffered sores from bed bugs and didn't have enough food to sustain them.

What's Next

You might assume that if a t-shirt costs $5.99, then a robot made it, but that isn't always the case. Better manufacturing processes in fast fashion and other industries could lead to improved working conditions for millions of people, but also may put some of those people out of their jobs. Sustainability goals set by the **United Nation** and other organizations have prioritized human rights in manufacturing and supply chain processes and automation.

The Impact

Ethical manufacturing promises more humane work environments, but could also potentially lead to disruption in developing economies. Even with extremely low wages, a workforce can sustain a local economy—when those wages are lost as workers are replaced by robots, the flow of money through the community can go from a trickle to a drought.

Watchlist

ABB Robotics, Aethon Inc., Alliance For American Manufacturing, Alphabet (Google), Amazon, Carnegie Mellon University, MIT's Interactive Robotics Group, National Association of Manufacturers, Tesla, ULC Robotics.

Robot Rights

HIGH DEGREE OF CERTAINTY

	INFORMS STRATEGY	ACT NOW	
LONGER-TERM IMPACT	REVISIT LATER	KEEP VIGILANT WATCH	IMMEDIATE IMPACT

LOW DEGREE OF CERTAINTY

"The rationale for robot 'rights' is not a question for 2076, it's already a question for now."

– Peter W. Singer, author of *Wired for War*

Key Insight

Some believe that we have moral obligations to our machines, and that, like people, robots should have rights too.

Why It Matters

We are seeing increased instances of humans bullying or abusing robots.

Examples

A recent study from the **Human Interaction With Nature and Technological Systems Lab** (HINTS) at the **University of Washington** discovered that children didn't show the same kind of empathy for robots that they do with other humans. In the study, 60% of the child subjects thought that a humanoid robot named Robovie-II had feelings—yet more than half of them thought it was fine to lock him in the closet. Researchers at **ATR Intelligent Robotics and Communication Laboratories**, **Osaka University**, **Ryukoku University**, and **Tokai University** in **Japan** conducted an experiment to mea-

sure human empathy toward robots. They deployed Robovie through a mall in **Osaka** without a human minder. If someone walked into the robot's path, it would politely ask the human to move. Adults complied—but children didn't. And if unsupervised, the children were intentionally mean, kicking the robot, yelling at it and bullying it.

What's Next

When it comes to our interactions with robots, what constitutes a moral violation? What rights should robots have, given that so many companies are building smart interfaces and cognitive systems? If we are teaching machines to think, and to learn from us humans, then what moral codes are we programming into our future generations of robots? Answering these questions will become increasingly urgent as robots proliferate in many aspects of our everyday lives.

The Impact

Do robots need worker rights, too? Researchers raise this question now, especial-

ly as robots are predicted to take on more meaningful roles within the workplace and in society. **The European Union** is already discussing whether there ought to be a special legal status of "electronic persons" to protect sophisticated robots.

Watchlist

ATR Intelligent Robotics and Communication Laboratories, Buddy, Honda, LG, MIT Media Lab, Mitsubishi, Osaka University, Panasonic, Ritsumeikan University, Ryukoku University, Sharp, SoftBank Robotics, Sony, Tokai University, Tokyo University, Toyota, University of Washington, Wyss Institute at Harvard.Mechatronics Lab, Buddy, Fujitsu, Groove X, Honda, Johns Hopkins Applied Physics Laboratory, LG, MIT Media Lab, Mitsubishi Heavy Industries, Nanyang Technological University, Panasonic, Ritsumeikan University, Samsung, Sharp, Shinpo Electronics, SoftBank Robotics, Sony, Tokyo University, Toyota.

Smart Dust

HIGH DEGREE OF CERTAINTY

INFORMS STRATEGY	ACT NOW
REVISIT LATER	KEEP VIGILANT WATCH

LONGER-TERM IMPACT · IMMEDIATE IMPACT

LOW DEGREE OF CERTAINTY

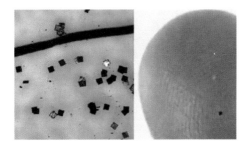

Smart dust developed by Hitachi.

Key Insight

These computers, no larger than a grain of dust, are so light they can stay suspended in midair.

Why It Matters

Smart dust, also known as "microelectrome-chanical systems" or MEMS, represent a new kind of atomic-level materials engineering.

Examples

If you watched the "Arkangel" episode of "Black Mirror" (season four), you're already familiar with smart dust. For years, re-searchers have been hard at work on minia-turization, as they try to shrink computers as much as possible, down to the size of grains of sand or specks of dust. Each particle-computer consists of circuits and sensors capable of monitoring the environ-ment, and even taking photographs. They can even harvest energy while suspended, using everything from passive WiFi and our body heat to power themselves.

It sounds fantastical, but the use of MEMS is already widespread. They're the accelerom-eter sensors for our airbag systems and are also found in biosensors. Scientists at the **University of California-Berkeley** developed what they call "neural dust," which com-prises microscopic computers that work alongside remote ultrasound to send and receive data about the brain. Meanwhile, researchers at the **University of Stuttgart** figured out how to print tiny 3D lenses—120 millionths of a meter in diameter, or about the size of a grain of sand.

What's Next

In health and medicine, this technology will dramatically change our approach to imaging. Rather than relying on our current endoscopic technology, which is bulky and invasive, a patient could simply inhale smart dust. Beyond medicine, trillions of smart dust particles could be released in the wind to measure air quality or take photos. But we must also consider other hazards and use cases: Would you know if you'd inhaled rogue smart dust on a windy day? In the fur-ther-future, could this technology be used to track us surreptitiously?

The Impact

We should see more interesting develop-ments in smart dust this year as the practi-cal application of always-on sensors grows.

Watchlist

Ambiq Micro, Defense Advanced Research Projects Agency (DARPA), Jeeva Wireless, Matrix Industries, Northrop Grumman, Psi-Kick, Purdue University, Stanford University, University of California-Berkeley, University of Stuttgart, University of Washington, University of Southern California Robotics Research Lab.

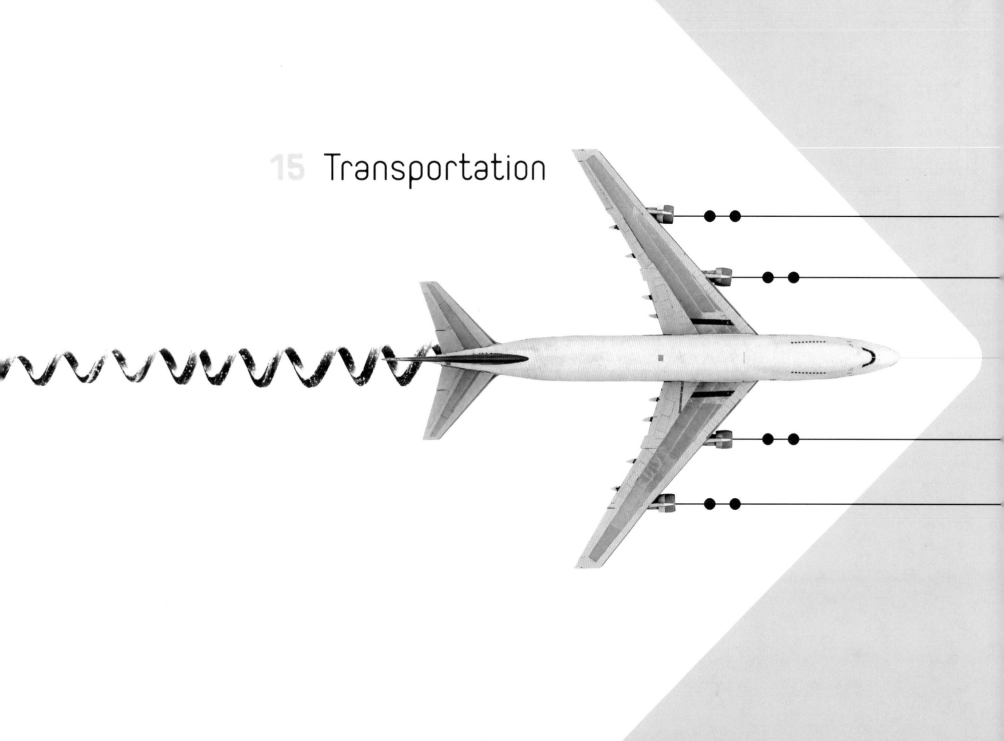

15 Transportation

Drones

Zipline's drones, which can carry about 4 pounds and travel at 68 miles per hour, have made more than 29,551 deliveries.
Credit: Roksenhorn

KEY INSIGHT

A commercial industry has boomed, and hundreds of thousands of drones are being used for media, land surveying, building and infrastructure inspections, and personal entertainment.

WHAT YOU NEED TO KNOW

Drones were used extensively during the coronavirus outbreak of 2020: to monitor residents and encourage them to stay indoors, to inspect traffic stops and hospitals, and to spray cities with disinfectants. A video clip went viral on a Chinese social media site, showing a drone breaking up a mahjong game—residents defied local ordinances to stay indoors. The government was reportedly using drones outfitted with infrared cameras to fly overhead and check for people who might have fevers.

China offers a glimpse into how drones will be used more in the near-future. Autonomous drones–capable of working independently and together as part of a larger fleet–are finding wider commercial use in natural disasters, for package deliveries, for smart city management, within warehouses, and on automated farms.

WHY IT MATTERS

As drone demand increases around the world, it's likely that consolidation will follow. Flight service providers, hardware startups, drone and aircraft manufacturers, asset and flight path management software, and data processing platforms will see a wave of mergers and acquisitions in the near future, which could make it difficult for new start-ups to compete.

THE IMPACT

Widespread future use of commercial drones will likely depend on standardizing regulations. If companies are forced to comply with patchwork regulations in different locations, it would make compliance burdensome.

WATCHLIST

Aerodyne Group, Airbus, AirDog, Bell Helicopter, Boeing, Boeing's Aurora Flight Sciences, Cora, Corgan, Cyberhawk, DJI, Dubai Road and Transport Authority, EHang, Embraer, Federal Aviation Administration, fiber optic cable providers, Hemav, Hover, Intel, Joby, Karem Aircraft, Lilium, Lockheed Martin Corp, Massachusetts Institute of Technology, municipalities and state legislatures, NASA, NASA Unmanned Aircraft System, oil and gas pipelines, Opener, Operation Zenith, Pipistrel Aircraft, security providers, shipping and port operators, Swellpro, Terra Drone, Toyota, Traffic Management, U.S. Coast Guard, U.S. Military, U.S. Navy, Volocopter, Walkera, Wisk, Yuneec International, Yuneec, Zipline.

⊘ TRENDS

Medical Supply Drone Delivery

Drone platform provider **Matternet** launched a new trial program with **UPS** in 2019 to deliver medical supplies—documents, blood samples, and other items—via a secure drone carrier. After a successful run, the two companies will provide the service to medical centers in the U.S. In 2020, **Jacobs Medical Center** and the **Moores Cancer Center**, which are located about a mile away from each other in **California**, will use secure drone delivery to move samples, documents and supplies. The flight will take a few minutes and will be monitored by a team of remote operators. Previously, UPS had tested a medical supply drone to deliver blood to remote areas of **Rwanda**.

Drone Operation Centers

As commercial drones take to our sidewalks and skies, drone control centers and specially-trained logistics experts with experience in geospatial data, predictive analytics and hardware will help manage fleets. In addition to optimizing and deploying fleets, commercial drone operation centers will work to determine the best delivery routes, how to minimize costs and the best way to reach consumers and partners.

Drones-as-a-Service

Ownership of powerful, commercial drones may be out of reach, financially, for some companies who need occasional—rather than ongoing—access to aerial logistics. The drone industry will likely borrow business models from other industries—including the car rental and scooter sharing industry—and may begin providing drones-as-a-service. This also reduces the need for specially-trained staff and licensed drone pilots.

Personal Home Drone Surveillance

Why bother with fixed security cameras when a flying drone could patrol your home? A number of new home drone surveillance startups are now testing new systems for homeowners. One example: **Sunflower Labs** has developed a three-part home drone surveillance system that includes flying and ground drones. Think of them as roving security guards that don't get tired or need bathroom breaks. The system relies on "Sunflowers," small 1.5-foot bulbs that resemble ordinary garden lights but are packed with various sensors. Placed around a home, the Sunflowers triangulate people and objects while a Bee—that's the name of the drone—flies itself around the property to monitor activity before returning to its Hive base station.

Flying Beyond Visual Line of Sight

Robots harnessing neural networks and artificial intelligence can make inferences and decisions when programmed to do so. That's because of sense and avoid technology. Last year, a host of new drones equipped with anti-collision sensors and transponders capable of transmitting waypoints were able to inspect many miles of oil and gas pipelines.

Drones cont.

Drone swarms move together and are used for light shows, military operations and reconnaissance missions.

Real-Time Mapping

Better cameras, faster processing, and smarter algorithms will soon help drones generate live maps while hovering in previously unknown areas. This will allow for fast data generation and, as a result, better insights. For example, some newer software systems like **DroneDeploy** can generate live thermal maps so that farmers and city managers can visualize temperature range variability in real-time.

Drones for Dangerous and Hard-To-Reach Areas

Smaller, rugged, A.I.-powered drones can access dangerous and hard-to-reach spaces. Companies now use drones to survey the insides of underground mines, ballasts of tanks and inside of nuclear facilities. Home and building inspectors now use drones to inspect rooftops and sides of buildings. Such use of drones could improve human safety, cut costs, and shorten downtimes.

Clandestine, Disappearing Drones

The **Department of Advanced Research Projects Agency (DARPA)** funded new research in drones capable of making deliveries—and then disappearing into thin air. The agency's **Vanishing Programmable Resources (VAPR)** program has already shown that it's possible to program a small chip to shatter on command. As part of the program, **SRI International** developed the **Stressed Pillar-Engineered CMOS Technology Readied for Evanescence (SPECTRE)**, which is a silicon-air battery technology that can self-destruct. It's also possible to get rid of certain parts of drones: Scientists at the **University of Houston** developed a new kind of circuit that dissolves when exposed to water molecules—when programmed or scheduled. Meanwhile, **San Francisco**-based **Otherlab** built a drone made out of mushrooms. Just after deployment, embedded spores begin to eat away at the drone, devouring it entirely in less than a week. Another **DARPA** program—the **Inbound, Controlled, Air-Releasable, Unrecoverable Systems (or ICARUS)** program—is working on vanishing drones and other gadgets to assist the **U.S. military** when carrying out operations. But disappearing drones don't just serve a military purpose. **Amazon** is working on self-destructing features in the event that one of its delivery drones fails. Rather than crash into people, homes, or cars, the drone would instead gently fall apart and glide down to a safe area.

Flying Taxis

The first flying taxi stations are opening in 2020. Electric vertical take-off and landing aircraft operators promise to make flying taxis available and affordable to everyone—and to alleviate traffic congestion in the process. Several companies built proof of concept designs for aircraft that would take off vertically, fly horizontally and fly short distances at an affordable price around metropolitan areas, and some are already flying. In late 2019, the **Volocopter 2X** made its first public flight in **Singapore**. **EHang** debuted a flying taxi that is rated to carry 575 lbs for 30 minutes at 80 miles per hour. **Berlin**-based **Lilium** is building a production facility for its new electric aircraft. **Kitty Hawk**, a startup funded by **Google's Larry Page** and run by **Sebastian Thrun**, who previously launched Google's self-driving car unit, entered into a joint venture with **Boeing** to launch flying taxi service **Wisk**. In February 2020, Wisk signed a memorandum of understanding with the government of **New Zealand** to start trials with its self-flying electric aircraft **Cora**. A number of other companies are working on such technology, **including Airbus**, **Joby** and **Toyota**. **NASA** is working with the **Federal Aviation Administration** on an **Urban Air Mobility**, or **UAM**, project to create the groundwork for the safety and security of this new short-distance aircraft. **Uber** has also provided guidelines for vertical takeoff and landing crafts to be able to travel at up to 200 miles per hour, at an altitude of 1,000 to 2,000 feet, and have a range of 60 miles. Uber's service is envisioned to serve concerts, festivals, and green spaces. (Today, you can book an Uber helicopter to include car service to and from heliports.)

Autonomous Underwater Vehicles

Drones aren't just for air and land—they can operate underwater, too. Autonomous underwater vehicles can reduce costs for monitoring, building and maintaining underwater assets. Changing the business dynamics for marine construction potentially increasing underwater land usage. Improved mapping of underwater surfaces will reduce the cost of laying the transatlantic cables that serve

as the backbone of the internet, enabling increased competition and connectivity. Military autonomous underwater vehicles could be used for security, intelligence, countermeasures, network infrastructure, and port security. These roles could be offensive or defensive.

Drone Air Lanes

Drone adoption will push the development of "air lanes" for both manned and unmanned aircraft where different types of aerial vehicles are grouped into categories and traffic lanes. **NASA** recently completed the development of a traffic management ecosystem for aerial devices that fly under 400 feet. The **Unmanned Aircraft System Traffic Management (UTM)** has been handed off to the **Federal Aviation Administration** for further development and implementation. Proactively constructing aerial infrastructure will let regulators relieve congestion, ensure safety and incorporate learnings from road and air travel. The development of regulation will be made at the city and state level because interoperability at a federal and global level will be less necessary for drone travel.

Follow Me Autonomously

"Follow-me" functionality popularized by consumer drones will drive the development of sense and avoid technology for autonomous vehicles of all sizes. Personal drones for photography will exponentially increase testing and accelerate the development of the technology. Drones that can automatically avoid crashes and avoid obstacles can increase the safety and versatility of drones. Autonomous conflict avoidance also reduces stress on the pilot, making indoor flight easier and expanding where drones can be operated. Many consumer drones available today have "follow-me" crash avoidance technology used for semi-autonomous flight. A subject is kept in the frame, and a separate pilot is not needed. This is ideal for capturing solo activities where the drone operator is in the field of view, perhaps doing backflips, cartwheels or smiling. Obstacle avoidance would be a logical stepping stone to fully autonomous drones, but getting there will likely require more energy efficient processors to do the necessary calculations onboard the drone. Connectivity technology like 5G will help minimize lag time between the movement of

the drone and the calculations performed in the cloud or via operator device.

Drone Swarms

Drone swarms are groups of drones that fly and move together. They are used in **China** as alternatives to fireworks and in dazzling light shows at **Disney Parks**. In the dark, lights on the drones can look like fireworks that move and light up in ways that defy physics. Beyond light shows, drone swarms are used in military operations and in reconnaissance missions. Future swarm technology could use what **Nora Ayanin**, a roboticist at the **University of Southern California**, calls "leveraging diversity in the control policy," where each drone is programmed slightly differently, so the one best suited to the task teaches the rest of the swarm how to act.

Transportation Trends

HIGH DEGREE OF CERTAINTY

INFORMS STRATEGY	ACT NOW
REVISIT LATER	KEEP VIGILANT WATCH

LONGER-TERM IMPACT   IMMEDIATE IMPACT

LOW DEGREE OF CERTAINTY

Locations of charging stations could shift traffic patterns, benefitting the local economies of some towns.

KEY INSIGHT

An autonomous vehicle is capable of sensing its environment and operating without human involvement while carrying some kind of cargo.

WHAT YOU NEED TO KNOW

The **Tesla** is well-known for its self-driving capabilities: It can park itself, drive on highways using auto-pilot, and drive through parking lots to pick up passengers. In 2020, several cars with autonomous features will come to market. Cars aren't the only autonomous vehicles, though. Trucks and ships are being developed with assistive technologies, which will require less direct human involvement while operating vehicles.

WHY IT MATTERS

As the autonomous vehicle industry starts to mature, there are numerous business opportunities for both startups and established companies. However the commercial sector moved faster than regulators, and in early 2020 **U.S.** lawmakers proposed a new regulatory framework to govern self-driving vehicles.

DEEPER DIVE

Levels of Automation

There are different levels of what's considered "self-driving." **The Society of Automotive Engineers** drafted a generally accepted definition of autonomous driving that goes from level zero to level five. The most advanced publicly available vehicles reached level two functionality, like **Tesla's** Autopilot or **Cadillac's** Super Cruise.

Level Zero

These cars contain features that may momentarily take control over the vehicle, but they do not have sustained control of the car. This includes anti lock brakes and electronic stability control.

Level 1

This incorporates "hands-on or driver assistance," in which the car works in conjunction with human control of the vehicle. Examples would be adaptive cruise control, where the car controls speed, or the use of "park assist" where the car controls steering.

Level 2

This is "hands-off / partial automation" where the car controls acceleration, braking, and steering, but the human is required to intervene at any point. A good example is **Tesla's** Autopilot feature, where the car follows lanes, accelerates to travel speed and decelerates for traffic and intersections.

Level 3

This would be "eyes-off / conditional automation," where the driver is not required to pay attention to driving for the majority of the time. But the driver must be prepared to intervene at certain moments when prompted by the car. An example would be the **Audi** Traffic Jam Pilot, where the car takes full control of driving in slow-moving traffic on highways.

Level 4

"Mind-off / high automation" includes technology that allows the vehicle to need no input or oversight, but it's restricted to specific roads or conditions. An example would be the **Google** Firefly Prototype, which did not have a steering wheel or pedal.

Level 5

"Steering wheel optional/full automation" means the car can operate anywhere and, in any conditions, that a human could without needing any human interaction. **Waymo** has a fleet of hybrid cars that it's testing for Level 5 automation in **Phoenix**.

How Autonomous Vehicles "Talk" To Each Other

Autonomous vehicles rely on internal software and sensors to perform basic functions. However, in order to achieve Level 5 autonomy—where vehicles drive themselves, along with other vehicles across all of our roads, highways, alleys, bridges, and driveways—they'll need to sense and communicate with each other. This will require additional work, and some questions still remain: Should vehicles talk to each other as part of a big, moving network? Or should vehicles communicate with infrastructure to send and receive all the data they need? (Or would there need to be some combination of the two?)

Vehicles will need to communicate with one another and to the road infrastructure to get real-time information on the road conditions and collaboration among vehicles. This will create new data streams to optimize road usage. **Audi**, **Qualcomm** and the **Virginia Department of Transportation** are testing cars that will interface with construction zones and traffic lights.

Multiple cars will travel together in groups of "platoons" in very short distances of each other, increasing the efficiency of communication between the vehicles and the roads on which they travel. The platoon approach is a frequent method of increasing the throughput on existing "dumb" highways—so vehicles communicate directly with one another. The platoon would require only one lead driver, or no driver, depending on the level of autonomation.

Waze's user-generated traffic data is an example of collaborative sourcing of transport information. **Cadillac's** Super Cruise semi-autonomous driving service relies on similar technology, using vehicles equipped with expensive LIDAR (Light Detection and Ranging) that scans the roadway ahead and provides accurate mapping of the road. Cars using the Super Cruise function that follow behind don't need to have their own LIDAR equipment.

Network protocols for vehicles and infrastructure communication must be developed, and it needs to be unfailingly reliable, fast, and secure. Vehicle communication protocols will likely intersect with 5G technology and node-based/mesh networks. Researchers are exploring Vehicular Ad Hoc Networks, which uses node-based rebroadcasting of information—a method that could potentially reduce the need for fixed infrastructure and could allow moving vehicles to take their network with them into areas with no connectivity. **Gotenna** uses similar local mesh networking to allow cell phone communication in areas without cell service.

Lawsuits and Restructuring

The pace of advancement slowed when **Waymo** and **Uber** entered a heated lawsuit over trade secret infringement and because of limited employee mobility across companies. The companies settled the suit, and a general truce emerged—but the freedom of information and exchange of ideas has been reduced.

Things perked up in November 2019 when **General Motors CEO Mary Barra** boldly announced that GM would restructure the company and focus on its electric and autonomous vehicle programs. Nonetheless, GM-backed Cruise delayed the 2019 launch of its autonomous taxi service in **San Francisco** to focus on further testing, without citing a new launch date.

❯ TRENDS

Cognitive Active Safety Features

Proactive driver safety functions are becoming more advanced as we get closer to autonomous driving. For example, **Driveri** is a dash camera that uses A.I. to monitor real-time road conditions to provide driving suggestions. The company partnered with fleets and commercial drivers to monitor driving behavior and also to teach people how to be better drivers. Vehicle manufacturers will continue to implement and tout active safety features as a way to drive consumer sales. The development cycles of car manufacturers will move faster than the historic 10-year cycles, as platforms become increasingly software-driven.

Electric Vehicles Cause Electricity Demand Spikes

Cars, trucks and buses aren't the only vehicles driving battery-powered transportation. Motorized bicycles, hoverboards, electric skateboards and battery-powered scooters are growing in popularity because their business models appeal to younger consumers who want to own less and want to live in cities that are becoming denser.

Tesla underscored the importance of the electrical grid when its vehicles' alerted owners in **California** that their electricity would be disrupted by wildfires. The early movers that build charging infrastructure along travel routes will have the power to shift traffic patterns and create a network advantage—similar to the way the interstate highway system created an economic boon for certain towns and sunk towns bypassed by the roads. Utility providers will be pressured to improve the grid resilience as domestic charging demands grow. Access and resilience of electricity grids will be key to economic prosperity in the future, as dependency grows for electric transportation.

Transportation-as-a-Service

The business models supporting transportation are starting to change as more players provide pay-per-use structures, such as ride, bike, scooter and car-sharing services. Ride-sharing services like **Uber**, **Lyft**, **Via**, and **Gett** are relatively well established, but the business model goes beyond cars. There are micro-mobility providers of electric and non-electric bicycles—**Citi Bike**, **Mobike**, **Ofo**, **Lime**—and electric scooter companies—**Bird**, **Spin**, **Lime**, **Skip**— and full-size gas and

electric motorcycles—**eCooltra** and **ioscoot**. Car rental companies like **Hertz** and **Avis** are now allowing rentals by the minute or mile in some locations, and other companies let people rent out their own vehicles to strangers—**Turo**, **Getaround**, **Zipcar**, **Koolicar**, **Drover**, **Carlease**, **Avis Budget Group**, **HyreCar**, **Hiyacar**, **Miveo Car-sharing Technologies** and **MaaS Finland**. Car manufacturers, too, are testing out new ownership models like **Silvercar** by **Audi**, **Care by Volvo** or **Porsche Passport**. As transportation shifts to service platforms, subscriptions or usage rates, traditional ownership, maintenance and depreciation will decrease in popularity. Consumers will choose such services based on their personal needs, flexibility and cost-efficiency.

Forced Updates To Firmware and Software

When a provider like **Microsoft** or **Google** changes a keyboard shortcut or switches the delete and archive button, the result can be a lot of frustration. Now consider when **Tesla** moves the horn or brake pedal... the result can be significantly more problematic. Or imagine there is a billing hiccup and your access to safety features is disabled during a road trip. In an ideal world, software that is always updated would be the safest and best experience possible. But software updates are often required and cannot be stopped. As more products are released in an evolving transportation platform, new features and functionality will be added via over-the-air firmware updates at a later date. Providers must increasingly learn to navigate the difficult path of introducing new features and improving customer experiences while balancing legacy experiences and muscle memory.

Analog Fallbacks

The saying, 'They don't make them like they used to' will soon become they *literally* don't make them like they used to and they can't be *repaired* like they used to.

As more functionality becomes digital-ly based, manual fallbacks will become more obscure and non-intuitive, leading to increasingly catastrophic failures when digital systems fail. Car locks, which are increasingly dependent on electricity, can become inoperable when the car battery runs out. There are plenty of examples: A man was trapped in his **Cadillac** for 13 hours and, tragically, a man and his dog died in a

Corvette when the car battery failed. Both vehicles had manual door release mecha-nisms designed as a fallback for electronic failure, but neither man could find the release mechanism. To make matters more tragic, one of the victims had the vehicle owner's manual yet still couldn't release the mechanism. What happens when cars no longer come with physical user manuals or if firmware updates change the product so much that physical manuals are no longer accurate? As vehicles become more auto-mated and require less mechanical know-how, consumers will focus more on other elements of the transportation. This will allow manufacturers to create new business models and drive brand preference with less emphasis on mechanical interactions. Hopefully, manufacturers self-regulate and ensure that emergency manual fallbacks are consistent and clearly indicated.

Exponential Growth in Autonomous Miles Data

More than 90% of traffic deaths are caused by human error. The traditional theory of algorithm development, meanwhile, dictates that the larger and richer the data set the better the resulting algorithm. **Tesla** vehicles

that use autopilot have begun to reach critical mass with an estimated total lifetime production of 200,000 electric vehicles. It is only with these higher autonomous miles that we begin to see shortcomings in the early algorithms for autonomous vehicles—mainly the challenge of identifying sta-tionary objects that results in catastrophic crashes. The network effect—drawing big data from autonomous car use—will be important to designing the safest auton-omous vehicles, which will, in turn, drive consumer preference. For manufacturers, autonomous algorithms mustn't be a "winner take all market" because the developer of the best algorithms could resell its IP. As the data set underlying autonomous driving gets larger and richer, the quality of the autono-mous driving should get better too. The data collected from miles driven with autono-mous technology will begin to grow expo-nentially as the install base reaches critical mass—and that should rapidly accelerate the improvement of driving algorithms.

Autonomous Last Mile Logistics

The first truly autonomous vehicles won't be transporting humans, but rather goods like pizza. That's because it's quickly becom-

ing safer and easier to manage the last mile of logistics using a small autonomous delivery vehicle. **Nuro**, a startup founded by former **Google** engineers, is developing autonomous vehicles for last-mile deliveries including take-out, groceries, laundry and packages. **JD.com** developed robots that delivered packages in June 2017. **SoftBank** and **Toyota** created a joint venture to create autonomous vehicles to deliver robot-made meals. They target the late 2020s to be in the market. **Dominos** and **Ford** are testing self-driving delivery technology in **Las Ve-gas**, **Ann Arbor**, **Michigan** and **Miami**. Auton-omous deliveries will help society transition and adjust to autonomous vehicles on public infrastructure as the vehicles will likely be small and slow-moving while delivering delightful experiences.

Mixed-Use Sidewalks and Drone Lanes

Our outdoor spaces are changing fast. Sidewalks now have pedestrian and electric scooter traffic. Small delivery drones drive alongside cars and trucks. Smart cameras and sensors are being used to detect how we're moving around our cities, and artificial intelligence systems can produce digital

Transportation Trends cont.

Waymo's self-driving vehicles are being tested in Phoenix.

twins of city blocks to pressure-test changes to traffic flow, population increases and public events. For example, **Strava Metro** is using the data from runners and cyclists to help urban planners design safer streets.

Supersonic Flights

After years of successful trans-Atlantic flights, the age of supersonic jet travel came to an end in October 2003, when **British Airways** permanently grounded the Concorde. Driven in part by the enthusiasm and excitement over faster, autonomous travel, these supersonic jets are being tested once again. **Japan Airlines** has invested $10 million in **Boom Technology** to develop supersonic jets, which will travel at 2.2 times the speed of sound—about twice as fast as a traditional aircraft. (Japanese Airlines has already pre-ordered 20.) **All Nippon Airways** is also researching supersonic flight. **Aerion, Lockheed Martin** and **GE Aviation** are developing a supersonic business jet that could carry 12 passengers. The new supersonic airplanes will allow flights to take off over land, which because of the sonic boom, had limited the success of the original Concorde. Fuel efficiency and safety concerns, however, could slow getting to market in the short term.

Autonomous Ships

Early in 2018, an oil tanker caught fire after colliding with another boat in the East China Sea, killing more than two dozen people. Safety is one of many reasons that companies are looking to automation in shipping. The **Yara Birkeland** is an electric container ship that is supported by radar, LiDAR, machine learning and computer vision systems, an automatic mooring system and a network for cameras. It is currently on schedule to transition from traditional human-crewed operation to fully autonomous operation in 2020. Electric ships that don't require people would offer cost savings throughout the entire shipping supply chain. They could be safer, solve labor shortages, and be better for the environment. The **International Maritime Organization** has begun a scoping exercise that will complete in 2020 after which practical drafting will start and lay the legal foundation for maritime autonomous surface ships.

THE IMPACT

Widespread adoption and use of autonomous vehicles promises fewer accidents, lower energy costs, optimized driving efficiency and reduced traffic congestion.

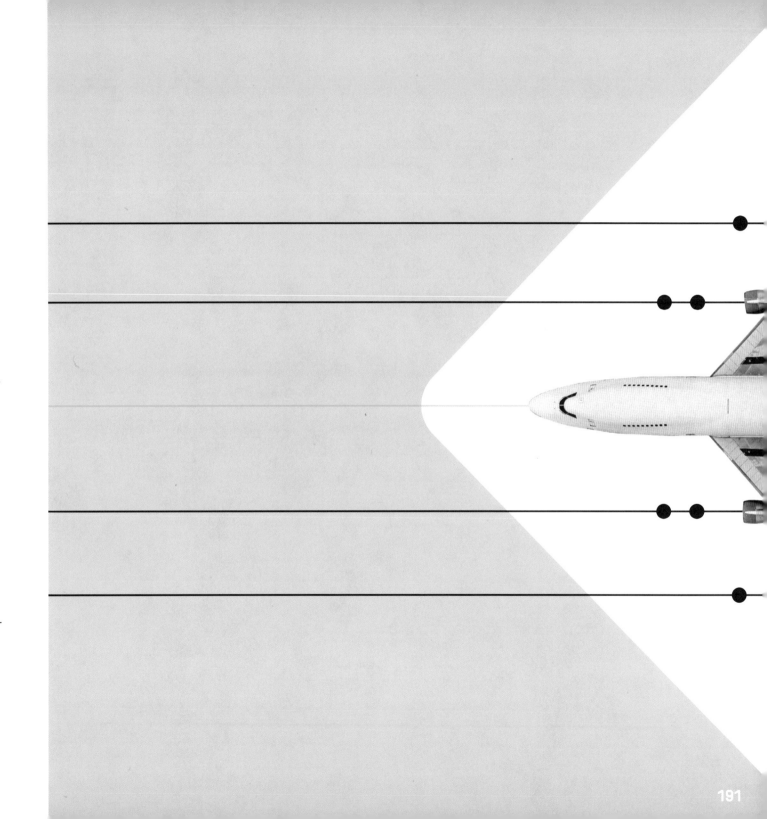

THE WATCHLIST

Ace Hardware, Aerion, All Nippon Airlines, Ample, Audi, auto manufacturers, Avis, Baidu, Bird, BMW, Boom, Bosch, Citibike, Delphi Automotive Systems, Dominos, Driveri, Ecooltra, FAA, Fiat Chrysler, Ford, GE Aviation, General Motors, General Motors, General Motors, Get, Hertz, Honda, Hyundai, infrastructure development players and investment banks, International Maritime Organization, Ioscoot, Jaguar Land Rover, Japan Airlines, JD.com, Kepler.gl, Kia, King Long, Kongsberg, lime, Lockheed Martin, Lockheed Martin, Lyft, Marin Teknikk, Mazda, Mercedes Benz, Mitsubishi, Mobike, NASA, National Oceanic Atmospheric Administration, Nissan, Nissan, NVIDIA, Ofo, Otto, Peterbilt, Porsche, Postmates, public utility companies, Rolls-Royce, Sidewalk Labs, Skip, Softbank, Solar Roadways, Spin, Starsky Robotics, Strava Metro, Subaru, Tesla, TomTom, Toyota, Turo, U.S. Army, Uber, Via, Virgin Group, Vision Zero NYC, Volkswagen, Volkswagen, Volvo, VW, Waymo, Waze.

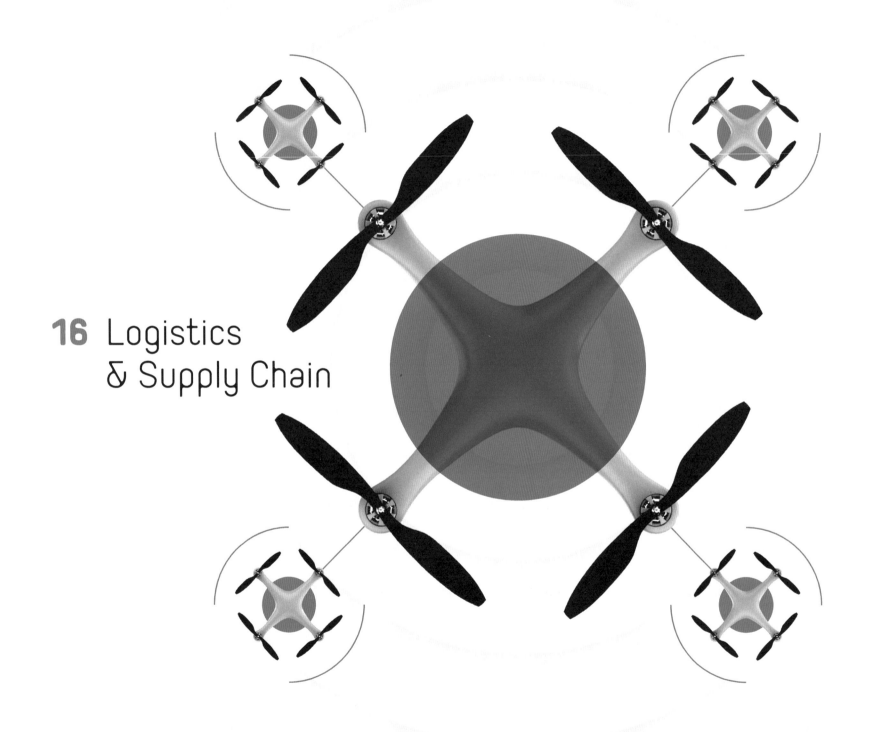

16 Logistics
& Supply Chain

Automating the Supply Chain

HIGH DEGREE OF CERTAINTY

INFORMS STRATEGY	ACT NOW
REVISIT LATER	KEEP VIGILANT WATCH

LONGER-TERM IMPACT / IMMEDIATE IMPACT

LOW DEGREE OF CERTAINTY

Autonomous mobile robots are performing more work in warehouses.

Key Insight

5G networks and new autonomous robots and vehicles will help optimize warehouse management.

Why It Matters

Autonomous mobile robots (AMRs) and autonomous guided vehicles (AGVs) will become more commonplace in 2020, which will bring cost-savings and efficiencies for businesses.

Examples

For the past few decades, robots have assisted humans with repetitive tasks. But in 2020, we will see a new class of autonomous robots and vehicles running on A.I.-powered logistics systems. Rather than relying on LiDAR SLAM (Simultaneous Localization And Mapping), a new class of robots use computer vision and A.I. In a warehouse setting, autonomous mobile robots assign global tasks, set paths and optimize tasks like picking. **Amazon Robotics**, which acquired **Kiva Systems** in 2012, leads the market in automated robots and now relies on a host of automated systems in its warehouses.

What's Next

Now in the midst of a transformation, the robotics industry will drastically impact the supply chain. Some researchers anticipate that 6 million mobile robots will be shipped within the next decade, shifting every sector of the global economy.

The Impact

Mobile automation in the supply chain is a quickly maturing market. While this means greater efficiencies and cost savings for businesses, it also portends job losses for workers who operate warehouse equipment.

Watchlist

Amazon Robotics, Boston Dynamics, Kuka Robotics, Mobile Industrial Robots, Okura, Omron, Rethink Robots, Robotic Industries Association, Universal Robots.

"Just because something works doesn't mean that it can't be improved."

– Shuri in Black Panther

Sustainability in Supply Chain and Logistics

HIGH DEGREE OF CERTAINTY

INFORMS STRATEGY	**ACT NOW**
REVISIT LATER	**KEEP VIGILANT WATCH**

LONGER-TERM IMPACT — IMMEDIATE IMPACT

LOW DEGREE OF CERTAINTY

Tetra Pak responds to sustainability shifts with renewable packaging.

Key Insight

Pressure from investors, customers, and governments—in addition to extreme weather events and trade tensions—has resulted in new efforts to build sustainability into the supply chain for many companies.

Why It Matters

A company's supply chain and logistics system can greatly impact the environment, human rights, and anti-corruption policies.

Examples

Swedish packaging company Tetra Pak requires third-party verification that its paperboard suppliers do not use wood from any form of deforestation that breaks the natural forestry cycle. A company cannot supply Tetra Pak if it fails to meet these requirements. Japanese chemical and cosmetics company KAO has been actively encouraging suppliers to reduce CO_2 emissions; at least 80% of its suppliers have set emissions reduction targets. The Zero Discharge of Hazardous Chemicals Programme (ZDHC), the Sustainable Apparel Coalition, and the Outdoor Industry Association are all working toward sustainability goals in the apparel industry. Some say that 2019 was the year that sustainability finally burst onto mainstream for the fashion industry. Esquel, a textile giant in Hong Kong, is working to make the apparel supply chain more environmentally friendly, and a number of designers including Gucci and Kanye West made sustainability pledges last year.

What's Next

Improving environmental, social, and economic performance throughout supply chains enables companies to find cost savings, as well as opportunities to increase productivity and optimize processes and systems. Building sustainable practices into logistics and the supply chain may be an aspiration today, but in the near future, it may be a requirement as extreme heat, air pollution, deforestation, water shortages, flooding, and worker health and safety issues make procurement less predictable. Regulators, too, are beginning to impose new restrictions on product development, manufacturing and shipping.

The Impact

The next decade will present significant opportunities for companies in manufacturing and consumer goods, as well as for those that manage logistics. Sustainability factors will impact growth and investor returns.

Watchlist

Companies in the fashion, consumer goods, shipping and manufacturing industries.

Rebuilding the Cold Chain

HIGH DEGREE OF CERTAINTY

INFORMS STRATEGY	ACT NOW
REVISIT LATER	KEEP VIGILANT WATCH

LONGER-TERM IMPACT · IMMEDIATE IMPACT

LOW DEGREE OF CERTAINTY

The cold chain supplies fresh sushi to your local grocery store.

Key Insight

Cold chains are temperature-controlled supply chains. We rely on them to deliver everything that requires low temperatures, such as medications, produce, and frozen foods.

Why It Matters

Climate change could result in new regulations that limit how the cold chain works, but new kinds of intelligent packaging and automated transportation systems mean new business opportunities.

Examples

For decades we've had access to fresh blueberries in February and fresh-squeezed orange juice throughout the year. Your local grocery store probably sells sushi featuring raw tuna and salmon farmed halfway around the world. The reason we can enjoy ice cream in the heat of the summer is the cold chain: a complicated system of storing and transporting food and medicine in exactly the right temperature range during the trek from farm, to factory, to the store. But in some areas of the world, the cold chain has contributed to climate change.

What's Next

If the temperature fluctuates or the cold storage fails, that puts a cold chain's cargo in jeopardy. Products could be contaminated or spoiled, which could mean millions of dollars lost. Companies are beginning to look at new sustainability opportunities to improve the cold chain. One area of interest is artificial intelligence in the cloud, which can help monitor temperatures and can also optimize travel routes. New packaging materials insulate food and medicine, keeping both at low temperatures without having to refrigerate entire trucks.

The Impact

We put an enormous amount of trust in the cold chain to protect the food and medicines we ingest. In a rapidly changing world with ongoing climate, economic and geo-political uncertainty, companies that use or rely on the cold chain should be invested in long-term planning.

Watchlist

AGRO Merchants Group, Americold, Cold Storage, Emergent Cold, Gardner Denver Holdings, Ingersoll-Rand, Kloosterboer, NewCold, Nichirei, Preferred Freezer Services, Versa Cold.

Additive Manufacturing and Printing

HIGH DEGREE OF CERTAINTY

INFORMS STRATEGY	ACT NOW
REVISIT LATER	KEEP VIGILANT WATCH

LONGER-TERM IMPACT / IMMEDIATE IMPACT

LOW DEGREE OF CERTAINTY

The electric Zeus motorcycle was produced using additive manufacturing.

Key Insight

Additive manufacturing allows us to create objects one layer at a time, and we can now do this using different materials.

Why It Matters

3D printing has moved from the fringe to the mainstream, offering new opportunities in medical and biosciences, manufacturing and art.

Examples

This year, a street-legal motorcycle produced using additive manufacturing processes will come to market. **Curtiss Motorcycle Company** and additive manufacturing company **Fast Radius** collaborated on the electric bike, which uses parts that require a hybrid of manufacturing approaches—including 3D printing.

Growth in new materials printing has made 3D printing a viable resource in the aerospace and automotive industries, which must meet stringent requirements for parts use. Last year, **Airbus** and **Materialize** created the first 3D-printed parts intended for use in the cabins of Airbus's commercial aircraft. And soon, "one size fits all" will take on a whole new meaning. If you're thinking Star Trek Replicator, you're not far off. Researchers are working toward scanning and producing objects in seconds—over time, this technology will be used in surgical centers to rapidly print replacement valves and joints using your own biomatter as models.

What's Next

Last year, **Chinese** researchers successfully printed ceramics capable of transforming over time in response to stimuli such as heat and light. It's a process known as 4D printing, and the practical applications are boundless. Imagine a heat shield that suddenly materializes during a fire, or a garden that plants itself when the ground has warmed to precisely the ideal temperature for each seed.

The Impact

We don't yet have international product liability and intellectual property standards, norms, and regulations that govern additive manufacturing and printing. A regulatory framework built to protect designers, patents, corporations and individuals is likely on the horizon.

Watchlist

Autodesk, Materialize, Kodak, Ethereal Machines, Northwestern University's Feinberg School of Medicine, University College Cork, Apis Cor, Organovo, MIT Media Lab, Airbus, GE, Formlabs, Aurora Labs, Arc Group, ExOne, Voxeljet, Stratasys, HP, Shapeways, MakerBot, University of Illinois Urbana, University College London.

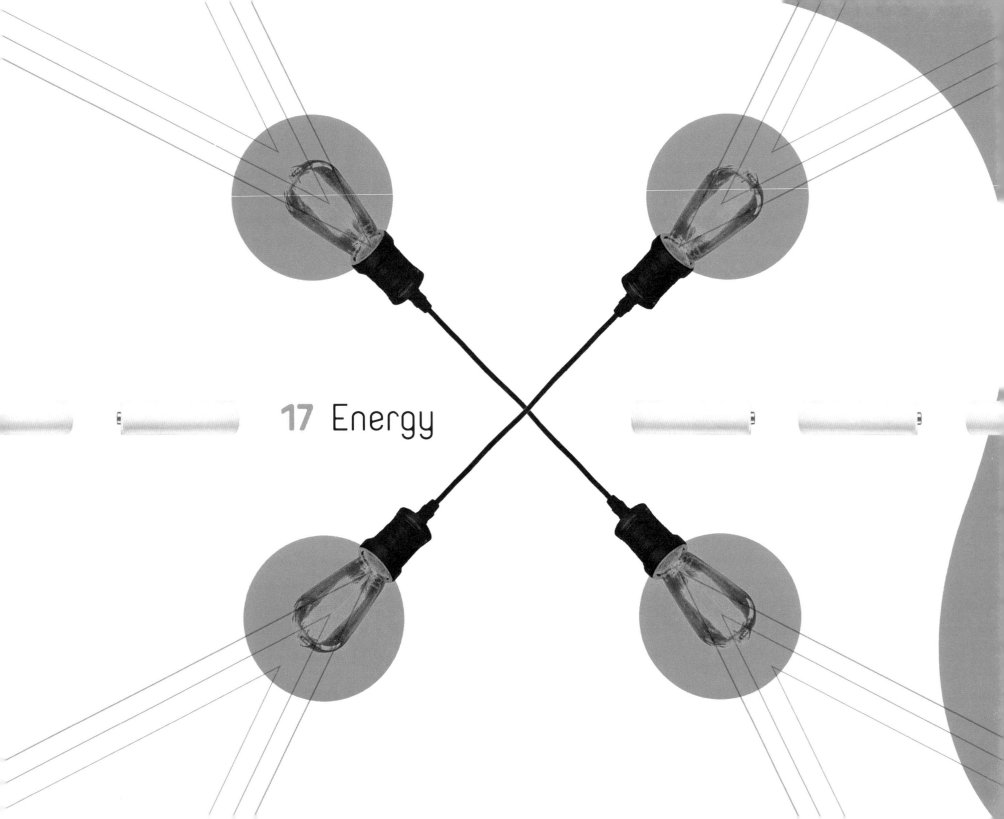

17 Energy

Grid Management

HIGH DEGREE OF CERTAINTY

INFORMS STRATEGY	ACT NOW
REVISIT LATER	KEEP VIGILANT WATCH

LONGER-TERM IMPACT · IMMEDIATE IMPACT

LOW DEGREE OF CERTAINTY

Key Insight

In many countries, the electric grid is a sprawling network of generators and connectors that links citizens to energy distributed by government agencies and private companies. Increased demands for power, combined with a failure to maintain or expand these grids, will pose new challenges over the next two decades.

Why It Matters

Utility companies aren't repairing and modernizing their equipment fast enough. In the wake of climate change and new power demands, managing the grid is proving difficult. And, like many countries, the does not currently have a comprehensive national electricity policy and isn't engaged in long-term planning in this field.

Examples

In 2019, a broken jumper wire from a transmission tower started the historic Kincade Fire in **California**. The blaze spread quickly and devastated thousands of homes and businesses. In the aftermath, **Pacific Gas & Electric**, California's biggest utility, decided to begin cutting power in anticipation of weather conditions—like fast, dry winds—that could lead to more of its lines going down. In October last year, the company abruptly cut power to 800,000 customers, which resulted in blackouts throughout **San Jose**, **Berkeley**, **San Mateo** and **Oakland**. Climate change has resulted in drier, hotter weather in some parts of the world, while in other areas ice has become more common. The problem: Our power networks weren't designed with these new environmental realities in mind.

Another big change on the horizon: lots of new power-hungry devices. Electric vehicles will soon be everywhere, which will cause a spike in electricity demand. So will streaming services, distributed computing applications, connected home appliances, and many other technological advancements.

What's Next

Researchers have been studying new ways to address grid management challenges. For example, **MIT** completed an interdisciplinary study on the future of the grid and outlined a series of steps that could be taken now to preempt anticipated issues, including ways to incentivize renewables, introduce computational tools to make better predictions about usage, explore new methods for wide-area transmission planning, and seize opportunities for energy conservation. We will start to see faster deployment of "microgrids," which can operate autonomously using artificial intelligence and can offer energy in developing countries, where as many as a billion people still live without electricity. Companies like **San Diego**-based **XENDEE** and **WorleyParsons Group** have developed cloud software tools for microgrids. And energy storage will improve—scientists in **Germany** and at **Northwestern University** in **Chicago**, for instance, are making advances in "singlet fission" technology to generate more electricity from solar cells.

The Impact

When the grid fails, it can cost millions of dollars, wreak havoc on public safety services, and put lives in danger.

Watchlist

ABB Group, American Electric Power, Cisco Systems, Dominion Resources, Electric Power Research Institute, Enel, Exelon Corporation, General Electric, IBM, ISO New England, Lahore University of Management Sciences, Masdar Institute, Microsoft, MIT Energy Initiative, National Grid, National Institute of Standards and Technology, New York ISO, Nexant, Pacific Gas & Electric, Tesla, Southern Company, Utility Wind Integration Group, Harvard Electricity Policy Group, and local and national governments worldwide.

Reversing Environmental Rules and Regulations

HIGH DEGREE OF CERTAINTY

LONGER-TERM IMPACT	

INFORMS STRATEGY	ACT NOW
REVISIT LATER	KEEP VIGILANT WATCH

IMMEDIATE IMPACT

LOW DEGREE OF CERTAINTY

Climate change protestors hold their placards high.

Key Insight

While citizens are demanding action on climate change, some governments around the world are now relaxing or eliminating rules and regulations designed to mitigate human-caused environmental damage.

Why It Matters

Thousands of scientists are warning that as temperatures and sea levels rise faster than originally projected, the impact of climate change will drastically change life as we know it.

Examples

New research from **Columbia Law School**, **Harvard Law School** and the **New York Times** revealed that the **Trump administration** has rolled back more than 90 environmental rules and regulations since taking office. It replaced the Obama-era **Clean Power Plan**, which set strict limits on carbon emissions from coal and gas-fired power plants and instead allowed states to set their own rules. It also relaxed a Clinton-era regulation that limited toxic industrial emissions. And it cut the reach of the **Clean Water Act**, removing millions of miles of streams and about half of America's wetlands from federal protection. **Brazil's President Jair Bolsonaro**, a climate skeptic, has pushed to open the **Amazon rainforest** to business and agribusiness. When fires ravaged the rainforests last year, he dismissed conservation efforts and said that pro-conservation NGOs had intentionally set the fires in an effort to undermine him.

What's Next

There are a number of global initiatives designed to combat and mitigate the effects of climate change, but ultimately each country designs and implements its own regulations. The **United Nations Global Compact** initiative is trying a different route, helping the world's corporations to achieve sustainable development goals by 2030.

Impact

Climate change impacts our global supply of food, human health, and our ability to work and move around, and disrupts the complex ecosystems in which we live.

Watchlist

United Nations, as well as companies and governments worldwide.

Green Tech

HIGH DEGREE OF CERTAINTY

INFORMS STRATEGY	ACT NOW
REVISIT LATER	KEEP VIGILANT WATCH

LONGER-TERM IMPACT

IMMEDIATE IMPACT

LOW DEGREE OF CERTAINTY

Key Insight

Sustainable technologies are built to reduce the human species' short- and long-term impact on the environment.

Why It Matters

Climate change and new regulatory efforts could force us to look for new, sustainable sources of energy.

Examples

This past January, **Microsoft** pledged it would be carbon negative in the next 10 years, and launched a $1 billion climate innovation fund. Also in January, **Black-Rock**—the world's largest asset manager with more than $7 trillion under management—announced that climate change would be a primary focus in all of its future investment decisions. Meanwhile, **China** is installing a record number of solar projects and wind turbines to deal with the country's crippling smog. The **Chinese government** will invest $560 billion over the next year to make green tech more accessible not only within China, but also for its export partners around the world. Wind and solar energy are getting a lift: Billionaire **Philip Anschutz**, who built his fortunes in oil and railroads, plans to build large-scale wind farms in Wyoming, while tech billionaire **Elon Musk** will work with a number of companies to build attractive solar panels that look more like slate shingles than the reflective rectangles we've seen to date—he, and others, are also developing new methods to create and store energy using battery systems. A team of researchers at **Massachusetts Institute of Technology** is developing offshore wind turbines that can store power on the ocean floor in huge concrete spheres. **Makani**, recently acquired by **Google X**, makes high-altitude kites to harness wind energy.

What's Next

Researchers at **University of California-Los Angeles** built bio-mimicking smart material that bends to follow the sun. Think of the technology as a responsive, artificial sunflower that can harvest energy and send it back to the grid. Compared to traditional solar panels, which are bulky and run afoul of some neighborhood association covenants, bio-inspired cell panels are much thinner and discreet, and work more efficiently. **European** scientists developed a new kind of wind turbine that transmits energy using a superconductor. The **EcoSwing** project uses high temperature superconductors and has already passed readiness tests for commercial use. **Heliogen**, a startup backed by **Bill Gates**, developed a new system to collect solar energy and concentrate its power. Large mirror panels point toward the sun— and toward each other—for a multiplying effect, which produces heat topping 1,000 degrees Celsius. Concentrated solar power can be used in industrial applications, like melting steel, but the hope is that someday it can be stored and distributed as needed.

Impact

Green tech is still a young market, but plenty of new technologies and scientific breakthroughs have people excited. Talk of regulation and global initiatives on climate change have garnered investor interest, which will likely grow in 2020 and beyond.

Watchlist

8minuteenergy, ABB Ltd, Akcome Science & Technology Co, Amazon, Apple, Argonne-Northwestern Solar Energy Research (ANSER) Center, Atlantica Yield PLC, Canadian Solar Inc, CropEnergies AG, Cypress Creek Renewables, EcoPlexus, Emerson Electric, Energcon, Energy Acuity, First Solar Inc, First Wind Solar, Friedrich-Alexander-Universität Erlangen-Nürnberg (FAU), Gamesa, GCL-Poly Energy Holding Ltd., GE, Global Pvq SE, Google, Hanergy Thin Film Power Group Ltd., Hecate Energy, Inox Wind, Intersect Power, JIANGS, Johnson Controls, Makani, Massachusetts Institute of Technology, Ming Yang, Motech, NextEra Energy, Nordex, Orsted, Pacific Ethanol, Panasonic, Power Company of Wyoming, Recurrent Energy, Renewable Energy Group, Samsung, Saudi Arabia government, Schneider Electric, Siemens, SoftBank, SolarCity, sPower, Suzlon Group, SunPower, Tesla, Toyota, United Power, Vestas Wind Systems, Vestas, WorleyParsons Group, XENDEE, Xinjiang Goldwind Science and Technology.

Renewable Energy

HIGH DEGREE OF CERTAINTY

INFORMS STRATEGY	**ACT NOW**
REVISIT LATER	**KEEP VIGILANT WATCH**

LONGER-TERM IMPACT

IMMEDIATE IMPACT

LOW DEGREE OF CERTAINTY

SUSTAINABLE DEVELOPMENT GOALS

The UN's sustainable development goals include a focus on renewable energy sources.

Key Insight

Renewable energy is collected from sources that can be replenished on a reasonable timescale. Renewables include wind, tides, geothermal heat, and sunlight.

Why It Matters

Last year, 400 global corporations committed to climate protection and sustainability goals, while 63 promised to convert their energy use to 100% renewables.

Examples

More than 100 cities across the globe report that as much as 70% of their energy production now comes from renewables, and at least 40 cities and 158 companies committed to dial that up to 100%. Hundreds more—both cities and countries— pledged to move to renewable energy production. Even oil-rich **Saudi Arabia** is working on a detailed, long-term plan to help diversify its economy and move away from oil.

What's Next

Renewables will take on greater importance in the coming decade. The **International Energy Agency** projects renewables will account for about 40% of energy distributed through the global power grid by 2040. In the next five years, we should see faster growth in green tech than ever seen previously.

Impact

The amount of clean, renewable energy bought by some of the world's largest companies has tripled since 2018. The **U.S. Energy Information Administration** says that renewables are "the fastest growing source of electricity generation."

Watchlist

Acciona Energia, Alterra Power, Atlantica Yield, Avangrid Renewables, Berkshire Hathaway Energy, Brookfield Renewable Partners, Enphase Energy, First Solar, GE Energy, International Energy Agency, Inve-nergy, MidAmerican Energy Anemos Energy Corporation, NextEra Energy, Ormat Technologies, Orsted, Pattern Energy, Siemens, SolarEdge, TerraForm Power, Tesla, U.S. Department of Energy, U.S. Energy Information Administration.

Charging Stations

HIGH DEGREE OF CERTAINTY

LONGER-TERM IMPACT	INFORMS STRATEGY	ACT NOW	IMMEDIATE IMPACT
	REVISIT LATER	KEEP VIGILANT WATCH	

LOW DEGREE OF CERTAINTY

Key Insight

In the coming years, an unprecedented number of charging stations for electric vehicles will come online, driving demand for a new kind of car and disrupting the traditional gasoline supply chain and retail business.

Why It Matters

Auto manufacturers are investing $225 billion to electrify their fleets in the next few years.

Examples

Ford launched an all-electric F-150 pickup truck and the electric Mustang Mach-E. **General Motors** will launch 20 new EV models by 2023, and **BMW**, **Nissan**, **Jaguar**, **Porsche**, **Audi**, **Volkswagen**, **Volvo**, and **Tesla** introduced EVs this past year, with more models to come. There are now more than 20,000 charging stations and 1,600 Tesla Supercharger stations in the **U.S.**, and more are being built this year.

Building new charging stations involves plenty of red tape with local utilities and real estate. Most networks are being installed by governments, utilities, and third-party companies. **California** leads the way: **Former Governor Jerry Brown** promised to get 5 million electric vehicles on the road by 2030 and 250,000 EV chargers in the ground by 2025. **Oklahoma**, **New York**, and **Colorado** state governments also recently unveiled plans to invest in networks of electric charging stations. **Electrify America** will put charging stations in 100 **Walmarts** in 34 states. The nation's largest charging company, **ChargePoint**, will open 2.5 million charging stalls by 2025, up from 53,000 according to the company. Another company, **EVgo**, created a modular fast-charging station that can be installed in a matter of days. **Google Maps**, **ChargePoint** and **PlugShare** will make it easier for people to find those electric vehicle charging stations from their smartphones, see the types of charging ports and prices and then rate and review them.

What's Next

To help EVs really take off, though, someone needs to reinvent the battery—and that's starting to happen. **Spanish** startup **Graphenano** built a battery out of graphene that charges a car in eight minutes, and will open the first battery manufacturing plant using this material. Solid state batteries promise to be safer, cheaper, and boost the amount of energy a battery cell can store—not to mention they may help cars charge faster. Such batteries also promise to bring the driving range for an electric vehicle more in line with what you'd get on a full tank of gas. By using solid materials instead of flammable liquids in batteries, automakers could benefit, because most existing electric vehicle batteries have hit the limits of their storage capabilities. Plenty are working on the task, including **Daimler AG**, **Fisker Inc.**, **Jiangxi Ganfeng Lithium Co.** in **China**, and spinoffs from the **Massachusetts Institute of Technology**, **Stanford University**, and **Tokyo Institute of Technology**. If they're successful, EV charging times could drop from several hours down to 10 minutes. (See also: Better Batteries.)

Impact

As more charging stations expand into communities everywhere, it will start to have a chilling effect on independent and corporate gasoline station chains, as well as on the local communities that are supported by them.

Watchlist

Blink CarCharging, BP, ChargePoint, Chevron Corporation, China National Petroleum Corporation, ConocoPhillips, Electrify America, Envision Solar, EV car manufacturers worldwide, Exxon Mobil, Google, Ionity, Kuwait Petroleum Corporation, Lukoil, Petro China, PlugShare, Royal Dutch Shell, Royal Farms, Saudi Aramco, SemaConnect, Sinopec, Suncor Energy, Tesla, the state governments for Colorado, California, New York, New Jersey, and Oklahoma, Valero Energy, vendors to gas stands, Volkswagen, Wawa.

Ultra-High-Voltage Direct Current and Macro Grids

HIGH DEGREE OF CERTAINTY

INFORMS STRATEGY	ACT NOW
REVISIT LATER	KEEP VIGILANT WATCH

LONGER-TERM IMPACT · IMMEDIATE IMPACT

LOW DEGREE OF CERTAINTY

China's major ultra-high-voltage transmission system is underway.

Key Insight

In the near-future, we will transport clean energy from production sites to areas where power is needed using a new kind of power grid being tested in **China**.

The Impact

Ultra-High-Voltage Direct Current can carry electricity farther with less loss, which will help feed China's relentless hunger for power. In addition to China, UHVDC will help large countries like **Brazil** and **India** deliver more power longer distances, which will help stimulate economic growth.

Why It Matters

A national direct-current macro grid could drastically lower emissions in an affordable way without compromising our access to electricity.

Examples

In the **U.S.** and throughout **Europe**, electricity is generated at a power station and then transmitted using alternating current. But that technology is inefficient over very long distances, and even smart grids haven't always been able to cope with climate change and our increasing consumer demands for heat and air conditioning. A new kind of transmission system—ultra-high-voltage direct current (UHVDC)—is being tested in **China**, which has invested $88 billion to build the future of UHVDCs and macro grids. **India** has made a similar investment.

What's Next

China has already moved ahead of the U.S. in developing this technology and is investing heavily in green technologies. The first 800,000-volt line, from a dam in **Yunnan Province** to **Shanghai**, has already been completed. Next up, the **Changji Guquan** system, spanning the east-west expanse of the country, which on its own can carry half the power needed to serve the entire country of Spain. China has made it known that it plans to transport clean energy all around the world, and its **Belt and Road Initiative** could help in that effort. Fifty years from now, it's conceivable that we're all reliant on China—rather than **OPEC** countries (**Saudi Arabia, the UAE, Venezuela, Iraq, Iran, Kuwait, Libya, Nigeria, Qatar, Algeria, Angola, and Ecuador**)—for our energy needs.

Watchlist

AGTransWest Express Transmission Project, ABB, China, GE, Hitachi, India, Mitsubishi Electric Corporation, Siemens, U.S. Department of Energy, and OPEC member nations.

Better Batteries

HIGH DEGREE OF CERTAINTY

INFORMS STRATEGY	ACT NOW
REVISIT LATER	KEEP VIGILANT WATCH

LONGER-TERM IMPACT IMMEDIATE IMPACT

LOW DEGREE OF CERTAINTY

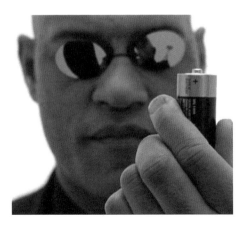

Morpheus describes the future of batteries in *The Matrix*.

Key Insight

It's a common first-world problem: Our devices never seem to have enough battery life, and just when we need power the most, we either forget our chargers or can't find a spot to plug in.

Why It Matters

Building a better battery has been an elusive challenge for decades—but we could make new headway in the coming years.

Examples

Researchers at **Monash University** developed a lithium-sulphur battery that can power a smartphone for up to five days, outperforming lithium-ion batteries. **IBM** researchers developed a new kind of battery with materials extracted from sea water instead of heavy metals like cobalt. Lithium-ion batteries have limits, which is why researchers at the **University of California-Irvine** are experimenting with gold nanowires housed in a gel electrolyte, which can last significantly longer than today's batteries. And scientists at **Ritsumeikan University** and **Panasonic** are trying to squeeze the last bits of untapped energy out of lithium-ion batteries.

What's Next

The problem with modern batteries isn't about making the power—it's about how to store enough of it. Startup **Ossia Inc.** built a wireless charging system that can power AA batteries from 30 feet away. **Form Energy** is trying to develop a "bidirectional power plant" that stores energy long-term, producing renewable energy and delivering it precisely when it is needed. Meanwhile, at **Google X**, a new project called **Malta** aims to capture more clean energy produced by using salt, and to store it on a large scale. Malta incorporates a grid-scale energy storage technology that saves electricity from renewable energy sources as heat inside large tanks of high temperature molten salt, and as cold in large tanks of chilled liquid. The system can discharge electricity back to the grid when energy demand is high—effectively "time shifting" energy from when it's produced to when it's most needed.

Impact

Battery improvements will drive growth in consumer electronics and electric vehicles.

Watchlist

Alphabet, Baseload Renewables, Daimler AG, Energous Corp, Fisker Inc., Form Energy, Founders Fund, General Motors, Graphenano, Huawei, Ionic Materials, Jiangxi Ganfeng Lithium Co, Khosla Ventures, Massachusetts Institute of Technology, MIT Department of Materials Science and Engineering, Nissan, Ossia Inc, Qualcomm, Solid Firm, Tesla, the Federal Communications Commission, Tokyo Institute of Technology, Toyota, University of California-Irvine, US Department of Energy.

Additional Energy Trends

⟳ TRENDS

Wireless Charging Everywhere

Laptops, earphones, mobile devices, and even portable batteries will be chargeable without wires in the coming years. This year we should see rollout of universal wireless chargers capable of powering our devices. Samsung phones now charge without wires—and can even transfer battery power to other similar phones. Energysquare and Unravel offer wireless charging for multiple devices at once.

Energy Trading Platforms for Blockchain

In 2018, companies in Singapore started buying and selling renewable energy certificates on a blockchain-powered system. Like carbon trading in other markets, Singapore's system, launched by utilities provider SP Group, allows for more transparency and lower costs because there is no central intermediary processing and verifying transactions. Meantime, a consortium that includes BP and Shell is now developing a blockchain-based platform to trade energy commodities.

Zero Carbon Natural Gas

In the future, we could see a natural gas plant capable of capturing all of its emissions at zero cost using a technology called carbon capture and storage, or CSS. While the tech has been around for decades, it hasn't been deployed at scale. Last July, U.S. startup Net Power successfully built a prototype plant that ran a full power cycle without releasing troublesome emissions into the air. It plans to scale up to a full-size plant by 2021. Wider adoption will likely be driven by new tax credits of up to $50 for each metric ton of emissions captured and stored by a power plant or factory.

Floating Nuclear Energy Plants

In an attempt to increase nuclear proliferation, Russia is working on a new kind of energy plant that can float and move with currents, thereby withstanding certain harsh environments. A barge called the Akademik Lomonosov is loaded with two nuclear reactors and in 2020 will produce enough energy to power 100,000 homes in the nearby town of Pevek.

Subsea Power Grids

Siemens and ABB are each building a new kind of distribution center underwater. Their subsea power stations would connect to wind turbines, generators, or power plants and could someday enable underwater factories. These power grids include transformers, switch-gear and variable-speed drives, and cabling so that operators back on land can monitor and adjust all of the systems. Testing should begin this year.

In the future, we could see a natural gas plant capable of capturing all of its emissions at zero cost using a technology called carbon capture and storage, or CSS.

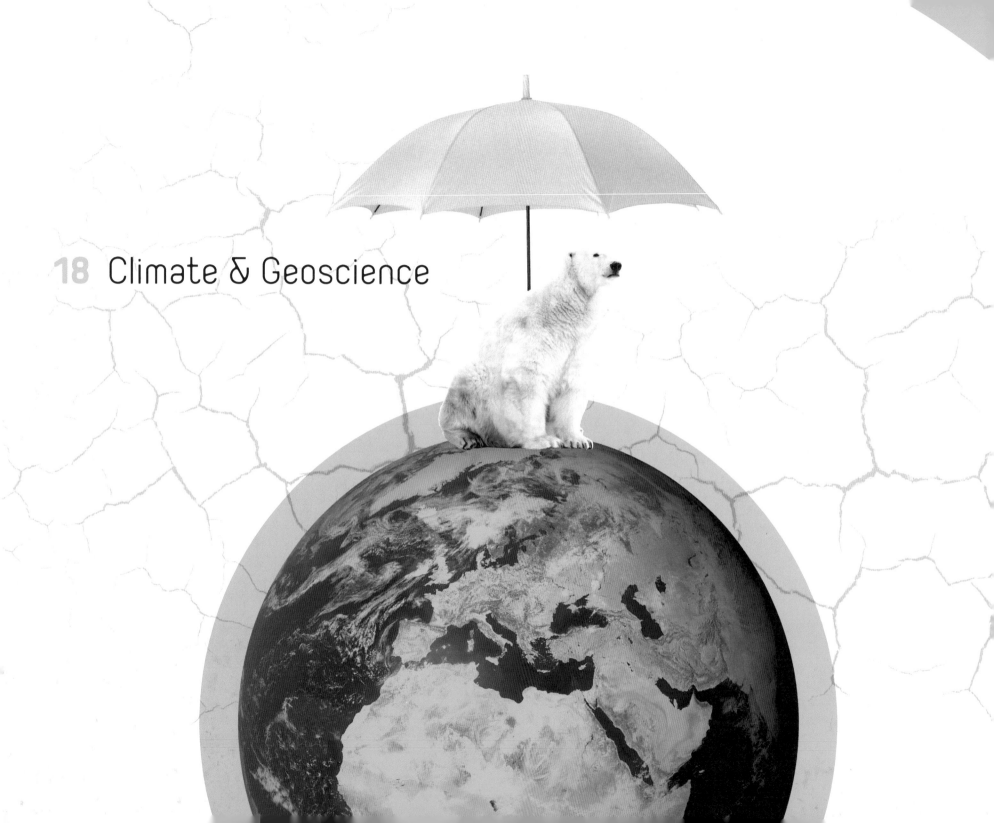

18 Climate & Geoscience

The Anthropocene Epoch

HIGH DEGREE OF CERTAINTY

LONGER-TERM IMPACT

INFORMS STRATEGY	ACT NOW
REVISIT LATER	KEEP VIGILANT WATCH

IMMEDIATE IMPACT

LOW DEGREE OF CERTAINTY

Earth's new geological layers show that humans have left a permanent mark on the planet.

Key Insight

We are in a new geological epoch defined by the permanent impact that humans have had on Earth.

Why It Matters

A new epoch is defined following a cataclysmic event—like the asteroid that collided with Earth and led to the mass extinction of the dinosaurs. Such events significantly and permanently alter the underlying sedimentary and rock layers beneath the surface of the planet, resulting in visible, measurable changes.

Examples

An international, independent team of scientists, called the **Anthropocene Working Group (AWG)**, has now found enough evidence to support the official declaration of a new geological epoch. The group, comprised of scientists who were in favor of, as well as those who were against declaring a new epoch, reached a consensus in early 2018. While much debate ensued, we are now seeing concrete, publicly-available research corroborating the designation. Scientists within the AWG and outside have determined that humans have left a permanent mark on the planet. The new geological layers we are creating are riddled with chemicals and industrial waste, pavement, plastic, nuclear fallout, everyday garbage, pesticide runoff and more. We've caused our sea levels to rise and our lakes and rivers to dry up, and extreme weather events are now a normal part of living on Earth.

What's Next

The "**Anthropocene**" (*anthro* for "man," and *cene* for "new") describes a new geographic epoch. (Our previous epoch, which began 11,700 years ago just after the last ice age, was called the "Holocene.") Being able to pinpoint an interval of time and the change it represents can help us set a different—and hopefully improved—trajectory for life on Earth.

Impact

Recognizing that humans have made a permanent, visible mark on the earth is the first step in studying the future implications for our planet.

Watchlist

Anthropocene Working Group, International Union of Geological Sciences, The Nature Conservancy, Union of Concerned Scientists, U.S. Geological Survey.

Unpredictable, Rising Sea Levels

HIGH DEGREE OF CERTAINTY

INFORMS STRATEGY	ACT NOW
REVISIT LATER	KEEP VIGILANT WATCH

LONGER-TERM IMPACT · IMMEDIATE IMPACT

LOW DEGREE OF CERTAINTY

Key Insight

We're getting better at understanding how ice sheets and sea levels change over time. This year, there will be more focus on trying to measure and interpret the rate of change.

Why It Matters

Rising sea levels could reshape countries and trigger mass-scale human migration.

Examples

Last year's historic floods ruined millions of acres of farmland, while coastal flooding wreaked havoc in **Alabama** and **Mississippi**. Blame warming temperatures. Scientists are developing new methods and models to understand changing sea levels, and artificial intelligence may help predict sea level rise and new human migration patterns. Researchers at the **University of Southern California** built a machine learning model that shows a ripple effect across the **United States**: As sea levels rise, people will move to land-locked urban centers such as **Atlanta**, **Houston**, **Dallas**, **Denver**, and **Las Vegas**, and rural **Midwestern** areas will see a disproportionately large influx of people relative to their smaller local populations.

What's Next

The federal **Global Change Research Program** predicts that we'll continue to experience heavier rainfall in the **Northeastern United States** and around the globe. We'll see sea levels continue to rise in the next century, perhaps by as much as eight feet. (Almost half of the 8-inch increase since 1900 occurred in just the last 25 years.) Meanwhile, earlier spring snowmelt and reduced snowpack will lead to chronic, long-term drought. Glaciers around the world are melting at alarming rates—but trying to predict how quickly large chunks will slide into the oceans has proven challenging for researchers. One of the research missions kicking off in 2019 will take 100 scientists to the **Thwaites Glacier**, where they will learn more about melting ice from **Antarctica** and how soon it could increase sea levels to a high enough point that coastal areas—**Manhattan** included—could be threatened.

To protect from future flooding, the **San Francisco International Airport** plans to construct a $587 million, 10-mile-long wall. In **New York**, the **U.S. Army Corps of Engineers** is studying how to build a six-mile-long barrier to protect the city from floodwaters during future storms. **The Union of Concerned Scientists** reports that the **Gulf of Mexico** and **East Coast of the United States** are experiencing some of the world's fastest rates of sea level rise. The group estimates that rising sea levels will put more than 300,000 coastal homes and 14,000 commercial properties at risk by 2045, and by the end of the century, more than $1 trillion worth of property could be impacted.

Impact

It is difficult to overstate how significantly rising sea levels will impact human and animal migration, our global supply of food, and our ability to move around. Insurers, city planners, businesses with global supply chains, and any business that relies on or provides logistics should be monitoring this trend carefully.

Watchlist

British-American International Thwaites Glacier Collaboration, Columbia University, NASA, NOAA, Union of Concerned Scientists, United Nations Intergovernmental Panel on Climate Change.

The Graveyard Point neighborhood in Central Texas after historic rainfall flooded the region.

Extreme Weather Events

HIGH DEGREE OF CERTAINTY

	INFORMS STRATEGY	ACT NOW	
LONGER-TERM IMPACT	REVISIT LATER	KEEP VIGILANT WATCH	IMMEDIATE IMPACT

LOW DEGREE OF CERTAINTY

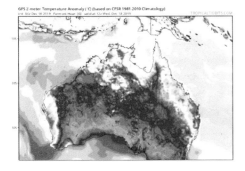

Australia recorded record-high temperatures in the past year. The darker red the map is, the higher above average the temperature is.

Data from December 2019.

Key Insight

An extreme weather event falls outside the norms of typical fluctuations in weather patterns. They became a more frequent and pronounced worldwide phenomenon in 2017, and we have been experiencing them since.

Why It Matters

2019 was one of the most disastrous years on record for extreme weather events, with floods, landslides, cyclones, tornados, and excessive heat that displaced more than 7 million people in the first half of the year alone. By year's end, more than a billion animals had died due to **Australia's** fires.

Examples

The past five years on Earth have been the hottest on record. Our globe's surface air temperature increased by about 1.8 degree Fahrenheit (1 degree Celsius) over the last 115 years, making it now the warmest it's been in the history of modern civilization. We've seen a number of record-breaking climate-related weather extremes. Starting in July 2019, the worst wildfires in decades ravaged **Australia**, devastating large swaths of the country, leading to at least 28 human deaths and 3,000 destroyed or damaged homes. By January 2020, the country's capital city of **Canberra** declared a state of emergency, due to encroaching fires. Forests continued to burn in **Alaska**, **California**, **Brazil**, **Russia**, **Indonesia** and **Africa**, while flooding wreaked havoc on **Arkansas**, **Louisiana**, **Mississippi** and **Missouri** last year. The **Greenland** ice sheet melted significantly, while huge expanses of the **Arctic** had little to no ice for long periods of time. In 2018, the **Mendicino Complex Fire** became the largest in **California** state history and gave birth to a new term: "firenado," or a whirling column of flames that destroys everything in its path. One such fire vortex topped out at 17,000 feet above the earth.

Researchers at **NOAA National Centers for Environmental Information** found that storms are moving more slowly than they did forty years ago, and that means they're sticking around longer and causing more damage. In 2019, dangerous, slow-moving superstorms including **Hurricane Barry**, **Hurricane Dorian**, **Tropical Storm Imelda**, and **Tropical Storm Fernand** caused more than $7 billion worth of damage.

A 2019 report by the **Bulletin of the American Meteorological Society** (BAMS) confirmed the link between the earth's rising temperature and extreme weather events. BAMS relied on a team of 120 scientists from 10 different countries and used historical observations and model simulations to produce the 17 peer-reviewed analyses collected in the special report.

What's Next

Extreme weather is our new normal. Researchers from the **Oeschger Center for Climate Change Research** at **Switzerland's University of Bern** reconstructed a global picture of temperatures for the past 2,000 years. Using six different statistical models, they found that while there have been short periods of cooler temperatures, overall the Earth is warming faster now than during any other time in the past two millennia.

Global warming is a serious concern. **The United Nations'** scientific panel on climate change issued a dire report, with scientific models showing that at our current rate, the atmosphere will warm as much as 1.5 degrees Celsius, leading to a dystopian future of food shortages, wildfires, extreme winters, a mass die-off of coral reefs, and more--as soon as 2040. That's just 20 years from now.

Large natural disasters can slow regional economic growth for decades, impact corporate and industrial productivity, and lead to post-traumatic stress among survivors. Extreme weather can also shift infectious disease patterns and compromise food security, safe drinking water supplies, and clean air. Economists estimate that bad weather has an impact of $3.8 trillion a year in the **United States** alone. It can drive up construction costs and cause flight cancellations. The rise of unpredictable, extreme weather will continue to force insurance companies to recalculate damage, building new models to better estimate the risk and

repercussions. Insurer **Aviva** has increased its **Canadian** home-insurance premiums by 6% since 2016, due partly to research into catastrophic risks. Extreme weather will also impact a wide range of sectors, from auto repair shops and home improvement stores to makers of sandbags and portable generators.

Impact

New R&D initiatives, emerging green technologies, new climate-focused investment strategies and global coalitions could help mitigate extreme weather. Businesses can do right by their investors and also do good for the planet by curtailing their contributions to climate change.

Watchlist

National Oceanic and Atmospheric Administration (NOAA), NASA, U.S. Department of Energy, U.S. Department of Homeland Security, House Armed Services Subcommittee on Emerging Threats and Capabilities, Columbia University's Earth Institute,

United Nations' Intergovernmental Panel on Climate Change, European Geosciences Union, University of North Carolina at Wilmington, Potsdam Institute for Climate Impact Research, National Center for Atmospheric Research.

Get ready for Snowspouts and Firenados.

"Snowspouts"—tornadoes spawned from snow, heavy winds, and low clouds—were spotted near Albuquerque last year.

"Firenados"—spinning vortexes of wind and flames—ravaged parts of the U.S. in 2018. One firenado towered 17,000 feet above the earth.

Human Migration Patterns Shift

HIGH DEGREE OF CERTAINTY

INFORMS STRATEGY	ACT NOW
REVISIT LATER	KEEP VIGILANT WATCH

LONGER-TERM IMPACT — IMMEDIATE IMPACT

LOW DEGREE OF CERTAINTY

Key Insight

Climate change is forcing people from their homes and communities, which can undermine a region's economic stability. To date, we don't have an official designation for "climate change refugees," but that's likely to change in the near future.

Why It Matters

Throughout the world, monsoons, droughts, and scorching heat are driving millions of people away from their homes in search of more hospitable environments—which makes climate change a national security issue.

Examples

Hurricane Maria in 2017 triggered a massive exodus from Puerto Rico, causing one of the largest migration events in U.S. history. By December that year, an estimated 215,000 Puerto Ricans had fled the island for the U.S. mainland. Researchers from the School of International and Public Affairs at Columbia University examined new flows of migrants worldwide and found that people who applied for asylum between 2000 and 2014 were increasingly on the move due to "weather shocks." A study by the Environmental Justice Foundation (EJF) says millions of Bangladeshi families could soon become climate refugees within their own countries. It's a problem that could soon get worse—a sea level rise of just 1 meter could result in a 20% loss of Bangladesh's current landmass. And it's not just Bangladesh that's at risk. By 2050, climate change is estimated to force 1.7 million people from their homes and businesses in low-lying southern regions of Mexico. Nearly 1.5 million Ethopians will also need to find new sources of food and water in the coming decades.

What's Next

It would be wise for intergovernmental organizations to begin talks about adopting official designation—as well as the corresponding protocols necessary—now, in preparation for near-future waves of climate refugees. Researchers at Columbia University published a study in the journal Science that predicts climate change could lead to 1 million climate refugees migrating into the European Union every year by 2100—creating unimaginable changes to our existing cities and infrastructure. The European Justice Forum worked with national security experts and retired military leaders to model scenarios for the future of climate change and human migration, and it concluded that the number of climate refugees could soon dwarf the number that has fled Syria in recent years. We could see a wave of migration from Africa, the Indian Subcontinent, and from island nations into Europe and the U.S.

Impact

A recent World Bank report also looked at the problem, projecting climate change could result in 143 million "climate migrants" by 2050, as people escape crop failure, water scarcity, and rising seawater. Most of them will flee developing countries in sub-Saharan Africa, Latin America, and South Asia. The World Bank offered a glimmer of hope: The future may not be as bleak if we work now to cut greenhouse gases drastically and plan for the socio-economic challenges of migrants, improving education, training, and jobs.

Watchlist

Center for Migration Studies, Cornell University, Environmental Justice Foundation, European Union, National Oceanic and Atmospheric Administration (NOAA), United Nations, United Nations High Commissioner for Refugees (NHCR).

We must prepare for a future wave of climate refugees.

Geoengineering

	HIGH DEGREE OF CERTAINTY	
INFORMS STRATEGY	ACT NOW	
REVISIT LATER	KEEP VIGILANT WATCH	
	LOW DEGREE OF CERTAINTY	

LONGER-TERM IMPACT / IMMEDIATE IMPACT

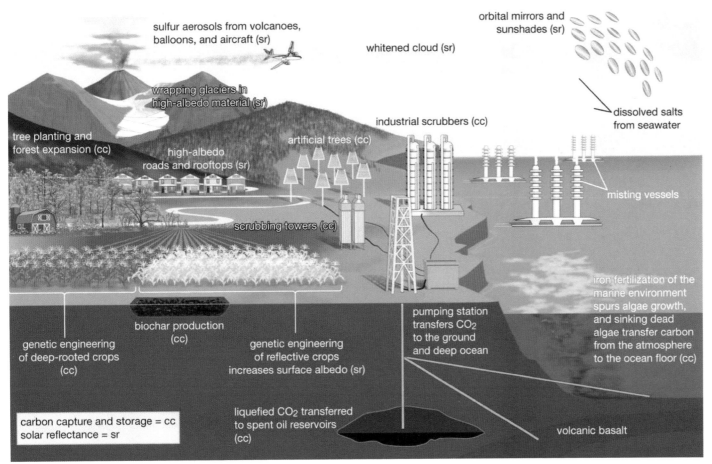

sulfur aerosols from volcanoes, balloons, and aircraft (sr)

orbital mirrors and sunshades (sr)

whitened cloud (sr)

wrapping glaciers in high-albedo material (sr)

industrial scrubbers (cc)

dissolved salts from seawater

tree planting and forest expansion (cc)

artificial trees (cc)

high-albedo roads and rooftops (sr)

misting vessels

scrubbing towers (cc)

biochar production (cc)

genetic engineering of deep-rooted crops (cc)

genetic engineering of reflective crops increases surface albedo (sr)

pumping station transfers CO2 to the ground and deep ocean

iron fertilization of the marine environment spurs algae growth, and sinking dead algae transfer carbon from the atmosphere to the ocean floor (cc)

liquefied CO2 transferred to spent oil reservoirs (cc)

volcanic basalt

carbon capture and storage = cc
solar reflectance = sr

Illustration courtesy of Encyclopedia Britannica.

KEY INSIGHT

To counteract extreme weather and climate change, researchers are looking to geoengineering—large-scale technological and scientific interventions to counteract the damage we've caused to the planet.

WHAT YOU NEED TO KNOW

Mirrors in space, capturing carbon dioxide, seeding clouds with particles, and injecting gasses into the atmosphere are all examples of geoengineering. We're at the earliest stages of research and exploration, but it's a controversial solution to our climate change problem. When Congress approved the $1.4 trillion spending package in December 2019, it included a small amount of money to further this research: $4 million in the National Oceanic and Atmospheric Administration budget and $15 million in the Department of Energy coffers.

WHY IT MATTERS

Scientists can run simulations using available data, but it's impossible to predict the second- and third-order implications of geoengineering in advance. Even so, the fate of the whole planet is at stake. The scientific community is divided on geoengineering because some of the proposed techniques could potentially adversely affect natural weather patterns. No one country can—or should—take a unilateral lead on geoengineering. **The National Academy of Sciences** is studying whether solar geoengineering research should be pursued, and if so, under what parameters.

THE IMPACT

Proposals for geoengineering projects are starting to gain wider public acceptance, which could influence regulators to allow experimentation in the years to come.

↻ TRENDS

Storing Captured Carbon with Algae and Bacteria

Scientists are building tubular bioreactors, filling them with green algae, and letting them eat away at the carbon captured from our environment. **Quebec City-based CO2 Solution** genetically engineered a strain of E. coli bacteria to produce special enzymes capable of eating carbon dioxide and converting it into a harmless bicarbonate.

Converting Carbon Dioxide into Building Materials

Carbon dioxide captured from industrial factories can be repurposed as building materials. Startup **Blue Planet** developed a way to convert carbon dioxide into a limestone coating that can be used to reinforce concrete. The company's bicarbonate rocks, also produced using captured carbon dioxide, were included in the reconstruction of the **San Francisco International Airport**. Meanwhile, in **Iceland**, the **Hellisheidi** geothermal power plant started a project that could turn carbon dioxide into a solid basalt rock.

Stratospheric Aerosol Scattering with Sulfur Dioxide

Also known as solar radiation management, this technique involves injecting tiny particles into the sky that would reflect sunlight back into space. The idea comes from volcanoes, with scientists pointing to an eruption 200 years ago that caused an unusual cold snap, triggering unseasonal summertime frosts. This remains a controversial area of research and has not yet been attempted at scale. The top climate scientist at NOAA received $4 million from Congress—as well as their permission—to develop this technique and another technique using sea salt particles in case the U.S. and other nations fail to reduce global greenhouse gas emissions.

Injecting Clouds with Sea Salt Particles

Inspired by maritime observations, this geoengineering technique would try to expand the coverage of the long clouds left by the passage of ocean freighters on the open water. An aerosol of sea salt particles and seawater vapor would be injected into these existing clouds, which would then expand and shade our oceans. The director of the **Chemical Sciences Division of NOAA's Earth System Research Laboratory** received a $4 million grant from Congress and permission to study these sea salt vapors. Meanwhile scientists at the **University of Washington** are working on increasing the whiteness and brightness of clouds by spraying trillions of particles of seawater into the clouds above the ocean, brightening them. The team's early computer models predict that if just 15% of marine clouds were brightened by 5% to 7%, it could offset warming by 2 to 3 degrees. **Swiss** scientists, meanwhile, are developing ways to eliminate cirrus clouds, those thin, wispy clouds made from ice crystals that form at high altitude and trap heat in the atmosphere. Other efforts include painting the roofs of large groups of houses white and laying reflective sheets in deserts.

Reflecting Sunlight

Some scientists are working on enormous, mirrored parasols to be launched into the stratosphere, which would reflect sunlight back into space and theoretically cool Earth's atmosphere over time. **The Keutsch Research Group** at **Harvard University** is hoping to launch the first ever major aerosol injection trial, known as the **Stratospheric Controlled Perturbation Experiment (SCoPEx)**. The scientists will use a balloon to inject huge amounts of aerosols, or extremely fine particles, into the upper atmosphere, reflecting sunlight. They plan to use a high-altitude balloon to lift an instrument package approximately 20 kilometers into the atmosphere. Once it is in place, a very small amount of material (100 grams to 2 kilograms) will be released to create a perturbed air mass roughly 1 kilometer long and 100 meters in diameter.

They will then use the same balloon to measure resulting changes in the perturbed air mass including changes in aerosol density, atmospheric chemistry, and light scattering. **Bill Gates** and other private donors put $16 million behind the Harvard projects, but some scientists warn the experiments are risky because they threaten to adversely disrupt natural weather patterns, potentially causing extreme flooding and drought in various parts of the world—mostly in poorer countries.

Sand for Glacier Melt

Sand is stronger than we once thought. One project from **Princeton University** scientist **Michael Wolovick** involves building massive piles of sand or similar materials dumped to the seafloor to build walls around glaciers, acting sort of like a scaffolding to prevent them from collapsing. Far beneath the surface of the ocean is warmer seawater. As the deposited sand moves closer to glaciers, it destabilizes their foundation, causing pieces to break off and melt into the ocean. Shoring up their foundation could keep glaciers supported in the icy upper layers of water, and theoretically prevent them from melting. It's not a method suited for all glaciers, but it can help.

Fertilizing the Oceans

Oceanic iron fertilization involves dumping enormous amounts of iron sulfate into wide expanses of the ocean. Theoretically, it would stimulate the growth of phytoplankton, the tiny sea life that absorbs carbon dioxide, releases oxygen, and is gobbled up by other creatures. This is key, because every year the ocean absorbs about a quarter of the carbon dioxide we emit into the atmosphere, changing the chemistry of the oceans and harming marine ecosystems. At the **University of the South Pacific in Fiji**, researchers are exploring how kelp forests and other seaweed habitats in the ocean could suck up carbon.

Enzymes to Eat Ocean Trash

The notorious mass of trash floating in the **Pacific Ocean** is bigger than we originally thought. It is actually two distinct collections of garbage, collectively known as the Pacific Trash Vortex. In 2018, researchers found that it is 16 times larger than original estimates, at least three times the size of France, or a total of 617,763 square miles. An estimated five trillion pieces of plastic float in the ocean, covering an area so large that environmentalists called on the **United Na-**tions to declare the Garbage Patch its own country dubbed "The Trash Isles." A recent report by the **British government** warned that the amount of plastic in the ocean could triple by 2050. The problem has prompted some innovative approaches to help clean up the trash. In the fall of 2018, the **Dutch** nonprofit **Ocean Cleanup** launched an ambitious effort to collect half of that Garbage Patch within five years, using a fleet of 60 autonomous floating "screens," or nets that collect debris as small as a centimeter in diameter, and are later retrieved by boats. A floater prevents plastic from flowing over the screen, while a skirt stops debris from escaping underneath. Algorithms pinpoint where to deploy, and real-time telemetry monitors the condition, performance, and trajectory of each screen. The system also relies on the natural ocean currents for energy; the rest of the electronics are solar-powered. In October 2019, Ocean Cleanup announced that the self-contained cleanup system is working. Another effort, the **Seabin Project**, cleans up oil and trash using floating receptacles with pumps and filtration centers set up in harbors, marinas, and other busy areas. **The 5 Gyres Institute** invites citizen scientists to contribute data on plastic pollution by offering them yearlong access to $3,000 trawls, or fine-mesh nets that can be used to capture plastic floating on the water's surface. Even if scientists succeed in cleaning up the marine garbage pile, it will require behavioral change among consumers and businesses to prevent future waste. Otherwise, more plastic will continue to pile up in the world's oceans.

WATCHLIST

5 Gyres Institute, Arizona State University, Blue Planet, Carbon Engineering, Carbon180, Chemical Sciences Division of NOAA's Earth System Research Laboratory, Chevron, ClimeWorks, Cloud Brightening Project, CO2 Solution, Columbia University, ExxonMobil, George Washington University, Global Thermostat, Hellisheidi, Incite.org, Keutsch Research Group at Harvard University, National Energy Technology Laboratory, Occidental Petroleum, Ocean Cleanup, Princeton University scientist Michael Wolovick, Silicon Kingdom Holdings, Silverlinings, European Union, National Oceanic and Atmospheric Administration, National Renewable Energy Laboratory, Seabin Project, Stratospheric Controlled Perturbation Experiment group, Swiss government, U.S. Department of Energy, the United Nations, University of Washington, YCombinator.

Corporate Environmental Responsibility

HIGH DEGREE OF CERTAINTY

INFORMS STRATEGY	**ACT NOW**
REVISIT LATER	**KEEP VIGILANT WATCH**

LONGER-TERM IMPACT

IMMEDIATE IMPACT

LOW DEGREE OF CERTAINTY

An aerial view of Apple's new campus as it was being built in 2017.

KEY INSIGHT

Large companies around the world are highlighting sustainability as part of their core values.

WHAT YOU NEED TO KNOW

Until recently, sustainability was little more than a buzzword and an afterthought. But we are now starting to see real change. In his January 2020 annual letter to CEOs, BlackRock CEO **Larry Fink** wrote that climate change has brought us to "the edge of a fundamental reshaping of finance" and "in the near future…a significant reallocation of capital." In the future, BlackRock, the world's largest asset management company, with more than $7 trillion under management, will vote against management and board directors when companies are not "making sufficient progress on sustainability-related disclosures and the business practices and plans underlying them."

WHY IT MATTERS

Many companies see corporate environmental responsibility as a value-add for all of their key stakeholders. Other companies can follow suit by developing long-term strategy, vision, and R&D plans to create new business opportunities that create value for shareholders while also helping the planet.

THE IMPACT

Corporate environmental responsibility is a growing concern among consumers and investors alike, who hope to see both economic value and good-faith efforts to mitigate the impact of business on climate change.

Sustainability as Corporate Identity

Unilever's Sustainable Living Plan sets targets for sourcing, supply chain, and production throughout its operations. A decade ago, CEO **Paul Polman** said that he wanted to double Unilever's business while cutting its environmental impact in half. **Allergan**, the maker of Botox, has developed ways to conserve water and energy in its operations and supply chain. Outdoor outfitter **Patagonia** sets the pace for every industry: They encourage repairing rather than replacing their products, use natural rubbers and upcycled plastic bottles, and are committed to minimizing or eliminating packaging waste. Last year, Patagonia took its sustainability efforts a step further, saying it would only produce its popular custom logo-embroidered vests and jackets for companies who can prove they align with Patagonia's corporate values.

Corporates Adopt Net-Zero Energy

Corporations have set ambitious goals to become net-zero energy consumers, which means that the energy they use will be equal to the amount of renewable energy created on their campuses. In 2019, **Google** was the global leader in corporate renewable energy procurement, signing contracts for 2.7 gigawatts of capacity. **Amazon**, **Microsoft**, and **Facebook** were also big buyers. Meanwhile, **Adobe** has made huge shifts to produce more renewable energy on-site. As of 2018, **Apple**'s campuses have been powered by 100% renewable energy.

Sustainable Shipping

It's no mystery that the shipping industry is a huge contributor to climate change, due to its carbon dioxide emissions and endless thirst for fuel. In an effort to limit that thirst, **Shell Oil** has devised a novel approach to fuel efficiency: air bubbles. The oil company installed a new system developed by London-based **Silverstream Technologies** on the hull of one of its ships, helping it move faster and more easily through the water. The technology relies on steel boxes welded to the ship's hull and air compressors, which together create a layer of microbubbles between the vessel and the water. The result: 5% to 12% fuel savings. New international environmental regulations went into effect in January 2020. The **United Nations' International Maritime Organization** now requires all international vessels except yachts to use fuels that contain no more than 0.5% sulfur—compared to 2019's limit of 3.5%. Shipping and cruising vessels, including **Carnival Cruise, Maersk, Norwegian Cruise Line, Grimaldi Group** and **Viking Lines**, are adopting more energy-saving technologies, because the required cleaner fuel may inflate fuel costs by 30% to 60%—an estimated $30 billion annually. Meanwhile, the market for hybrid and electric boats is growing. The world's first electric barges now chug between ports in **Amsterdam** and on the coast of **Belgium**. The vessels, made by **Dutch** company **Port Liner**, have been dubbed "Tesla ships." Eventually, the hope is that these sorts of ships will also operate autonomously. Hybrid boats are making waves, too. Powered in part by solar energy, they reduce a watercraft's weight, cut down on noise, boost passenger capacity and cut emissions.

Corporate Meteorologists

Virtually every business will be impacted by extreme weather events, sea level rise, and global warming. The financial models and predictive systems that guided companies in the past will need to be adjusted for weather-related impacts. For example, a food and beverage company that uses vanilla in their products will rely more intensively on weather data to better predict possible shortages of the ingredient. Some companies, including **Mars Chocolate** (maker of M&Ms and **Dove**), now employ a team of meteorologists. Their job: analyze the impact of weather events on the company's supply chain, financial models, production, and distribution.

"The eyes of all future generations are upon you. And if you choose to fail us, I say—we will never forgive you."

– Climate activist Greta Thunberg at the U.N. Climate Summit in 2019.

Reducing Corporate Reliance on Plastics

Plastic has long been the bane of the environment, piling up in oceans and landfills. We now know that, when exposed to the elements, plastic releases methane and ethylene, two greenhouse gases that exacerbate climate change, according to new research by the **University of Hawaii**. There are efforts to mitigate plastic's ills, however. Last year, researchers at the **University of Portsmouth** accidentally discovered a plastic-eating enzyme that could help break down larger pieces of plastic and aid in recycling efforts. **French** biotech company **Carbios** will produce a new generation of plastics for bottles, packaging, and film that include enzymes to trigger biodegradation after use. **Recycling Technologies**, based in the **UK**, hopes to turn traditionally unrecyclable plastics into "plaxx," or plastic, wax, and oils. Meanwhile, corporations are stepping up: **Origin Materials** will make "plastic" bottles from sawdust and cardboard. **Evian** has promised to use recycled plastic in all its water bottles by 2025. **Starbucks** pledged to eliminate plastic straws in 2020. **British** supermarket **Morrisons** will bring back traditional brown paper bags for loose fruit and vegetables, and a number of cities have banned plastic bags at grocery stores.

WATCHLIST

Adobe, Allergan, Amazon, Apple, BlackRock, Carbios, Chevron, Evian, Facebook, Google, Infarm, Innventia, Microsoft, MIT Media Lab, Morrisons, Origin Materials, Patagonia, Port Liner, Recycling Technologies, Saltwater Brewery, Shell Oil, Silverstream Technologies, Starbucks, Tomorrow Machine, Unilever, United Nations, University of Hawaii, University of Minnesota, University of Portsmouth.

Inventia and Tomorrow Machine created dishes that never needed washing.

19 AgTech & Global Supply of Food

Aeroponics, Vertical Cultivation and Indoor Plant Factories

HIGH DEGREE OF CERTAINTY

INFORMS STRATEGY	ACT NOW
REVISIT LATER	KEEP VIGILANT WATCH

LONGER-TERM IMPACT · IMMEDIATE IMPACT

LOW DEGREE OF CERTAINTY

Japan is home to the world's largest "pinkhouses," indoor plant factories that tend to emit pink light.

KEY INSIGHT

With extreme weather hampering traditional agriculture systems, new techniques are endeavoring to cultivate grains and produce that can be grown in spite of our changing climate. The availability of sensors, new kinds of irrigation, better lighting, and efficient ways to capture and process data is helping to modernize the agricultural sector—a transformation that will decentralize farming.

WHAT YOU NEED TO KNOW

Decentralized food production is popular worldwide and could become a market of $700 billion over the next decade, according to a report by the **Union Bank of Switzerland**.

WHY IT MATTERS

Our existing global food system is a significant driver of climate change. The food system is also vulnerable to the effects of climate change. We're facing long-term existential risk in the global food supply, but we're also seeing tremendous new research and opportunity in AgTech.

⊕ DEEPER DIVE

Smarter Farms

The agriculture industry is abuzz over projections that by 2050, we must increase agriculture production by 70% to meet projected demand. Traditional farming methods won't cut it. That shortfall has spawned a new generation of AgTech startups—nearly a dozen accelerators have popped up in the sector since 2013. Yet small farmers are slow to experiment with and adopt new technologies. If a technology doesn't work, it can kill an entire harvest and a year's income. The tech needs of a current farmer aren't flashy yet. They want tech to digitize their field notes, and to use apps to track people and equipment, monitor valves and irrigation systems, store historical records of pest problems, spot irrigation leaks, and monitor water wells.

⊕ TRENDS

Aeroponic Growing

Aeroponic systems don't require soil. Instead, nutrient-fed water nurtures plants that grow in a soilless growing medium. The root systems are exposed to extra oxygen, and the closed-loop irrigation technique requires 95% less water than plants grown in traditional soil. Seeds are planted into an organic foam-like material, which cradle plants as they grow over time. There's an added benefit: If plants must be treated for disease or pests, there won't be any chemical runoff into nearby streams and lakes.

Vertical Farming Grows Up

Amazon's Jeff Bezos and **SoftBank's Masayoshi Son** have both invested in vertical farming, the burgeoning industry in which crops are grown in stacked layers inside of climate-controlled environments. In the past, the expense of robots, artificial light, and other equipment made vertical farms difficult to scale. But that's changing as the ecosystem matures and technology improves. Today, thanks to brighter, cheaper LED light bulbs, cloud-based A.I. systems, and more available agricultural sensors, vertical farms can now cultivate lettuce, spinach, basil, garlic, and snow peas. They

tend to deliver 10 to 20 times the total yield of conventional farms with far less waste. Vertical farming projects now scatter the globe, settling mostly in urban centers such as **Baltimore** and **Chicago**.

Indoor Plant Factories

Many countries lack the land mass or infrastructure to produce high-quality produce, so they're bringing traditional agriculture indoors and underground, using high-tech robotics, irrigation, and lighting systems to cultivate food. In the **U.S.**, **80 Acres Farms** is building a fully automated indoor farm the size of one-and-a-half football fields just outside of **Cincinnati, Ohio. Japan** leads the world when it comes to indoor plant factories, with more than 200 now up and running. The government subsidized many of these operations, and they thrive thanks to **Japanese** consumer demand for fresh, local, pesticide-free food. Near **Kyoto**, the **Kansai Science City microfarm** uses artificial intelligence and collaborative robots to raise seedlings, replant, water, adjust lighting, and harvest fresh produce.

In **Kameoka** (also near Kyoto) a company called **Spread** uses machines and robots to cultivate plants to produce between 20,000 and 30,000 heads of lettuce per day. It may take only 40 days for plants to mature before they're shipped to nearby supermarkets in Japan. Plants thrive elsewhere in the world, too. In **California, Iron Ox** built a fully autonomous, hydroponic indoor farm that uses two robots to plant, maintain, and harvest produce. Those two bots can do the equivalent of 30 acres of outdoor farming in just a single indoor, automated acre.

Big Data for Better Produce

Researchers at **Massachusetts Institute of Technology** now crunch data to come up with "plant recipes" that can improve indoor food production even more. Using complex algorithms and sensors attached to plants growing in hydroponic systems, the researchers track everything from carbon dioxide and temperature to water and plant tissue health, analyzing the best conditions and systems for growing the most nutritious, tastiest foods possible.

THE IMPACT

Overpopulation means the world must feed an estimated 9 billion people in 2050. If you're a human who eats food, you should care deeply about the global food supply. With our global weather patterns and climates in flux, it's plausible that the world's agricultural centers today won't be capable of sustaining commercial farms in the near future. Today's agriculture system alone won't work.

WATCHLIST

80 Acres, AeroFarms, Bowery Farming, Bright Farms, AGCO, BASF, Bayer AG, Chiba University, Claas, Del Monte, Detroit Dirt, DowDuPont, Fujitsu, GP Solutions, Grove Labs, Growing Underground, Iron Ox, Iwatani Agrigreen, Japan Plant Factory Association, Japanese Ministry of Economy, John Deere, Komatsu, MIT, Mitsubishi, Monsanto, National Federation of Agricultural Cooperative Association (Japan), Plenty, Sungenta, Tomiyama Corporation.

"This is called farming! You kids are gonna grow all kinds of plants! Vegetable plants, pizza plants."

– The Captain in Wall-E

SCENARIO · FUTURE TODAY INSTITUTE RESEARCH TEAM

Growhouse-to-Table is the New Farm-to-Table

NEAR-FUTURE OPTIMISTIC SCENARIO

Restaurants have smaller walk-in refrigerators because they now grow their own produce and harvest it just before preparing meals. Compact, self-sustaining indoor vegetable gardens fit within the existing space of a commercial kitchen. Special lights help reduce the growing time necessary for plants to reach maturity. Elite chefs not only grow their own foods, they develop and culture special varieties to complement their recipes.

Precision Agriculture

HIGH DEGREE OF CERTAINTY

INFORMS STRATEGY	ACT NOW
REVISIT LATER	KEEP VIGILANT WATCH

LONGER-TERM IMPACT · IMMEDIATE IMPACT

LOW DEGREE OF CERTAINTY

New tools will help farmers predict crop yields based on environmental factors.

Key Insight

Using sensors, algorithms, and optimization analytics, farmers can now quantify the progress of every single crop—down to a single cherry tomato hanging on a particular vine.

Why It Matters

Precision agriculture can help increase crop yields and profitability while reducing the costs associated with watering, fertilizing and treating crops for pests.

Examples

The University of Georgia became one of the first research institutions to apply big data to farming in the mid-1990s. This new farm management approach involves a variety of technologies, including GPS, sensors, collaborative robotics, autonomous vehicles, autonomous soil sampling, telematics, and lots of machine learning. Vestiges of precision agriculture have been around since farmers started using GPS alongside their tractors, but advancements in robotics, data collection, and insights have meant new opportunities. Farmers can now vary irrigation and fertilizer automatically using new technologies.

What's Next

Modern agriculture relies on efficient management and accurate predictions. Researchers at the University of Illinois combined seasonal climate data and satellite images with the USDA's World Agricultural Supply and Demand Estimates to build new kinds of prediction models—they hope this will help farmers predict crop yields in advance given environmental factors. South Dakota State University invested $46 million in a new facility to study the future of precision agriculture and is developing new precision ag courses set to start in 2021. New technologies on the near-future horizon include drones equipped with smart cameras, data mining to understand crop blossoming and ripeness, and new analytics dashboards to help farmers make better decisions.

The Impact

As 5G becomes more widely available this year, precision agriculture applications will improve and usage will expand.

Watchlist

Amazon, Arable, Blue River Technology, Bosch, CropMetrics, Descartes Labs, DuPont, Farmers Business Network, Farmers Edge, Google, Honeywell, Planet Labs, SAP, Semios, Sentera, Smart Ag, Syngenta, TerrAvion, University of Georgia College of Agricultural and Environmental Sciences, University of Georgia's Center for Agribusiness and Economic Development, University of Illinois, United States Department of Agriculture.

Deep Learning for Food Recognition

HIGH DEGREE OF CERTAINTY

LONGER-TERM IMPACT	**INFORMS STRATEGY**	**ACT NOW**
	REVISIT LATER	**KEEP VIGILANT WATCH**

IMMEDIATE IMPACT

LOW DEGREE OF CERTAINTY

Disease detection app Plantix helps farmers see what's wrong with their crops.

Key Insight

Deep learning is being used to identify food for a number of reasons: to help computers have more robust conversations with us about the content and origin of what we're eating, to calculate the number of calories in a dish, and to spot spoiled or tainted food.

Why It Matters

Artificial intelligence and deep learning now help food manufacturers and farmers determine nutritional deficiency and detect disease. It helps consumers learn more about the provenance of our food.

Examples

Plantix, a cloud-based A.I. system, lets farmers identify pests and disease in their crops just by uploading photos of suspicious plants. The system will use image recognition to cross-reference with a database of various species, and within a couple minutes offer assessments of potential problems. Perhaps the plant is not getting enough water or needs a micronutrient. **California** start-up **Abundant Robotics** and **Israeli**-based **FFRobotics** are both developing automated picking systems that scan and "read" produce to determine when it's ripe. **SomaDetect** lets dairy farms monitor milk quality using optical sensors and machine learning. **Blue River Technology** uses deep learning to automatically detect and spray weeds.

What's Next

Deep learning will soon help determine exactly how much to feed livestock and will adjust quantities and mixtures of nutrients to optimize their health. Computer models will calculate the nutritional value of food before you've taken your first bite. Researchers at the **University of Massachusetts** now use deep learning for computer-assisted dietary assessments, while scientists at **Microsoft** already incorporated their deep learning prototypes for recognizing popular Asian and Western foods into the **Bing** local search engine. At the **MIT Media Lab**, students are at work on an organic barcode that's invisible to us, but could be read by machines—it could be used to help consumers more easily trace produce as it moves around the world. Machine learning also lets chefs and at-home cooks determine which foods taste best together, select complementary ingredients, and offer food suggestions for various tastes.

The Impact

Deep learning can be used to find and sort problem products on food assembly lines, and it can help growers better identify crop disease. Deep learning for food recognition could soon present a number of opportunities for agricultural companies, farmers, food manufacturers, restaurants, chefs, and health-minded consumers.

Watchlist

Abundant Robotics, Alphabet, Apple, Blue River Technology, Carnegie Mellon, FFRobotics, IBM, John Deere Labs, Microsoft, MIT Media Lab, Penn State University, Plantix, PlantJammer, PlantVillage, Prospera, SomaDetect, University of Maryland, University of Massachusetts, University of Tokyo.

Big Tech Gets into Farming

HIGH DEGREE OF CERTAINTY

INFORMS STRATEGY	ACT NOW
REVISIT LATER	KEEP VIGILANT WATCH

LONGER-TERM IMPACT / IMMEDIATE IMPACT

LOW DEGREE OF CERTAINTY

Microsoft's new FarmBeats program applies the IoT to agriculture.

Key Insight

Technology companies are getting into the agriculture business.

Why It Matters

Farming is a difficult, often unpredictable business. But it's one that could be drastically improved through data collection and predictive analytics.

Examples

In November, **Microsoft** launched FarmBeats on Azure marketplace, which is a sort of internet of things for farms. The effort is a multi-year plan to modernize agriculture with data analytics, and it is being tested on two U.S. farms in which Microsoft has invested. The system uses unlicensed long-range TV white space to to connect and capture data from solar-powered sensors, while drones gather aerial footage of crops. The data are mined and refined using machine learning algorithms, which then send analysis back to farmers with recommendations for how to tweak their resource use. The company also helped launch **Grand Farm**, a partnership between farmers, businesses, government, and entrepreneurs in **North Dakota**. Over three years, Grand Farm will help upskill workers to drive agricultural and new business innovation. **Walmart**—which we think of as a technology company as well as a retailer—is opening its own meatpacking plants and dairy processing facilities in an effort to drive down costs. Meanwhile **Amazon's Jeff Bezos** has invested in vertical farming. (See: Aeroponics, Vertical Farming, and Indoor Plant Factories.)

What's Next

Farm analytics is an active area of R&D and investment. There are a number of startups actively building products and services for agriculture, which points to consolidation over the next few years.

The Impact

The agriculture market is worth an estimated $5 trillion and has serious implications for the survival of growing human populations.

Watchlist

Amazon, EarthSense, John Deere, Microsoft, Monsanto, Pollen Systems, Solinftec, TeleSense, Trace Genomics, Understory, Walmart.

Additional AgTech & Global Supply of Food Trends

A hydroponic farm growing many rows of butter lettuce, basil, mint, and other herbs.

⊙ **TRENDS**

Artificial Trees

CO2 is the undisputed culprit when it comes to climate change. But what if we could just suck it out of the air? Trees do that naturally, but after years of deforestation, we simply do not have enough of them to make a sizable impact. In January 2020, **Ireland**-based **Silicon Kingdom Holdings** and scientists at **Arizona State University** started manufacturing artificial trees that can absorb carbon dioxide. About the size of a poplar tree, the "leaves" are plastic-like discs that absorb CO2 in the air and wind. When filled, the leaves drop down into the "trunk," a barrel at the base and into pipes that collect the liquid CO2 for resale to beverage companies. **Columbia University** has a similar project in the works. Another approach is to convert atmospheric CO2 into carbon nanofibers that can be used for consumer and industrial products, including wind turbine blades or airplanes. Chemists at **George Washington University** are experimenting with what they dub "diamonds from the sky," so-named because diamonds are made from carbon. The scientists bathe carbon dioxide in molten carbonates at 750 degrees Celsius, then introduce atmospheric air, an electrical current of nickel, and steel electrodes. The carbon dioxide dissolves and carbon nanofibers form on the steel electrode.

Intelligent Packaging

Advancements in agriculture both depend on and will generate new investment in smart packaging. The nascent market for sustainable smart packaging is on the rise, ranging from moisture-control and temperature sensors incorporated into QR codes, to antimicrobial and edible packaging—even packaging that "eats" itself after it is no longer needed. Meanwhile, researchers at the **University of Minnesota** are developing new kinds of polymers that will self-destruct or "unzip" when exposed to light, heat, or acid. **Stockholm**-based **Tomorrow Machine** and **Innventia** developed a self-cleaning plate and cup made from a superhydrophobic coating that rejects dirt. The upshot: It never needs washing. **Saltwater Brewery** in **South Florida** designed plastic rings for its six-packs of beer to be biodegradable and edible. So, rather than turtles getting caught in the plastic rings, the material becomes food for them. **Berlin**-based **Infarm** created a renewable sheet of plastic that folds to create a self-contained package. It uses seaweed-based agar-agar gel to grow microgreens and herbs that don't need water. Tomorrow Machine has also developed packaging made from caramelized sugar and coated wax. Designed for rice, oil and smoothies, you crack the package like an egg and melt it in water. This kind of active and intelligent packaging used for meat has been shown to extend shelf life and cut costs.

Insect Agriculture and Bug Proteins

While some cultures eat a variety of bugs as part of their daily diets, bug-based cuisine isn't a worldwide phenomenon. That could change with the introduction of bug-based proteins. There's an environmental argument to eating crickets rather than chickens: Raising and consuming insects produces significantly less greenhouse gasses, doesn't require extensive land and water, and inflicts less long-term damage to the planet. Bugs are good sources of protein,

fatty acids and fiber, and they have been an important part of the diet of cultures around the world. Previously, cultivating insects had been limited to a small, experimental group of startups. The **U.S. Department of Agriculture** has awarded $1.45 million in research grants for bug proteins in the past few years. The **North American Coalition for Insect Agriculture** (NACIA) says the market could top $1 billion by 2023.

Cellular Agriculture

Cellular agriculture refers to the production of **agricultural** products from **cell** cultures, and it's key to producing lab-grown meat. In 2013, the **University of Maastricht** introduced the world to the first lab-grown hamburger patty, and it cost $330,000 to create. Since then, a number of startups have been working on various techniques to culture—rather than harvest—meat that has the same chemical structure of what would have come from an animal. Fast food chains like **Chipotle** now offer **Impossible meat**, a beef substitute made from genetically-modified yeast. Many **U.S.** grocery stores now sell ground Impossible meat, too. **Clara Foods** serves up creamy lab-grown eggs,

fish that never swam in water, and cow's milk brewed from yeast. **Perfect Day** will focus on yogurt, cheese, and ice cream—sans the cows, and instead grown inside a lab. **Memphis Meats**, **Beyond Meat** and **Aleph Farms** are working on lab-grown chicken and beef using pea protein and other plant materials. **Eclipse Foods** is a plant-based dairy company that makes an ice cream base. **New Wave Foods** makes algae-based shrimp, while **Finless Foods** makes fish flesh. The clean meat movement is heading towards acellular agriculture, which doesn't require starter cells extracted from muscle biopsies. Instead, it generates meat from microbes. This will allow researchers to someday soon cultivate milk, chicken, and eggs. It will take years before producers can scale production to meet demand, and there is no guarantee everyone will adopt the meatless meal. In 2018, the U.S. beef industry took aim at the nascent industry, filing a petition to bar non-animal products from the definition of meat and creating a consumer campaign against lab-grown meat. Yet retail sales of plant-based meat grew to $1 billion in 2019, up 56% from 2015—while retail meat sales remained flat, according to **Nielsen**. **French** lawmakers also

passed a law that bans vegetarian companies from calling their products "bacon" and "sausage." Still, in the future, you might buy meat at a local microbrewery, which instead of beer, "brews" meat. Or, for that matter, you might print your hamburger at home.

Off-Planet Terraforming

Terraforming—literally, "earth shaping"—is a concept from science fiction. People re-form another planet to make it resemble Earth, in order to support human life. But as humans begin serious off-planet exploration (see: Space and Off-Planet Trends), we will need to develop new agricultural techniques suitable for space. One key to terraforming might be in our current microbes, which are capable of surviving harsh environments like the **Atacama Desert**. Of course, we might even invent entirely new forms of life using synthetic biology. To advance terraforming from theory to reality, we'll need a host of new robots that can be trained to mine for resources and build an ecosystem that can sustain human life. In addition, we will need hybrid-skilled researchers with backgrounds in biology, botany, agriculture, robotics, and physics.

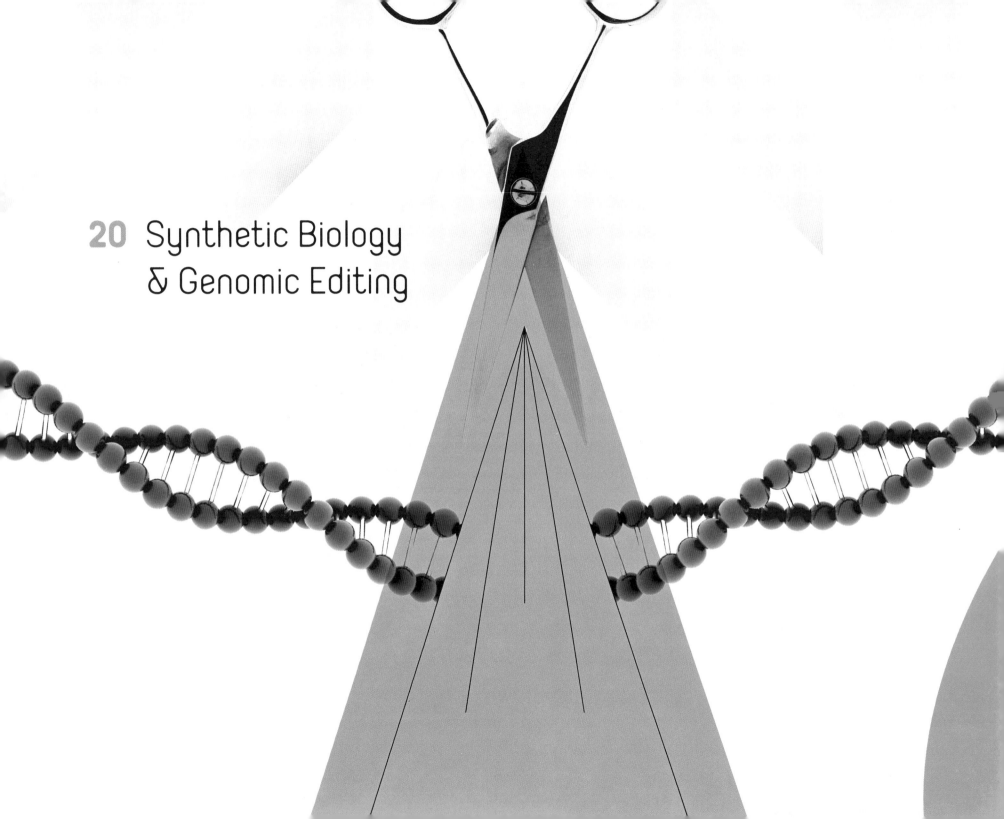

20 Synthetic Biology & Genomic Editing

Synthetic Biology

HIGH DEGREE OF CERTAINTY

INFORMS STRATEGY	**ACT NOW**
REVISIT LATER	**KEEP VIGILANT WATCH**

LONGER-TERM IMPACT · IMMEDIATE IMPACT

LOW DEGREE OF CERTAINTY

Scientists are experimenting to reprogram E. coli.

KEY INSIGHT

Synthetic biology is a relatively new interdisciplinary field of science that combines engineering, design, and computer science with biology. Researchers design or redesign organisms on a molecular level for new purposes, to make them adaptable to different environments, or to give them different abilities.

WHAT YOU NEED TO KNOW

Synthetic biologists are working to develop new kinds of proteins that might someday replace the animal meats we consume. Industrial biologists are investigating how to build new enzymes that could help break down plastics.

WHY IT MATTERS

Synthetic biology will someday help repair defective genes, rid the planet of toxins, destroy cancer cells, and help mass-produce proteins for our consumption. It could be a key to a healthier planet. Since 2018, more than 100 synthetic biology startups have collectively raised $3.8 billion.

⊘ DEEPER DIVE

Synthetic Biology vs Genetic Engineering

While synthetic biology might sound similar to genetic engineering, they are different fields. In general, modifying an organism by editing a single gene doesn't count as synthetic biology. Engineering rice so that it can withstand extreme heat results in an improved strain of rice, which could also be accomplished through breeding over a long period of time. But if you wanted rice that could not only stand up to extreme heat but could also serve as a convincing substitute for beef, you'd need to engineer that rice with a suite of new genes that would result in an entirely new genetic code. Synthetic biology involves creating an organism that doesn't already exist in nature.

Weird Science

There have been some exciting developments in this field in the past decade. **Swiss** researchers figured out in 2012 that it's possible to program mammalian cells to do basic math. Researchers at the **University** of California at San Francisco engineered E. coli that can be programmed to find and move along designated paths.

Synthetic Medicines, Drinks and Fuel

Imagine a future in which you no longer take medication—instead, your cells are simply reprogrammed to fight off whatever ails you. Or biting into a thick, juicy Tomahawk steak, grilled to perfection—and vegan-friendly, because it is made from plant-based proteins. **Exxonmobil** has even partnered with **Synthetic Genomics** to research how to make fuel from algae.

A, C, T, G, X, Y, Z

Our DNA is made up of base pairs, which you've no doubt seen in a double-helix illustration. Each base includes an A-T or C-G, and the combination of pairs is what makes up our phenotype—our visible, personal traits and characteristics. But what if it was possible to include new bases? In 2014, scientists successfully added new bases and discovered additional possibilities that worked, at least in E. coli.

THE IMPACT

Synthetic biology could be a far more realistic way to mitigate the problems of climate change than seeking off-planet solutions (like colonizing Mars).

WATCHLIST FOR SECTION

Aleph Farms, Arcadia Biosciences, Arzeda, Atomwise, Autolus, Azitra, Baker Lab at the University of Washington, Beam Therapeutics, Bolt Threads, Calysta, Cargill, CB Therapeutics, Checkerspot, Codagenix, Codexis, Delft Advanced Biorenewables, Distributed Bio, DNS Script, EdiGENE, Fauna Bio, Gilead Sciences, Ginkgo Bioworks, Global Bioenergies, Google Calico, Google Deep Mind, Impossible Foods, Inscripa, Lygos, Memphis Meats, Microsoft Research, Moderna, Motif, Oxford Biomedica, Poseida Therapeutics, Precision BioSciences, Princeton University, Riffyn, Scout Bio, Sherlock Biosciences, Shire Pharmaceuticals, SNIPR BIOME, Sphere Fluidics, Stanford University, Strand Therapeutics, Strateos, Symlogic, Synthace, Twist Bioscience, Vedanta Biosciences, Verve Therapeutics, Vestaron, Wild Earth, Zymergen.

⊘ TRENDS

Single-Nucleotide Polymorphism (SNP) Profiling

Researchers are developing a new technique that might someday enable us to upgrade our children before they're born. Think of a SNP as a single genetic letter (A,T,C,G). Tinkering with the order of those letters could allow us to optimize our genetic code for the best possible outcomes. This doesn't mean creating babies with a certain hair or eye color, but rather lowering the odds of future heart disease or diabetes. The procedure requires IVF for now: embryos can be SNP-profiled, and the best possible combination would be used for the pregnancy. Future generations would have those traits passed forward.

Super-Fast Molecule Discovery

Synthetic biology is being used to discover and produce molecules on demand. The **Defense Advanced Research Project Agency (DARPA)** and the **MIT-Broad Institute** Found-ry tested whether new molecules could be generated for practical use. By combining artificial intelligence and synthetic biology, the team delivered six out of the 10 requested designer molecules in just 90 days.

Designer Cells

Researchers had previously developed artificial cells that come very close to the real thing, but last year, scientists at the **University of California-San Diego** discovered a technique that creates cells capable of sending protein signals to other cells and triggering behavior—mimicking what biological cells do on their own. Artificial cells will soon have practical applications in precision medicine, which is the customization of healthcare. What happens as designer cells and synthetic biology evolves? Could we predict all of the implications? Probably not, because as cells randomly mutate, new generations could function in ways we've not yet imagined. Don't get too excited: We're not talking about engineering synthetic humans (yet). Programming

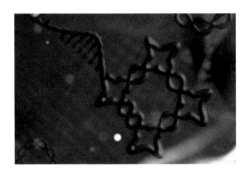

Hao Yan, a researcher at Arizona State University, designed a knotted DNA structure.

"But everyone belongs to everyone else."

– World Controller Mustapha Monda in *Brave New World*

individual cells to perform useful tasks will still take some time. But the possibilities are many/thought-provoking/exciting. The future of synthetic might, by design, include a kill switch to enable self-destruction after a task has been completed or if we change our minds later on.

Molecular Robotics

A team of scientists at **Arizona State University** and **Harvard University** created single-stranded DNA—which is capable of self-folding into origami-like shapes. It turns out that RNA can be used, too—and both can be produced inside of living cells. In 2018, scientists at the **California Institute of Technology** built a DNA-based version of tic-tac-toe with self-assembling DNA origami tiles. Molecular robotics will someday be used on all life forms to provide targeted therapies as well as genetic augmentation. Scientists at the **Wyss Institute for Biologically Inspired Engineering** at **Harvard University** discovered that both robots and our DNA share the ability to be programmed in order to perform tasks. Also, just like our next-gen robots, molecules can self-assemble, and can react to their environments. In the future, molecular robotics will offer

new opportunities to advance medicine and agriculture.

Building Full Chromosomes

The **Human Genome Project-read (HGP-read)**—an initiative to sequence the human genome and to improve the technology and costs associated with sequencing DNA—wrapped up in 2004. But now there's a new initiative: the **Human Genome Project-write (HGP-write)**. This is a synthetic biology initiative, and it's a massive-scale collaboration to synthesize new species of microbes, plants and animals.

Creating Synthetic Wombs

In an experiment at **Northwestern University's Feinberg School of Medicine**, researchers successfully printed and implanted synthetic ovaries in mice that resulted in a successful pregnancy. In 2017, researchers at the **Children's Hospital of Philadelphia** created an artificial womb called a "biobag" and used it to successfully keep premature lambs alive and developing normally for 28 days. We are still years away from synthesizing and growing a full-sized organic womb—but the biobag represents an intervention

that could help the thousands of premature babies born before 25 weeks each year.

Synthetic Age Reversal

Last year, synthetic biologist **George Church** and a team at **Harvard's Wyss Institute** combined three different gene therapies related to cellular decay into a single compound to see if it might reverse obesity and diabetes while also improving kidney and heart function. Remarkably, the technique seemed to work—in mice.

Genomic Editing

HIGH DEGREE OF CERTAINTY

INFORMS STRATEGY	**ACT NOW**
REVISIT LATER	**KEEP VIGILANT WATCH**

LONGER-TERM IMPACT

IMMEDIATE IMPACT

LOW DEGREE OF CERTAINTY

Many animals have been cloned since Dolly the Sheep.

KEY INSIGHT

Genome editing is a quickly-developing, game-changing field promising to influence the future of life on our planet.

WHAT YOU NEED TO KNOW

Mapping the human genome has been a long and difficult process. Recently, sequencing technology has become more accessible and affordable to research labs, which can enable them to work towards personalized medical treatments for vexing diseases like cancer.

WHY IT MATTERS

Advancements in genome editing will have a profound effect on all living things, potentially helping us to live longer, healthier lives.

⊙ DEEPER DIVE

Our CRISPR Decade

Ten years ago, researchers unveiled a gene editing technique called CRISPR-Cas9, which allows scientists to edit precise positions on DNA using a bacterial enzyme.

More recently, new technologies have made CRISPR gene editing more affordable. The implications are tremendous. Mosquitoes carrying malaria could be edited so that they no longer carry the disease through future generations, and so that millions of humans in high-risk regions are no longer exposed to the disease. There are therapeutic possibilities in human medicine as well. Editing our genetic code could mean eradicating certain genetic diseases—like cystic fibrosis—so they can't be passed along to our babies, and liver cells could be edited to lower the bad cholesterol levels in families carrying inherited mutations. World-renowned geneticist **George Church** and his team used CRISPR to modify pig organs, making them safe to be used in human liver, kidney, heart and lung transplants.

CRISPR enters key clinical trials

This year, CRISPR will face a few key trials that will test its ability to treat genetic diseases and mitigate the growth of cancerous cells. In one trial, CRISPR will be used to

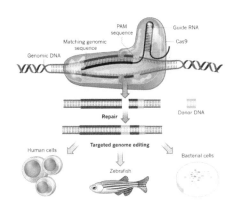

CRISPR-Cas9 is a technique that allows scientists to edit precise positions on DNA using a bacterial enzyme.

disable genes in T-cells to help a cancer patient's immune system effectively fight malignant cells from growing. It will also be used as a method of improving vision in people with an inherited condition that causes progressive blindness, and as a treatment for sickle cell disorder.

China's Genetically-Edited Babies

In 2015, **Chinese** researchers edited the genes of a human embryo. It was done in a petri dish, but scientists quickly sounded the alarm, because it wasn't difficult to see how CRISPR could be used to modify embryos during the in vitro fertilization process. Since then, plenty of experimentation on human embryos has ensued in **China**, and late in 2018, we learned about a team of researchers led by **Dr. He Jiankui** at the **Southern University of Science and Technology in Shenzhen** who not only used CRISPR in conjunction with IVF, but purportedly eliminated the CCR5 gene in a pair of twin girls. That modification, the scientists hoped, would make the twins resistant to HIV, smallpox and cholera throughout their lives. If true, this would be the first instance of genetically modified humans—and we haven't yet developed global norms and stan-

dards governing humanity's position on this sort of human enhancement. In December 2019, Chinese state media revealed that Dr. He's work had resulted in additional births beyond the twins. Authorities arrested him and sentenced him to three years in prison for "illegal medical practices."

Designer Humans

The revelations that a Chinese doctor had genetically edited human embryos that resulted in live births created a global panic. The scientific community lambasted Dr. He, while governments around the world were quick to publicly condemn the use of CRISPR for designer babies of any kind. Many nations, including the **U.S.**, have regulations banning gene modification for that purpose. This will be a very difficult area to traverse heading into the future, especially with no global standards for modification. Genetic modification that aims to eradicate disease, however, could be a boon for humanity: **Harvard University's Stem Cell Institute** started using CRISPR to modify sperm cells so that they could not pass on the genes responsible for Alzheimer's disease. Back in 2017, the first known attempt to create a genetically-modified human embryo in

the **United States** took place at the **Oregon Health and Science University**. Researchers there successfully corrected a genetic mutation causing a deadly heart condition. (The critical difference: These experiments did not result in pregnancy or live birth.)

Meanwhile, researchers at **Stanford University** have discovered that some people could be immune to part of the CRISPR process. One of the primary tools used, Cas9, is typically created using the same bacteria that causes strep throat. Some people's immune systems can naturally fend off the infection, and this research calls into question whether the CRISPR technique could be effective across all—or just part—of the human population.

⊗ TRENDS

Gene Vandalism

Sometimes the gene editing process results in breaking the double strands of a DNA's helix. That results in what synthetic biologist **George Church** calls "gene vandalism." As cells try to repair the break, it often results in unintended modifications and mutations that cannot be easily controlled, and worse, could be dangerous. Gene vandalism is on the rise as more researchers experiment with CRISPR.

Prime Editing

A new CRISPR, which scientists call "prime editing," could make the editing process much more precise and result in more accurate modifications. As impressive as CRISPR is, it can sometimes change the wrong genes or accidentally break apart strands of a DNA's double helix. A refinement to the CRISPR technique affords more precision and versatility.

Organoid Development

In 2008, researchers for the first time created cerebral organioids—tiny blobs grown from human stem cells that could grow into brain-like tissues. They helped scientists understand some of our brain functions, and have since been used to research autism spectrum disorders and diseases like the Zika virus. Advancements in artificial intelligence will help catalyze research, eventually leading to more complex and realistic organoids that resemble "mini-brains." Organoids aren't conscious—yet—and as experimentation progresses scientists will need to develop ethical standards. There are regulations in place, but this is another field that is developing faster than existing legal frameworks. The **Brainstorm Project** at the **National Institutes of Health** is bringing together scientists and ethicists to develop a set of recommendations.

Super Pigs

In 2019, a massive outbreak of swine fever devastated **China's** stock—nearly a quarter of the global pig population died. The disease was first reported in August 2018, but it took the **Chinese government** a very long time to take action. Paradoxically, the disease spread because the Chinese government took some very positive steps to curb pollution. After new regulations went into effect, industrial pig farmers couldn't upgrade their facilities fast enough, which led to farm closures and a re-routing of the pork supply. As pigs got sick, they were shipped all around the country, which helped the disease spread. China consumes a tremendous amount of pork, and it will take years to rebuild the swine population. Enter genome editing: There are now dozens of gene editing experiments and research projects underway in China to develop new breads of disease-resistant, climate-acclimating super pigs intended for consumption. All of this research could have a spillover effect in other areas of agriculture and medicine, and it could help speed along new regulations.

Unregulated Pet Cloning

In 2019, **China's** first cloned cat was "born." **Sinogene**, a **Beijing**-based commercial pet cloning company, sequenced, cloned, and delivered a cat named Garlic for a 22-year-old businessman. Pet cloning is an unregulated business, and while it wasn't the first pet to be cloned in the world, it was the first for China. **The United States** and **South Korea** are other existing markets for pet cloning.

A Shortage of Genome Storage

One of the fastest-growing datasets in the world is made up of our human genetic data. By 2025, we may be out of data storage space for human genomes, according to estimates by the **University of Illinois at Urbana-Champaign**. As precision medicine, CRISPR, and gene therapy technologies continue to advance and improve, our storage needs will explode, along with the computing power and requirements for acquiring, distributing, analyzing, encrypting, and safeguarding our genomics data. As technology becomes increasingly intertwined with biology, we're realizing that we didn't plan ahead for adequate storage capacity, and that we didn't create sufficient technology workflows for properly storing all that data. **Australia's Garvan Institute of Medical Research** is looking into different processes and workflow to reduce the genomic data footprint going forward.

Additional Biotech Trends

○ TRENDS

DNA Storage

In 2018, scientists from **Microsoft Research** and the **University of Washington** achieved a new milestone: They figured out how to create random access on DNA at scale. They encoded 200 megabytes of data—35 video, image, audio and text files ranging from 29KB to 44MB—to synthetic DNA. To date, scientists have stored a $50 Amazon gift card, an operating system and a film (*L'arrivée d'un train en gare de La Ciotat*, a foundational black-and-white French short film made in 1896) on human DNA. Researchers at **Columbia University** and the **New York Genome Center** think that DNA could potentially be used in advanced computer systems, and they're not alone. The **U.S. Defense Advanced Research Projects Agency (DARPA)** announced its own DNA storage project in 2017. It seems like a weird branch of biological science, but there are practical reasons for human computing: DNA could solve our future data storage problems. It's durable, too: Evolutionary scientists routinely study DNA that is thousands of years old to learn more about our human ancestors. **Twist Bioscience**, a DNA storage startup, figured out how to make hyperdense, stable, affordable DNA storage: Their robots deposit microscopic drops of nucleotides on silicon chips and can create a million short strands of DNA at a time. The end result will be a tiny, pill-sized container into which we will someday fit hundreds of terabytes of capacity.

Microbe-Engineering As a Service

Synthetic biology is an emerging field that builds new life: replacement organs and soft tissue, as well as entirely new kinds of organisms never before seen on Earth. **Zymergen**, based in the **San Francisco Bay Area**, is developing original microbes for making specialty polymers, which have applications in military equipment and electric vehicles. In 2018, it raised $400 million in its third round of funding from **SoftBank Vision Fund**, **Goldman Sachs**, **Korea**-based **Hanwha Asset Management** and others. Synthetic biologists at **Ginkgo Bioworks** build custom-crafted microbes for their customers, which have included designer bacteria enabling crops to fertilize themselves.

Microbiome Extinction

We may all be guilty of causing a mass genocide, which is happening right now in our guts and in the environment. The widespread use of antibiotics, along with diets rich in processed foods, have led to a staggering decline of microorganisms in wealthy nations. During the past 12,000 years of human evolution, we've shifted nature's balance—our diets are now relatively narrow, compared to our far-distant ancestors. Recently, scientists studied modern hunter-gatherer tribes in **Tanzania**, **Peru**, and **Venezuela**, whose microbiota have 50% more bacterial species than those in the West. Unlike those tribes, we no longer hunt and eat wild flora and fauna. Those from wealthier countries now eat very little dietary fiber, a limited variety of fruits and vegetables, and only four species of livestock: sheep, poultry, cattle and pigs. Worse, widespread use of antibiotics in farm animals—not to prevent disease, necessarily, but to increase weight gain and therefore the volume of meat available—means that we're ingesting compounds that are helping to destroy our own microbiomes. We humans are complex, composite organisms, made up of layers and layers of cells. Researchers now think that our gut microbiome is directly linked to everything: our metabolism, immune system, central nervous system, and even the cognitive functions inside our brains. It's an inherited problem: Most of our microbiomes are passed from our mothers as we pass through the birth canal. A number of researchers are now looking at the future of our microbiomes. **Cambridge, Massachusetts**-based **Vedanta** is making gut bacteria that can be turned into drugs and counts the **Bill & Melinda Gates Foundation** as one of its investors. **San Francisco**-based start-up **uBiome** has launched several at-home microbiome tests (though for the time being you need a subscription to take one). The **American Gut Project**, the **American Gastroenterological Association** and **OpenBiome** will track 4,000 patients over 10 years to learn about fecal microbiomes. Investors have poured more than a billion dollars into microbiome startups since 2016.

Genetic Screening

New genetic screening techniques to test embryos before implantation are making their way into fertility centers. **Menlo Park, California**-based **MyOme** and **New Jersey**-based **Genomic Prediction** now use the genetic sequences of parents along with cells retrieved during a biopsy to generate an embryo's entire genome. Next, they use algorithms to calculate the probabilities of certain ailments. Couples can then select the embryos they like, based on those results. While both companies are disease focused for now, it is also possible to calculate scores and optimize for other genetic traits like height and intelligence.

Biological DVRs

The source code for humanity is stored in our DNA. As we age the sequence might stay constant, but there are chemical changes that occur to our DNA. Observing those changes could lead to new techniques to halt or even reverse age-related disease. **Columbia University** researchers discovered that it might be possible to record and store information about cells as they age. The technique—a sort of biological DVR—is achieved using the CRISPR-Cas system over a period of days. In the future, this could allow researchers to very closely study how,

exactly, we age. If we can quantify aging at a cellular level, maybe we can reverse it.

Superbugs, Viruses and Phages

In January 2020, a new coronavirus named 2019-nCoV (also known as novel coronavirus or Wuhan coronavirus) spread rapidly throughout **China**. As of February 6, there were 28,256 cases in China alone, and 3,800 were critical according to **World Health Organization** data. The death toll from the virus had surpassed 560. Thousands of people were quarantined on cruise ships outside of **Yokohama, Japan** after 10 passengers were diagnosed. The **U.S.** and **Australia** temporarily barred foreigners who'd recently visited China from entering their countries, companies like **Apple** and **Starbucks** closed their stores, and airlines including **Delta** and **British Airways** cancelled flights. As of this report's printing, we didn't yet know what caused the virus or how it was spreading. It joined a host of superbugs already rampant elsewhere in low-income countries. Researchers will be testing phages—specially programmed viruses that can target a bacteria that causes illness without harming us—in the coming year. That's good news for

countries where the overuse of antibiotics has led to medicine-resistant superbugs. As for the coronavirus, the outbreak will be top of mind throughout 2020, as governments explore how they can more easily collaborate to contend with global health emergencies. Months before the outbreak, researchers at **Johns Hopkins** ran a simulation of a hypothetical, treatment-resistant coronavirus outbreak spawned at a pig farm in **Brazil**. Unlike the 2019-nCoV, this one was extremely lethal, and in the simulation 65 million people died in just 18 months. Despite these massive hypothetical risks, most governments underspend on emerging disease research.

Building a Comprehensive Human Cell Atlas

Researchers are working on the first-ever comprehensive map of all of the 37.2 trillion cells that make up the human body. A large team of scientists—including 130 software engineers, mathematicians, computational scientists, biologists, clinicians, and physicists—hailing from **Israel**, the **Netherlands**, **Japan**, the **UK**, the **U.S.**, and **Sweden** are hard at work mapping the human body on a

cellular level. Although a cell atlas has long been theorized, new biological tools and more powerful computers have turned this one-time vision into a reality. The team working on the atlas believes that they can draw comprehensive reference maps for all human cells in the body. A human cell atlas would give the medical community a new way of understanding how our bodies work and how to diagnose, monitor, and treat disease.

Opportunities and Risks

VERY NEAR TERM

Pest Control vs Ecological Weaponization

Genome editing can be used in mosquitos, which carry malaria—a disease that kills millions of people worldwide each year. The technique alters a section of the mosquito's DNA, making it impossible for future generations of the insect to spread malaria to humans. However, some security experts warn that the same process could be used with malicious intent—to rapidly spread a biological weapon that could be impossible to stop.

10–15 YEARS AWAY

Longer Lifespans vs Overpopulation

Some argue that genome editing could be used to give humans longer lifespans and to lower mortality rates—which would result in a devastating strain on our global supply of food and greater environmental degradation. On the other hand, genome editing is also being researched to create heartier plants and double-muscled livestock for human consumption.

20 YEARS AWAY

Healthier Babies vs Modification for the Wealthy

Genomic editing will help eradicate heritable diseases such as cystic fibrosis, Tay-Sachs disease, Huntington disease, and Leigh syndrome from the population. The same techniques could be used additively, tweaking our musculoskeletal composition and I.Q. Very wealthy parents might be offered options to edit and enhance their future children. This will create a new divide between modified humans and non-modified humans. The best jobs and opportunities will be held for modified humans resulting in a new bio-engineered caste system.

Biointerfaces & Wearables

Biointerfaces

HIGH DEGREE OF CERTAINTY

LONGER-TERM IMPACT	INFORMS STRATEGY
	REVISIT LATER

ACT NOW
KEEP VIGILANT WATCH

IMMEDIATE IMPACT

LOW DEGREE OF CERTAINTY

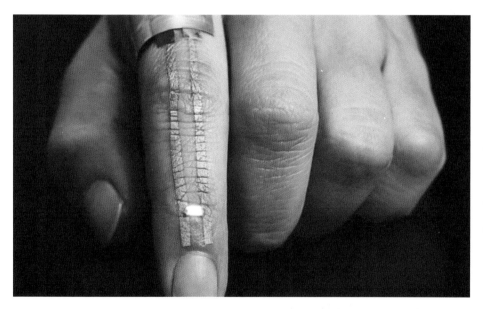

New sensors can be worn like temporary tattoos. Image courtesy of Takao Someya Group at the University of Tokyo.

KEY INSIGHT

Biointerfaces act as intermediaries between a biomaterial (cells, organs, muscles, or entire bodies) and technologies.

WHAT YOU NEED TO KNOW

New techniques developed in the past few years are leading to breakthroughs in research on biointerfaces, which range from microscopic ingestible robots to "tattoos" that function as medical sensors.

WHY IT MATTERS

New kinds of skin-based interfaces and ingestible devices could be a key to humans living longer, healthier lives.

THE IMPACT

These technologies have the potential to greatly reduce the complexity and intrusiveness of administering medicine and tracking biometrics, increasing quality of life and enabling more detailed insight into one's health and wellness.

WATCHLIST FOR SECTION

Apple, Caltech, Carnegie Mellon University, Case Western Reserve University, Center for Humane Technology, Chinese University of Hong Kong, Common Sense, Defense Advanced Research Projects Agency (DARPA), Tufts University, Duke University's Center for Neuroengineering, Elon Musk, Facebook, Food and Drug Administration, Federal Communications Commission, Google, Google's Soli, Harvard University's Wyss Institute, Harvard-MIT Division of Health Sciences and Technology, Institute for Basic Science, Johns Hopkins Applied Physics Laboratory, Johns Hopkins University, Sant'Anna School of Advanced Studies, MIT's Department of Mechanical Engineering, National Academy of Science, Neuralink, Northwestern University, Penn State University, Seoul National University, Stanford University, StarLab, Tufts University, Gemelli University Hospital, University of California-Berkeley's School of Information, University of California at San Diego, University of Chicago, University of Southern California, University of Texas at Austin, University of Tokyo, University of Washington's Center for Sensorimotor Neural Engineering.

⊙ TRENDS

Nanomesh Temporary Tattoos

Imagine wearing a temporary tattoo instead of taking a handful of pills every day. Research is underway on nanomesh technology as a diagnostic and drug delivery tool. Scientists at the **Institute for Basic Science** and **Seoul National University** in **South Korea**, the **University of Texas at Austin**, the **University of Tokyo, Stanford**, and the **University of California-San Diego** are all working on electronic second skins. **Lexington, Massachusetts-based MC10** has already created microscopic, organic semiconductors and carbon nanotubes that stretch and flex and can be powered wirelessly. Called **BioStampRC**, the sensors are far thicker than a tattooable, but the principle is the same, and it's only a matter of time before the technology shrinks.

Dissolving Bioelectronics

For many people, implanted electronics are required to live a healthy life, but the machines require surgery, can be costly, and the devices sometimes need replacement parts. In 2018, scientists at **Northwestern University** revealed new research on flexible, dissolvable electronic materials. In one case, they showed how the materials could be used during surgery. If nerves have been severed, doctors suture them back together and reawaken them using electrodes and gentle electrical stimulation—but they typically don't have enough time in the operating room to provide restorative therapy beyond what would be minimally required. The team demonstrated that dissolving electrodes could be used to wirelessly transmit the electrical signal and stimulate repaired nerves for several days, which could cut recovery time in half. Once the therapy was finished, the materials broke down and were excreted. The study was done in rats, but it shouldn't be long before we start to see clinical applications in humans.

Programmable, Ingestible, and Implantable Microbots

Tiny robots capable of delivering medicine to a specific area of the body, or assisting with micro-surgery, are here: They can be steered, threaded, and unfolded to patch wounds, dislodge swallowed objects, perform biopsies, and deliver targeted medications. Researchers at the **University of California-San Diego** proved in 2015 that a nanobot, propelled by gas bubbles, had successfully delivered medicine inside of a live mouse without causing injury. **Caltech** scientists developed an autonomous molecular robot, made of a single strand of DNA, that can treat the inside of the human body like a distribution warehouse. The nanobot can travel around, pick up molecules, and deposit them in designated locations. Scientists have been working on nanobot technologies such as these for the past decade. Late in 2018, scientists at the **Chinese University of Hong Kong** unveiled a new way to use nanobots within the body. Millions of tiny, magnetic shape-shifting nanoparticles

MC10's wearable sensors are helping researchers run virtual clinical trials.

Biointerfaces cont.

A muscle cell resting on a bed of nanobots.

are able to extend, merge, and collaborate in a swarm. In practical terms, this means that a surgeon could direct the swarm to deliver targeted medicines during surgery. In 2019, researchers at **MIT's Department of Mechanical Engineering** figured out how to create arrays of nanoscale magnets that respond to magnetic fields using a technique called electron-beam lithography to make magnetically reconfigurable robots that are the size of a few micrometers. In one instance, they made a microscopic bird-like structure that can flap its wings and move as directed. This could someday allow surgeons to perform operations on individual blood vessels or to manipulate single cells. The grand hope with all of these technologies is that nanobots will replace one-size-fits-most medications and therapies, treating our specific ailments in a highly personalized way without causing side effects.

"Smart thread" uses electrical currents to transmit information to doctors after surgery. Think of it as a sort of temporary system that connects to a smartphone or other medical device and can report on your glucose levels, diagnose an infection, and alert hospital staff if your body is chemically out of balance. Researchers at **Tufts University** have embedded nano-scale sensors and electronics into surgical thread that can be used for suturing. Meantime, researchers at the **University of California-Berkeley's School of Information** are experimenting with color-changing smart threads. These non-surgical threads are coated with thermochromic paint that changes color when jolted with electricity, and could be used as discreet components of visual alert systems, for example. Smart thread is just coming out of experimentation, but initial test results show that it can be successfully used as a diagnostic device.

Nearly a decade ago, **Microsoft** experimented with "skinput," which projected a digital overly onto a person's arm and turned it into an interactive interface. You could answer a call by tapping your fingertips together or press your palm to skip a song in your playlist. With Microsoft's **Hololens 2** extended reality headset, simple taps against your skin can be used to activate features. **Google's** Soli is advancing this skinput idea: In December 2018, the **Federal Communications Commission** approved Google's proposed tests of a new chip that uses radar to track micromotions. Soli is a miniature radar that understands human motion at various scales—from the tap of your finger to the broader movements of your body. We're already transitioning from physical to digital touchscreen buttons; soon skinput may teach consumers to live without any buttons at all.

Wearables

HIGH DEGREE OF CERTAINTY

INFORMS STRATEGY	ACT NOW
REVISIT LATER	KEEP VIGILANT WATCH

LONGER-TERM IMPACT — IMMEDIATE IMPACT

LOW DEGREE OF CERTAINTY

Sony's wearable air conditioner hopes to keep you cool on the move in the heat of summer.

KEY INSIGHT

More than 1,000 wearable devices are now available to consumers and to the enterprise. Wearable computing systems include watches, earbuds, sensors, headbands, fabrics, and other devices.

WHAT YOU NEED TO KNOW

The latest generation of devices no longer require a smartphone or computer to see and report data, adjust settings and archive information. This is known as "independent connectivity," and it will become the norm in 2020.

WHY IT MATTERS

The **International Data Corporation** measured 31% growth in the wearables market during the fourth quarter of 2018 alone, but the holiday season wasn't an anomaly. Growth has continued along an upward trajectory through 2019. **The Future Today Institute** estimates that by the end of 2020, global wearable device sales could top $370 million.

◉ DEEPER DIVE

A Replacement for Smartphones

Globally, smartphone shipments are in decline. **Apple** will no longer report sales numbers for its phones—a clear signal of what's on the horizon. And even as new form factors enter the consumer marketplace in 2020 (dual-sided phones and models with foldable screens), the functionality isn't improving at a fast-enough rate to merit tossing out existing phones for new ones. In the next 10 years, we will transition from a single device that we carry to a suite of next-gen communication devices that we'll wear and command using our voice, gesture, and touch. This future came into clearer view in January 2020, when Apple reported $20 billion in wearable product sales for the previous year. This growth in wearables has eclipsed the company's growth in phones—and made the wearables division itself worth as much as a Fortune 150 company.

Strategy for Wearables

Entertainment, media, and technology companies should develop strategies for wearable systems. Key questions to answer include:

- How will your organization interact with consumers via wearables?

- How will consumer expectations change as a result of wearables? For example, will they want to physically feel the impact of a football player making a tackle? Can broadcasters transmit shows with real-time translation? How will consumers get news stories via wearables?

- What are the ethical considerations of using wearables to send content? To receive it?

- How might your organization use neurotechnology some day? What would be your data governance requirements?

- What is the business case for wearables within your organization?

- How might your organization glean personal data from your customers via their wearables? How actively transparent will you be about this data capture?

THE IMPACT

We are transitioning from devices that we carry to devices that we wear. As price points drop and 5G networks are built, wearable devices will enter the global mainstream.

WATCHLIST

Amazon, Amazon's Echo products, Android, Apple, Athos, Center for Brain and Cognition at the University of California-San Diego, Center for Wearable Sensors at the University of California-San Diego, Digitsole, Ekso Bionics, Facebook, Google, Google's Fitbit, Halo, Harvard University's Wyss Institute for Biologically Inspired Engineering, Sacros Robotics, HTC, Intel, Johns Hopkins University, Magic Leap, Microsoft, MIT Media Lab, Motiv, Muse, Neuralink, NextMind, Nike, Oculus VR, ORII, Oura, PayPal, Pivot Yoga, Proteus, Quanttus, Ringly, Robotics Institute at Beihang University, Samsung, Sign-IO, Signal, Simon Fraser University, SmartThings, Soliyarn, Sony, Spire Health, Starkey, Thalmic Labs, Trimble, UnderArmour, University of California-Los Angeles, University of California-San Francisco, University of Chicago, Welt Corp, Withings.

⊘ TRENDS

Cloud-Based Wireless Body Area Networks

Wireless Body Area Networks (WBANs) communicate information from your wearable devices back to medical servers, app manufacturers, and your home computer. Sensors operate inside devices that monitor your heart rate or oxygen level, collect data, send it back to a central hub (most often, your smartphone), and then relay the information to a medical team or healthcare monitoring service. There are many benefits: Rather than moving into an assisted living facility or spending a lot of time in the hospital, patients can live at home and receive virtual care. Cloud-based systems allow for the continuous transmission of your data and real-time analysis for issues like chronic disease (hypertension, high blood pressure, asthma). This trend is still in very early stages and will accelerate as 5G networks proliferate, because a more advanced network will lead to less lag and could help secure personal data.

Adaptive Wearable Technologies

Artificial exoskeletons and soft exosuits improve human mobility after a traumatic incident, serving as replacements for human limbs. Advanced articulation mechanics and neurointerfaces are generating big strides in this field. The hard exoskeletons used today will soon evolve into smaller, more modular components and designs. Researchers at the Robotics Institute at Beihang University are developing new lower-body mechanisms that are lightweight and respond to the wearer in real time. Meanwhile, scientists at Harvard University's Wyss Institute for Biologically Inspired Engineering are researching how to transition from soft exosuits to implanted interfaces—think tiny sensors worn beneath the skin—which could someday help to control neuromuscular activity to help people with sever impairments regain mobility.

Commercial Full-Body Exoskeletons

Movies like *Iron Man* and *Avatar* depict mechanized suits that can give average humans superpowers. This year, more practical versions of these apparatuses will be made available for commercial applications. **Sarcos Robotics's** Guardian XO is a battery-powered suit intended for construction sites, mines, and factories. Built to enhance worker productivity, the suits help people lift heavy loads—up to 198 pounds—without back strain. **Ekso Bionics**, which develops medical-grade exoskeletons, created a vest intended to help workers more easily perform high exertion overhead tasks.

Wearable Air Conditioners

For many years, **Japanese** and **Chinese** workers who must wear protective suits during summer's intense heat have used wearable fans to keep cool. These tiny fans generate air inside their suits, while ventilation flaps let body heat escape. Now, miniature, wearable air conditioners will come to market for the rest of us. **Sony** developed the Reon Pocket, which relies on a phenomenon known as the Peltier effect, which moves heat between objects using electrical currents. In place of a servomotor and fan, this flat device is embedded into a shirt. Your mobile phone controls the thermostat and the wearable Reon Pocket can cool or heat your body by 23 degrees or 14 degrees Fahrenheit, respectively.

Brain-Machine Interfaces (BMIs)

University of California-Los Angeles computer scientist **Jacques J. Vidal** first talked about "brain machine interfaces" in the 1970s. Since then, the term has grown to encapsulate technologies that serve as interfaces between the internal workings of the brain and the external world. Researchers are finding new ways to connect humans and mammals directly to computers. Last year, **Elon Musk's Neuralink** unveiled a robot capable of implanting tiny, ultrathin threads deep into the brain. It's a step toward Musk's vision of advanced brain-machine interfaces—small, wearable computers with these thread-like components embedded directly into our brain tissue. The **Pentagon** has been working on similar projects that use both threads and pulsating lights. Much of the research to date has focused on rehabilitation: With these human-machine interfaces, people can communicate via thought alone, which promises new options for those suffering from stroke and paralysis. Startups **Neurable** and **Trimble** are collaborating on brain-computer interface projects in transportation, architecture, and engineering. **Paris-based NextMind** secured

$4.6 million in funding to bring noninvasive brain command technology to the gaming industry. **Facebook** has been working on several BMI projects, including a noninvasive headband that would read thoughts before we say them aloud. In one partnership with the **University of California-San Francisco**, researchers place sheets of electrodes on the brains of volunteer test subjects to see how much of their thoughts can be read. Facebook, which also owns **Oculus VR**, is working toward a headset that might someday allow us to control music or virtual reality environments simply by thinking.

Smartwatches

Consumers can choose among hundreds of different smartwatches from traditional watchmakers and big tech giants. Some models, like the newest **Apple Watch 5**, no longer require a mobile phone for pairing—they can connect directly to cellular networks and can perform much of the same functionality as our phones. As the **Future Today Institute** forecasted in 2016, smartwatch adoption is contributing to a decline in the growth of the smartphone market.

The Apple Watch 5 is one of the world's most popular wearable devices.

Wearables cont.

The Neuralink could someday be wired directly into your brain.

Rings and Bracelets

Last year, **Amazon** unveiled the **Echo Loop** smart ring, which functions as a speaker-phone, digital assistant, and smart sensor. It's essentially a wearable Alexa. **PayPal** has been researching its own connected ring, intended for fast and easy payments without having to dig around for your phone or credit card. The **Motiv** and **Oura** rings track sleeping habits, while the **ORII** ring lets you make calls. **Google's** acquisition of **Fitbit** made major news last year, and it was seen as a move to combat Apple's domination in the watch market. Rings and bracelets aren't meant as replacements for smart-watches per se, but if you're a developer looking for single-task application opportunities, rings and bracelets offer a good alternative to more programming-intensive watch interfaces.

Hearables / Earables

In-ear computers, otherwise known as ear-ables, are here. **Sony's 360 Reality Audio** is a new format that uses Sony's object-based spatial audio technology to enhance sound—setup requires that you allow photos of your

ears to be scanned, analyzed, and stored on Sony's servers. **Apple's AirPods** may soon include biometric sensors to monitor temperature, perspiration and heart rate during exercise or sports. **Starkey's Livio AI** uses A.I. and an array of sensors to modulate external sound—if you're someone who complains that restaurants or public places are too loud, this device may help you hear better, while also acting as a digital assistant. New iterations will track lots of different health and behavioral metrics, like cognitive activity and how you're engaging with other people, and it will translate 27 different languages in near real-time.

Head Mounted Displays

One increasingly common form of wearable devices is the type of headsets used for virtual and augmented reality. What's next: they will soon collect your biometric data and other personal information in order to provide added functionality. The **HTC Vive** tracks your movement, while controller sticks send haptic signals to your brain as you work your way through simulated environments. (See also: Mixed Reality.)

Connected Fabrics

In the past, connected clothing has required wires and sensors, which can make fabrics stiff or uncomfortable. That's starting to change, and it will likely lead to more smart clothes for the masses. A process called "reactive vapor deposition," for instance, is being used to engineer fabric with smart circuitry embedded into the cloth. Start-up **Soliyarn** is working on imperceptible, flexible sensors woven into self-heating gloves for the **U.S. military**. Athletic wear is another key market for connected fabrics. Soliyarn is working on smart pajamas and sleep-sensing masks, while others are developing pajamas that can emit infrared energy to help your muscles recover faster from a hard workout. **Pivot Yoga** makes connected yoga pants—you read that right—that monitor your downward dogs and help you adjust your form. The connected clothing syncs to an app, through which a digital assistant will tell you when to turn your left hip or to move your legs a few inches back on the mat. **Spire Health** makes a fabric-coating that can be attached to bras and underwear to help track your breathing and stress level.

Smart Belts and Shoes

Welt Corp sells a smart belt that can detect falls—and it sends push notifications if it senses that you've eaten too much. **Nike's** self-fastening **Electric Adaptable Reaction Lacing** shoes adjust to the contours of your feet. **French** insole manufacturer **Digitsole** makes connected insoles that fit inside the existing shoes of cyclists and runners and record and communicate their activity data—plus, they can keep your feet warm. **Baltimore**-based **Under Armour** makes connected running shoes, which rely on foam soles with accelerometers, gyroscopes, batteries, and Bluetooth modules. The shoes collect and store data, allowing you to go out for a run without having to bring along your smartphone. They also set a baseline the first time you use them, and then track distance, stride length and your running cadence over time.

Smart Gloves

In **Kenya**, a researcher invented smart gloves that can translate sign language into speech. The gloves, called **Sign-IO**, use gesture recognition and sensors embedded in the gloves. **Canadian** researchers at **Simon Fraser University** designed a set of interconnected gloves to help transmit the sense of touch through the internet. When someone moves her fingers in one glove, her actions are sent to her partner wearing the other. **Sony** has been filing patents for haptic glove controllers, which would simulate the physical sensations of slicing, punching, and shooting.

Touch-Sensitive Materials

Researchers are developing new prosthetic skins and limbs that restore not just movement, but touch as well. In 2018, researchers at **Johns Hopkins University** in **Baltimore** created an electronic skin to help restore a sense of touch to amputees. Dubbed "e-dermis," it recreates the sense of touch (including pain) by sensing physical stimuli and sending those signals back to the peripheral nerves. Interdisciplinary researchers at the **Center for Wearable Sensors** and the **Center for Brain and Cognition** at the **University of California-San Diego** are combining materials science and psychophysics to map exactly how humans perceive touch. This research lays the groundwork for the advanced prosthetics of the future.

We've already seen some exciting developments. Neuroscientists at the **University of Chicago** are experimenting with touch-sensitive robotics and rhesus monkeys, whose neural-sensory biology is most similar to humans. They successfully simulated the sensation of touch by stimulating certain areas of the brain. A team of scientists from the Sant'Anna School of Advanced Studies and the Gemelli University Hospital in Rome developed a bionic hand that transmits a realistic sense of touch; it's already in use, restoring sensation to a woman who lost her hand in an accident 25 years ago.

The Decade of Connected Eyewear

DR. BRIAN WOOLF, O.D., CEO OF WOOLF EYE LAB

This is the decade of connected eyewear. The world's largest technology companies—Apple, Amazon, Google, Microsoft, Facebook—are all working, in some way, on connected devices that you wear over your eyes.

These smart glasses will offer a number of key benefits, mostly in the way we interpret information. Humans evolved to see objects clearly from afar—a useful ability as we wandered the Savanna and spotted threats and opportunities at a distance. Today, however, that distance vision poses a problem, because we spend so much of our time staring at all sizes and shapes of screens, many at close range. The result is tired eyes, headaches, and blurry vision at the end of a long day. These are just a few of the problems caused by Computer Vision Syndrome, and it's becoming more prevalent.

Our eyes weren't made for this. A little primer on how the eye works: In a completely relaxed state, our eyes focus light received from a distance into a sharp point at the back of the eyeball, on a layer of tissue called the retina. Transitioning from distance vision to close vision, we must adjust our focus so that the light from this new, nearer source is once again sharp and defined when it reaches the retina. To do this, we tighten a small muscle in our eyes that bends the lens into a different shape, causing the light to be focused correctly. But it requires active energy to keep that muscle constricted and keep our near vision sharp. Doing that wasn't a big deal when we sat for a few hours honing sticks into spears or weaving reeds into baskets. But in the modern era, we're spending eight, twelve, even fourteen hours a day focused intently on screens, something our eyes were never designed for—and it's taking a toll. In the past decade of seeing patients, I've counted sharp increases in myopia, or nearsightedness, as the body tries to adjust to constantly looking up close. Technology is moving way faster than our bodies can evolve, and it's causing problems.

Smart glasses promise to help. Instead of projecting light at you—the way a phone screen does, for example—these wearables project light into you, emulating the way you would receive light from a distant object. There's no need for internal eye focusing to get a sharp, clear image—even though the device might be right next to, or even touching the eye, the images presented appear to you as though they're coming from far away.

When it comes to smart glasses and augmented reality, things really get interesting. We've come to understand that the eyes are just conduits to get raw information to the brain, where it's processed—this sensorial and cognitive phenomenon is what we call vision. When virtual information is projected onto the retina, as it would be through an AR headset or smart eyewear, the eye is happy to pass that information along to the brain just the same as if it had been received from your physical environment. This means well-rendered digital elements and virtual overlays very quickly get integrated into our personal system of vision and become part of what we perceive as our reality.

I've used multiple prototypes of new extended reality headsets, such as Magic Leap and Microsoft's HoloLens2. It's remarkable how quickly you take in the new information these devices present you with, and how seamlessly it becomes part of the world you're living in. Unlike virtual reality, which is fully immersive and in current iterations can have a general feeling of artificiality to it, new augmented reality technologies digitally map your environment, and the images they project for you interact with and react to the real world you're standing in. For instance, you might see your desk as you would with your naked eye, but also see a digitally generated miniature dinosaur walking around on it. That dinosaur "knows" not to fall off the edge of the desk, and if it bumps into your lamp, it will move around it. Using Magic Leap, I put a digital wall sticker on the far side of my room, and when my session was over and I took off the device, I was genuinely surprised the sticker was gone. It had already become an accepted part of my surroundings.

Over the decade, as this technology becomes more ubiquitous, the possibilities will become endless. We'll switch from looking at information on handheld screens to using devices like Magic Leap, which send information directly to our eyes, more or less the way nature intended. Our brains live in a dark silent cave and only know what's going on in the outside world because of what our sensorial organs report back to it. Through AR, we can utilize our eyes and ears to send information that we've created—rather than information we've passively received—to our brains for processing, allowing us to manipulate our perception and convince our brains that whatever we'd created is in fact the real world. We can essentially become all-powerful architects of our own audiovisual reality.

Of course this poses plenty of potential problems. We may end up with two classes of people: those who can afford this new augmented reality world, and those with only traditional human vision. And as we now begin to confront the reality of deepfakes and other sources of false information, other dangers arise. For instance, what if you could hack into a person's system of vision and create a false reality that was indistinguishable from "true" reality? It would call into question today's notion that to verify a fact or occurrence, one must "see it to believe it."

What is clear, however, is that these new connected glasses will be the future. They can feed us information in the way we've evolved to receive it, and, as a result, we can process it faster and more completely. It's a lot easier to react to a bear jumping out of the woods at you when you see it happening in real time—versus reading a push notification on your phone that says "A bear has jumped out of the woods at you." With smart eyewear you'll get more information with less distraction, and with less strain on your eyes. Ultimately, that's good for everyone.

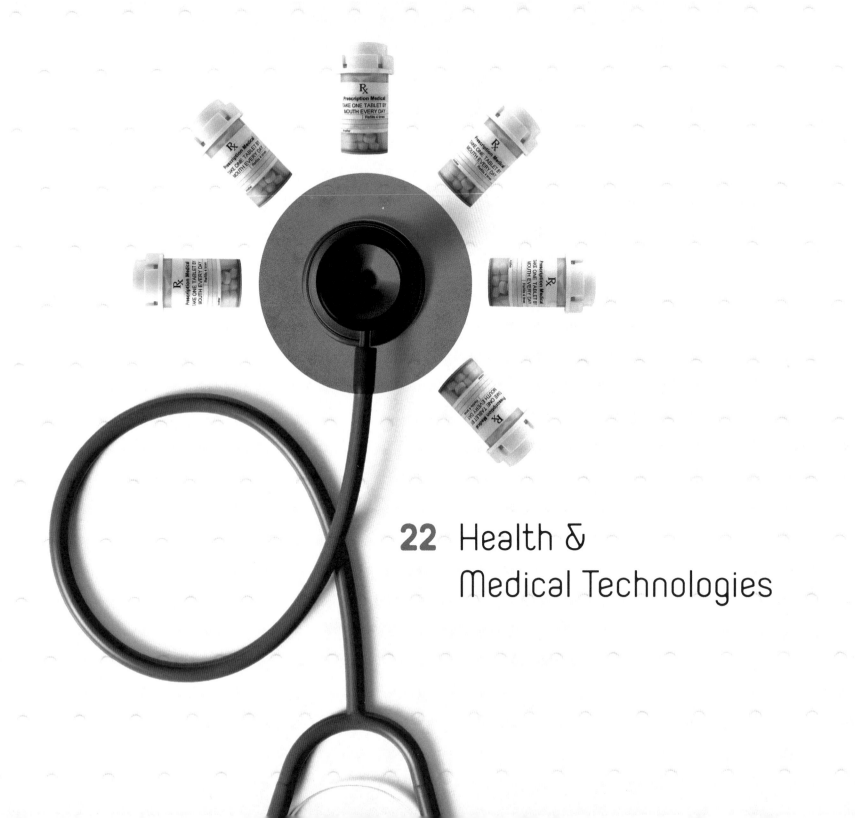

22 Health &
Medical Technologies

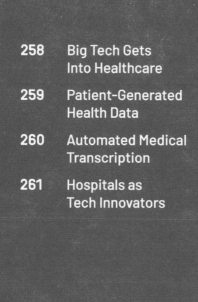

Big Tech Gets Into Healthcare

HIGH DEGREE OF CERTAINTY

LONGER-TERM IMPACT	**INFORMS STRATEGY**	**ACT NOW**
	REVISIT LATER	**KEEP VIGILANT WATCH**

IMMEDIATE IMPACT

LOW DEGREE OF CERTAINTY

Key Insight

The future of healthcare could soon look very different than it does today as **Google**, **Amazon**, **Apple**, **IBM**, and **Microsoft** disrupt health and medicine.

Why It Matters

The world's largest tech companies are leading various health initiatives, which include basic scientific research, research investments in the healthcare application process, developing innovative health insurance models, creating new clinics, and enabling the capture and analysis of personal health data via interactive devices.

Examples

Last year, **Microsoft** and **China's Tencent** captured more than 70% of all startup investment deals made in digital health. Meanwhile, **Amazon** made its health strategy more clear. **Haven**—Amazon's joint health insurance venture with **JPMorgan** and **Berkshire Hathaway**—hired 50 people and will roll out health plans to its employees in 2020. Amazon also made a $2 million investment in **Boston**-based **Beth Israel Deaconess Medical Center** to improve patient care and efficiency in operating and emergency rooms with its **AWS** cloud and A.I. tools. Its **Alexa** voice assistant was deemed HIPAA compliant last year—no small feat—which paves the way for hospital and pharmaceutical partnerships. Amazon's **PillPack** integrates its online pharmacy with some of the biggest insurance providers in America. **Amazon Care**—a hybrid in-person healthcare system and virtual clinic where Amazon employees get live, in-app visits from doctors and nurses—has acquired or partnered with numerous healthcare providers for A.I. research. **Google** is equally aggressive about healthcare. About 7% of the searches performed on Google are health and medicine related. In 2019, Google's **Project Nightingale** teamed up with **Ascension**, one of the largest health-care systems in the **U.S.**, to mine and analyze personal health data across 21 states. Goo-gle and **Alphabet**-owned **Verily** worked on A.I. and computer vision solutions for medical imaging analysis. Google's electronic health record voice assistant **Suki** became a helpful resource for some doctors. Don't forget that Google acquired **Fitbit**, as well. **Apple** continued its move into electronic health records, upgrading its **Health App** to include personal data as part of a massive partnership with the **Department of Veterans Affairs**. Within Apple's employee health clinics, patients get free genetic screenings courtesy of the company's partnership with genetic testing startup **Color**. Apple watches and earbuds are also being oriented for integration within its healthcare ecosystem.

What's Next

Big tech companies are now competing to recruit top medical talent, to establish research partnerships, and, of course, to get access to our data. They each have ambitious health strategies that we will see unfold in the coming years.

The Impact

Healthcare is a $3 trillion market, and with its inflated pricing and outdated systems, it is particularly ripe for disruption.

Watchlist

Alibaba, Alphabet, Amazon, Apple, Baidu, Berkshire Hathaway, Google, IBM, JPMorgan, Microsoft, Tencent, healthcare providers, hospitals, and government agencies.

Amazon pushed quickly and assertively into the healthcare space in 2019.

Patient-Generated Health Data

HIGH DEGREE OF CERTAINTY

INFORMS STRATEGY	ACT NOW
REVISIT LATER	KEEP VIGILANT WATCH

LONGER-TERM IMPACT · IMMEDIATE IMPACT

LOW DEGREE OF CERTAINTY

We are generating data through wearable devices like this Fitbit Versa.

Key Insight

Demand for patient data is on the rise. Hospital records contain sensitive personal information, and the ability to integrate that data with the latest-and-greatest technologies often means making that data accessible to tech companies.

Why It Matters

Individuals are generating a trove of data that could contribute to their healthcare provider's patient assessments and subsequent strategies. Packaging all that data—and figuring out how to make use of it—is still a challenge.

Examples

From **Google's** Fitbit, to **Apple's** Watch and Airpods, to smart scales we use at home, there are hundreds of devices that can collect and monitor our health using various inputs. New software from companies like **Validic** allow doctors to collect this other data and incorporate it into their medical records—with patient consent. **GE Health-care**, **Meditech**, **Allscripts**, **eClinicalWorks**, and **Cerner** are all building products to make better use of our data.

We also generate data at the doctor's office, and under federal law in the U.S., that data must be filed and stored electronically. The medical community and public health sector are now trying to find ways to make good use of all that information. Differential privacy measures could enable hospital systems to anonymize our private details while still making our data useful to researchers.

What's Next

A challenge for tech companies is de-identifying our data so that our privacy is protected and federal regulations are met, and to free up that data for use in training A.I. systems. Safeguarding and maintaining vast genetic and personal health data will be paramount as consumers purchase their own genetic testing kits through third-party companies like **23andMe**.

On a near-weekly basis, hackers target hospitals and doctors, holding patient data for ransom. In May 2017, hackers used the WannaCry malware to break into the **UK's National Health Service**, crippling the nation's hospitals and clinics. In January 2018, hackers used a remote access portal to break into a rural Indiana hospital and restrict access to patient data. They demanded four bitcoin to restore data access. The timing was awful: A serious ice storm had caused a spike in emergency room visits, and the community was battling a flu outbreak. The volume of patient data has sparked a new field within the life sciences business: patient data security. **Veeva Systems** builds tools that prevent unauthorized access.

Watchlist

Amazon, Allscripts, Apple, Cerner, eClinical-Works, GE Healthcare, Google, HumanAPI, IBM, Manulife Financial, Medicaid, Medicare, Meditech, Microsoft, Qualcomm, Validic, Veeva Systems, Vivify, national health systems.

Automated Medical Transcription

HIGH DEGREE OF CERTAINTY

INFORMS STRATEGY	ACT NOW
REVISIT LATER	KEEP VIGILANT WATCH

LONGER-TERM IMPACT · IMMEDIATE IMPACT

LOW DEGREE OF CERTAINTY

In 2019, Amazon announced its medical transcription service.

Key Insight

Dictating patient notes is a core task in a clinical practice. Artificial intelligence promises faster transcriptions, as well as real-time diagnostic analysis.

Why It Matters

Transcribing recordings is a tedious process that relies on excellent sound quality and a good understanding of medical terminology—not to mention confidentiality. Making the process more efficient and effortless could improve operations throughout hospitals and medical practices.

Examples

In order to meet compliance regulations, a strict protocol must be followed for the transcription to be legally performed by a third party. But what if the transcription is performed in real-time? Not only would it be easier and more cost-effective for building patient records, but an additional layer of machine learning could help doctors learn even more about their patients during visits.

What's Next

In December 2019, **Amazon** launched **Amazon Transcribe Medical** and a companion service called **Amazon Comprehend Medical**. Both are intended to make medical practices more efficient. Transcribe Medical does what its name says: It runs voice recognition on audio of doctor-patient interactions and transcribes the conversations directly into an electronic medical record. In a private practice without medical residents, this frees the doctor from having to move between the patient and her computer to enter symptoms and other information. Comprehend Medical is intended for developers to help them use unstructured medical text in diagnostic tools. AWS's software is designed to be integrated into devices and apps using an API. **Microsoft's** Azure and **Google** Cloud are also working on similar systems.

The Impact

The biggest challenge for tech companies will be proving the compliance and accuracy of their systems. Imagine an error in which "hyperglycemic" (high blood sugar) is mistakenly recorded as "hypoglycemic" (low blood sugar).

Watchlist

Alphabet, Amazon, Apple, Google, IBM, Microsoft, Nuance, Stanford University, healthcare providers, hospitals, and government agencies.

Hospitals as Tech Innovators

	HIGH DEGREE OF CERTAINTY	
INFORMS STRATEGY	ACT NOW	
REVISIT LATER	KEEP VIGILANT WATCH	
	LOW DEGREE OF CERTAINTY	

Jefferson Health is pioneering a new tech-inspired culture within healthcare.

Key Insight

Medical and health knowledge is increasing exponentially, and new artificial intelligence systems promise to transform how we understand and care for patients. Some hospitals are now evolving into centers for innovation in technology as well as healthcare.

Why It Matters

The future profit generators of hospitals could be an evolution from our current system, which relies heavily on insurance systems. Investing in health innovations and emerging technologies could be alternate profit centers.

Examples

In **Philadelphia**, **Dr. Stephen Klasko**, president of **Thomas Jefferson University** and CEO of **Jefferson Health**, spearheaded dozens of initiatives to transform the city's entire hospital system. Klasko often says that medical schools are designed to "suck the creativity" out of their students, so he instead started looking to **Silicon Valley** to gain inspiration for new hires at Jefferson Health with backgrounds in design, technology, and creative problem solving, and who happen to be interested in the medical sciences. The hospital system is actively partnering with and investing in health and medical startups—a drastic shift from other hospital systems which instead tend to focus investments in brick-and-mortar real estate.

What's Next

The future of health tech includes home diagnostic equipment, A.I.-powered clinical decision support tools, and sensor-embedded clothing that can improve the quality of hospital stays. Hospitals that can maintain consistent contact and interaction with patients both on- and off-site will have a better shot at keeping them healthy throughout their lifespans. Jefferson Health has partnered with a startup that is carbonizing hemp—the result is soft fabrics you can sleep, work, and exercise in that can be easily integrated with technology to give you real-time metrics on your health and communicate that information with your healthcare provider, too.

The Impact

Roughly 6.5% of Americans had one or more hospital stays in 2017. Great quality of care in hospitals can mean better, healthier lifestyles once patients return home.

Watchlist

Alphabet, Amazon, Apple, Google, IBM, Jefferson Health, Microsoft, Stanford University, Yale University, healthcare providers, hospital networks.

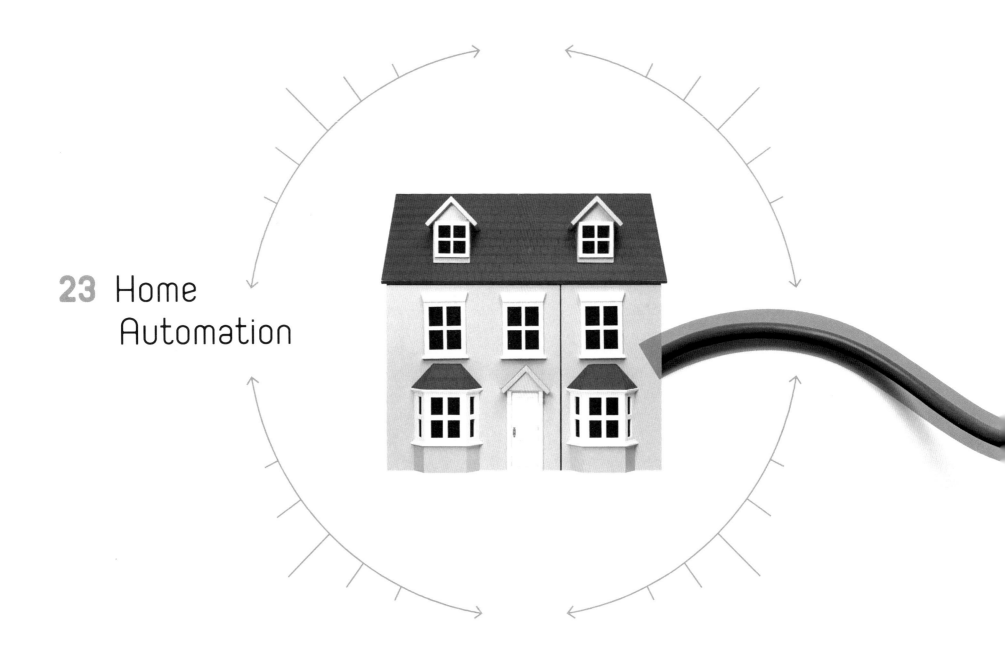

23 Home
Automation

Home Automation

HIGH DEGREE OF CERTAINTY

INFORMS STRATEGY	**ACT NOW**
REVISIT LATER	**KEEP VIGILANT WATCH**

LONGER-TERM IMPACT · IMMEDIATE IMPACT

LOW DEGREE OF CERTAINTY

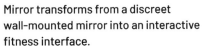

Mirror transforms from a discreet wall-mounted mirror into an interactive fitness interface.

KEY INSIGHT

Connected appliances, lights, thermostats, plugs, and other devices can be networked inside a home to automate everyday tasks.

WHAT YOU NEED TO KNOW

The U.S. market has seen a steady year-over-year growth in home automation products. Security systems and smart speakers account for the largest share of devices sold so far. There are still competing interoperability standards and protocols.

WHY IT MATTERS

This is one of the fastest growing sectors of consumer technology in North America.

THE IMPACT

Estimates vary, but researchers forecast that the value of the global smart home market could range between $160 billion and $240 billion by 2025.

WATCHLIST FOR SECTION

Amazon, ADT Pulse, Amazon Neighbors App, Amazon Turnkey, Apple, Arlo Ultra, August Home, Bosch Home Connect, Botrista, Brilliant Control, Carnegie Mellon University, Comcast, Connect, Dyson, Ecobee, Ecovacs, Electronic Frontier Foundation, Facebook, Federal Trade Commission, FET Kitchen, FightCamp Gym, Google, Google Home Hub, Google Nest, Honeywell, Huawei, Husqvarna, Hydrow Rower, IBM, Ikea, Innit, iRobot, JaxJox Kettlebell, KitchenAid, Lennar, Logiech, Logitech, Microsoft, Mirror, Nanit, Nest, Peloton, Philips Hue, Rachio, Realogy, Ring, Roku, Samsung, Siemens, SimpliSafe, Sleep Number, SmartThings, Sonos, Tonal, Truveon, Whirlpool, Worx, Wyze, Yeelight, Zigbee Alliance, ZTE.

◌ DEEPER DIVE

Consolidation in Home Operating Systems

There are lots of smart home devices now available in the market, but increasingly few platforms are capable of connecting them all together. The companies behind those platforms should come as no surprise: **Amazon**, **Apple**, and **Google**. Devices are ubiquitous and increasingly affordable, but the real revenue won't be from device sales anyway—it will come from the monetization of information captured by those devices in their data-rich domestic environments.

In 2020, speaker manufacturer **Sonos** sued Google in two federal court systems for patent infringement, but its legal action had less to do with patents and more to do with how Google and Amazon built the smart home infrastructure that companies like Sonos rely on. Back in 2013, Sonos partnered with Google, giving engineers detailed diagrams on how the Sonos systems worked. At the time, Google was not yet making speakers. Three years later Google Home was unveiled, a product that applied a Sonos-like approach to make speakers communicate with each other. Since its launch, Sonos had advertised its speakers on Google and sold them on Amazon, and the company used both ecosystems to reach its customers. When Amazon and Google entered the smart speaker market with cheaper alternatives and far greater potential reach, Sonos sued. Amazon, which sells Echo devices similar to Sonos speakers with multi-room music playing functionality, claims that it hasn't infringed on Sonos's technology. Likewise, Google's defended itself, saying it had been in productive IP conversations with Sonos for several years. The case is analogous to several others brought by smaller tech companies accusing the tech giants of taking their ideas, their technology, and their market share. To be fair, startups show their technology to bigger tech companies all the time for a variety of reasons: to gain access to platforms and device ecosystems, for possible investment or acquisition, and to develop applications for consumers. (Usually agreements are signed beforehand, however, to protect everyone involved.)

New Social Contracts

Every time you open a website, use a social media platform, or access the hundreds of available digital tools and services, you are either explicitly or implicitly agreeing to a company's legal terms. Nearly all of us scroll to the checkbox and click to agree without reading. Those documents are very, very long and if you didn't attend law school, they can be confusing and difficult to understand. Researchers at **Carnegie Mellon** calculated how much time it would take to read all the terms of service, privacy policies, and other legal documents we're served—they estimated it would take us each approximately 76 business days, reading 8 hours a day, to get through all the paperwork we're shown in an average year.

And yet people are increasingly concerned about their privacy. As smart home technology becomes more universal, the success of everyone in the ecosystem—home builders, OEMs, platforms, ISPs, and app developers—will depend on the successful management of our data. Building trust in our home automation systems will unlock shared value for businesses. To get there, we will need a new social contract for smart homes and those who live in them.

THE IMPACT

One key development for 2020 is the widespread extension of devices into our homes as the broader consumer electronics market continues to grow. By 2023, we expect one third of the world's population to own at least one computing device (smartphone, laptop) and to either have access to or own one additional connected device, such as a smart plug, speaker, or pedometer. Today's devices and those introduced over the next decade promise to give consumers access to bundled entertainment packages, shopping platforms, and other personal services benefits—all of which rely on our personal and behavioral data.

Google's Nest Hub helps manage connected devices in a smart home.

Home Automation cont.

❯ TRENDS

Digital Emissions

The average person isn't aware of how much data they're shedding. Collectively, our homes are starting to produce digital emissions, which includes all the data not actively used and processed by devices. Bits of information in that network include things like your body temperature as you watch TV, the ambient hums and creaks that your home makes at night, and the communication pings your devices make. Digital emissions aren't harmful to the environment, but they're an untapped resource to be mined and analyzed—with transparency and permissions, of course.

Interoperability

Smart home technologies aren't necessarily easily interoperable. A Google speaker won't interact with devices running on Amazon's smart home platform, for example. While savvy users can buy smart cameras that can run on open source tools, the average family typically needs to make a decision and run either **Google**, **Apple**, or **Amazon** gear. In 2019, the three companies joined the **Zigbee**

Alliance to explore ways to make their device ecosystems more interoperable.

Retrofitting Old Homes with New Tech

As smart home devices become more ubiquitous and affordable, people are working to retrofit old homes with new technologies. Purchasing a smart fire alarm system is easy enough, but it could be a challenge to install and maintain it in a home with aging or outdated wiring, for example. For now, many systems require a strong cabled internet system to work properly. That could change, though, as 5G networks become more prevalent and smart home technologies are able to work wirelessly without latency issues.

Forced Bundling and Planned Obsolescence

A decade ago, companies that sold printers made tweaks to their technology to prevent generic ink cartridges from being used. That same technique is starting to be used in connected home appliances and devices. A few years ago, **General Electric** started requiring consumers to replace water filters in its refrigerators with new versions that

included RFID chips. If you didn't buy one of theirs, which is substantially more expensive than other brands of filters, you didn't get water. As more smart home appliances become available, we anticipate arbitrary technical barriers that make the devices beyond a certain period of time. That leads to a thorny question: Could we be causing future environmental damage by forcibly bricking our devices every few years? For example, if a company retires an operating system for its smart refrigerator, should consumers still have the right to at least use the refrigerator in its traditional function for temperature-controlled storage? If not they'd have to throw it away, creating unnecessary and potentially harmful waste.

Real Estate and Home Building Powered by Platforms

Big tech companies are getting into the real estate market. **Amazon** partnered with **Realogy** in 2019 to help launch its **TurnKey** home buying platform on Amazon.com. The system connects buyers to real estate agents and Amazon move-in experts who will help select smart devices for your new home and will connect them for you. Amazon has also run a trial program with **Lennar**, America's largest home builder, to develop

and build brand-new smart homes powered by Amazon's technology.

Smart Cameras

In 2018, **Amazon** announced a new feature for its **Ring** doorbells. The system automatically recognizes people, making it easier for homeowners and tenants to see and track everyone coming to their home or apartment. There are added features, too: In some communities, local police are asking residents to opt in to a program giving law enforcement access to camera footage. Patents filed by researchers at Amazon show a version of the camera technology with a field of view that extends beyond the doorstep, to driveways, streets, narrow passageways between or behind buildings, and virtually anywhere the smart cameras are placed. **Google's Nest** system similarly identifies faces and allows users to input names, and it can be trained to recognize friends, family, and those who consumers don't want near their homes. Smart cameras automatically detect a face, zoom in, and follow that person as they move around. Millions of hours of security camera footage are now being uploaded regularly from these devices. Consumers can access it, share and repost it as they want, and give third parties access to footage as well. To allay privacy concerns, Nest released a firmware upgrade that turns on a light on each camera anytime it's recording.

Smart Camera News Networks

Amazon's Ring includes an app called **Neighbors** that allows users to post the videos they've recorded—it also encourages them to post videos and photos of suspicious activity, crime, and other notable occurrences within neighborhoods. As of August 2019, 225 U.S. police departments could retain the right to request video footage from Ring doorbell users. In addition, anyone can download the free mobile app and gain access to videos posted, even if they aren't Ring users. The app shows video clips that can be annotated by uploaders, while a "News Team" supplements the feed of videos with short stories about burglaries, fires, and other events—some of which is pulled from sources like the **Associated Press**. The app, however, can easily be manipulated: There are numerous instances of people uploading and intentionally mis-tagging photos of people, reporting "suspicious" activity without any real evidence or data, and submitting purposely racist content.

Networked Smart Devices

For the past decade, researchers have worked on something called device handoff, aiming for more efficient communication among devices across a network. In 2020, our smart home appliances will increasingly collaborate on the backend. For example, **Innit**'s platform lets kitchen appliances talk to one another, even if your appliances come from several different brands. In 2019, Innit teamed up with **Google Home Hub** and other smart displays to further connect your kitchen. There are lots of other options: the **Bosch Home Connect** smart kitchen line connects to **Nest Protect**. If you forget that pizza in the oven and it starts to catch fire, your Nest smoke detector will tell the oven to turn itself off. In the coming year, we'll see more integrations across brands and appliances.

Interactive Fitness Equipment

The last few years saw the launch of smart fitness equipment, including mirrors, bikes, and treadmills. **Peloton**'s connected bike and subscription model have chipped away at popular rivals **SoulCycle** and **Equinox** by allowing bike owners to join live group classes from home. Last year, the company launched its **Peloton Tread**, a connected treadmill with a companion app that leads users through a variety of running and training classes. The **JaxJox Kettlebell Connect** is a kettlebell set that tracks your movement using Bluetooth. **Mirror** is an interactive gym masquerading as—you guessed it—a full-length, wall-mounted mirror. A coach leads recorded or live classes and the mirror interface actively helps you adjust your form. Meanwhile, **Tonal** is an interactive fitness mirror that comes with adjustable arms for resistance and weight training. The system will automatically detect your performance and increase or decrease the resistance accordingly during your workout. The **Hydrow Rower** is a connected rowing machine with adjustable resistance levels and pre-recorded workouts. **FightCamp Gym** is a connected punching bag with corresponding classes accessible from iOS devices.

The End of Remote Control

Video content creators must improve tagging, titles, and meta-data automation—and fast. In 2020, more remote controls will be equipped with voice recognition systems. Subscribers to **Comcast's Xfinity** already have access to voice-controlled remote controls, which allow users to search for actors, ask questions about shows, and bypass the button-navigated menu system to quickly find what they want to watch. We tend to associate remote controls just with our televisions, but you can expect to see new uses for remotes in the years to come. However, as digital voice assistants become more integrated with various consumer electronics, smart remotes will give way to embedded speakers and microphones within our devices. **TCL Roku TVs** will soon be equipped with far-field microphone arrays. **Samsung** will keep its remotes for now, but they will start to rely heavily on its smart assistant. All of this sounds exciting—unless you are hoarse, are a non-native English speaker, have a thick accent, or are unable to speak.

Smart Appliance Screens

Major appliance manufacturers are including smart screens in upcoming models, supported by **Alexa** and **Google Assistant**. The **Samsung Family Hub** smart refrigerator and **Whirlpool Cabrio** washing machines will allow users to interact with the devices via touchscreens and smartphones. The smart screen interfaces offer customization—new specialty cycles and programs can be downloaded from the internet.

You're an Amazon, Apple, or Google Family in our Digital Caste System of the Future

MID-FUTURE CATASTROPHIC SCENARIO

In the year 2035, Apple households tend to be wealthier and older. They can afford all of Apple's sleek, beautiful hardware. Apple's smart glasses, connected toilets, and custom refrigerators carry on its long tradition of pricey products that are intuitive and easy to use. Apple's system comes with voice interfaces and a choice of two soothing voices. But convenience comes with a cost: Apple's A.I.s cannot be overwritten. In an Apple home running the air conditioner, you can't open the door for more than a minute or the system will start beeping incessantly. If there's sufficient daylight detected by the sensors embedded in your light bulbs, then the Apple system keeps the light switch on lockdown.

We saw a preview of Google's connected home a decade-and-a-half ago at the 2018 South By Southwest Festival in Austin, Texas. Back then, the tagline was "Make Google do it," and attractive spokesmodels took small groups around the three-story home to interact with A.I.-powered appliance screens and connected frozen daiquiri makers. Google's system is less intuitive, but it makes better use of our data—and it offers different levels of service and access. For those who can afford the upgrade fees and have enough tech savvy, Google Green gives families the ability to manually override their systems, and they can connect a greater variety of things—such as coffee makers and outdoor irrigation systems—to their homes. Green families pay for the privilege of opting out of marketing and advertising, though their data is still collected and sent to third parties. Google Blue is an affordable option with limited unlocking privileges and some additional permissions, but Blue families are still subjected to marketing. Google Yellow is the lowest tier. It's free but comes with no override abilities, a small selection of available devices and appliances, and it has limited data protections.

Amazon went in an interesting, but ultimately smarter, direction. A few announcements Amazon made in the fall of 2018 went largely unnoticed, such as the launch of its AmazonBasics microwave, which includes a voice interface. Users could put a bag of popcorn in the microwave and ask Alexa to pop it. Tech journalists wrote the microwave off as a novel, silly use for Alexa, and missed the bigger picture: The system was actually designed to get us hooked on subscription popcorn. That's because the microwave tracks both what we're heating up and what we're ordering on the Amazon platform. A new box arrives before you ever have the chance to run out.

Because Amazon was smartest in its approach working with federal, state, and local governments—offering them deep discounts at Amazon.com, patiently working through procurement requirements, and building and maintaining cloud services customized specifically for their needs—it became the preferred platform for certain social services in the United States. That is how Amazon discovered how to leverage the long tail of government funding.

Low-income families now live in Amazon Housing, which has replaced city-funded public housing programs in the United States. By every measure, they are far superior to any public housing ever provided through our previous government programs. Amazon Homes are completely outfitted with connected devices in every room. The former Supplemental Nutrition Assistance Program (previously known as the Food Stamp Program) is currently hosted by Amazon, which provides steeply discounted Amazon-branded food and drink, as well as household products, toiletries, and books.

Unsurprisingly, this program works seamlessly. There are never delays in funds being distributed, it's easy to look up the status of an account, and all transactions can be completed without ever having to wait in a long line at a government office. Those living in Amazon Homes must buy most of their things through Amazon while their data is scraped, productized, and monetized for various initiatives. Amazon's A.I.s are the most pervasive, following Amazon families everywhere they go to collect valuable behavioral data.

The lack of interoperability between A.I. frameworks and systems led to segregation by our data and household, and that is why we now have a digital caste system. By choosing Google, Apple, or Amazon, you are forced to align your family values with the values of the corporation. Apple families are rich, maybe a little less A.I.-savvy, and live in fancy houses. Google families might be rich and techy, or middle class and fine with marketing, or complacent enough that having a lot of choices in life doesn't matter all that much. There is no way to sugarcoat Amazon families: They're poor, even if they have free access to cool gadgets.

Families are locked into their de facto home operating systems, and that designation travels with them, even being passed from generation to generation. It's easier for a Google Yellow family to port into the Blue or even Green level than an Amazon family to port into the Apple system. That's why most families that could opted in to Google when they had the opportunity.

Your status is visible to all of the A.I.s you interact with. Self-driving taxi services like Lyft, Uber, and CitiCar don't pick up Amazon riders with as much frequency, and cars sent to them tend not to be as nice. Waymo cars exclusively pick up Googlers. For Greens, the car is preset to the rider's desired temperature and ambient lighting scheme, and it drives along the rider's preferred routes. Yellows are subjected to advertising their entire trip.

Advertising isn't the only headache for Yellow Googlers. One downside to all the subsidized (or free) gadgets, appliances, and gear offered to Google Blue, Google Yellow, and Amazon families is that it's impossible to disconnect the A.I. health and wellness minders, which continually monitor, diagnose and nudge. When they were built, computer scientists defined health and wellness with rigidity out of necessity. Now the collective values of A.I.'s earlier tribes are an oppressive souvenir of a simpler time. A failure to comply with health and wellness minders results in a litany of alerts and punitive restrictions.

Remember those Amazon Lockers, that you may have used many years ago to pick up all the things you ordered on the Amazon app and on Amazon.com? They made their way into Amazon Housing. The U.S. Health and Human Services Department thought nudging poor people was a clever way to improve health and wellness, so the department issued new policies requiring all public housing units to be outfitted with Locker technology. The Lockers may look like ordinary pantries, refrigerator doors and closets, but they act like A.I.-powered juries. If an Amazon Housing customer hasn't had her exercise that day, the Locker system will decide to keep the freezer closed and won't let her eat ice cream.

It's not impossible to intermarry—occasionally an Amazon will marry into an Apple family—but that old adage "opposites attract" no longer applies. All of our A.I.-powered dating services now match us based on our data, and what tech giant we've aligned ourselves with can be a major criterion. On the one hand, we no longer suffer under the tyranny of choice, since dating A.I.s have drastically reduced the selection of possible suitors. But some of the choices that once made us uniquely human—like opting for May-December romances, or dating someone our parents don't approve of—are less available to us now. In America, society is beginning to feel uncomfortably Huxleian, as we acquiesce, get married, and have babies with our fellow Apples, or Google Blues, or Amazons.

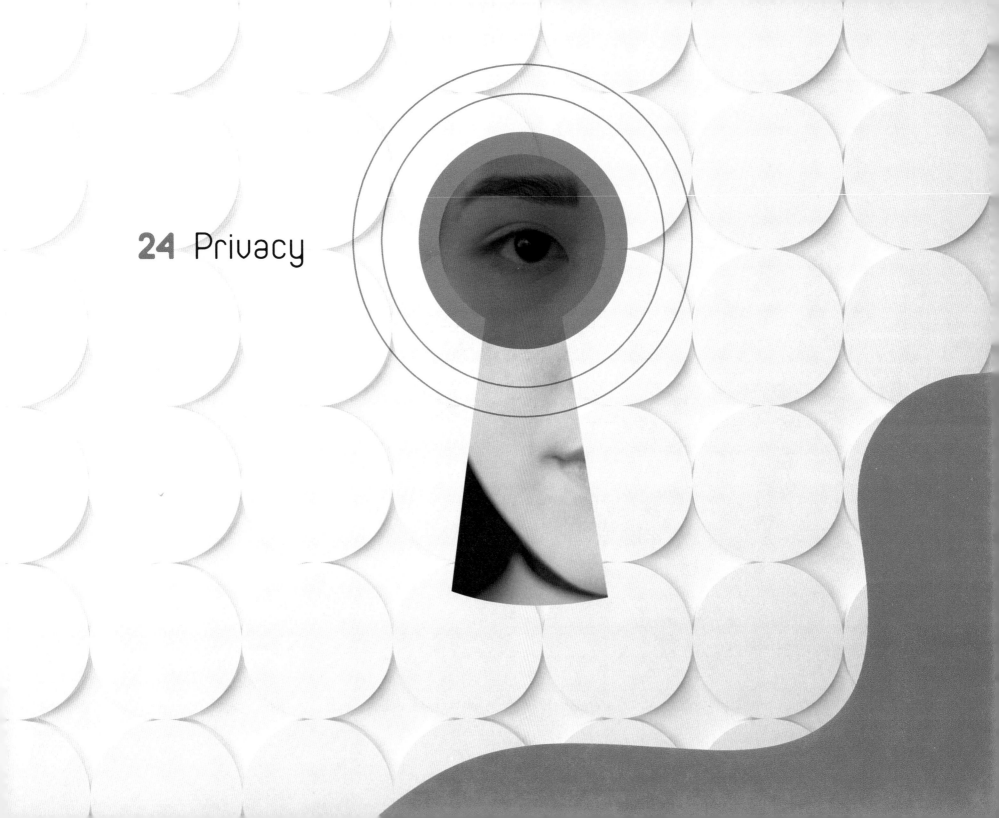

24 Privacy

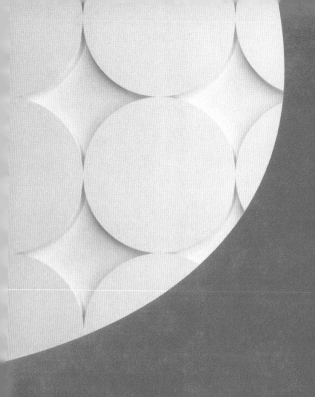

Privacy

HIGH DEGREE OF CERTAINTY

LONGER-TERM IMPACT

INFORMS STRATEGY	ACT NOW
REVISIT LATER	KEEP VIGILANT WATCH

IMMEDIATE IMPACT

LOW DEGREE OF CERTAINTY

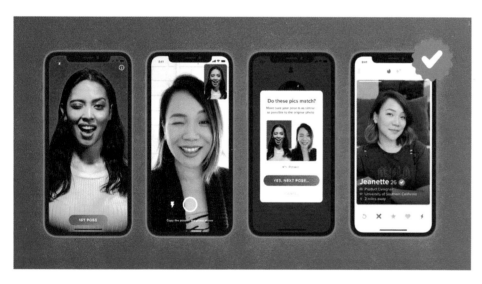

Keybase represents the next generation of encrypted messaging networks.

KEY INSIGHT

In the digital era, our data is currency. But as connected devices and systems become more popular, privacy is a growing concern. New technologies, mobile applications, gaming systems, websites and e-commerce platforms have made personal data more accessible and easier to collect, while advanced A.I. systems can now use those data to sort and categorize us. Often, this happens without our knowledge or oversight.

WHAT YOU NEED TO KNOW

In the year since the massive **Cambridge Analytica** scandal, questions remain about the right to privacy in an age of surveillance capitalism. While some data is used legitimately to improve products and services, other data is used to capture our attention, anticipate our choices and nudge us to particular decisions.

WHY IT MATTERS

Numerous advocacy groups, trade associations, tech companies and legislators are now debating a number of issues related to privacy, including rights to data ownership and portability, a digital bill of rights, and standardized tools that would allow people to protect their digital privacy.

Law, Country	Year it went into effect	Response
General Data Protection Regulation (GDPR) EU	2018	While GDPR is known as the world's strictest privacy law, some critics say the law lacks enforcement. Arguably, the biggest legacy of GDPR is the string of similar legislation it has inspired around the world.
Personal Information Security Specification, China	2018	Inspired by the EU's GDPR, China's law specifies how personal data should be collected, used, and shared. It's a uniquely Chinese plan: the law is meant to build consumer trust without undermining the government's ability to gain access to that data as it pleases—and to exert control when necessary.
California Consumer Privacy Act, California, USA	2020	This new law is known as California's GDPR. While there are still many outstanding questions regarding the law's interpretation and enforcement, Microsoft was one of the first tech companies to commit to extending CCPA privacy protections to all of its US customers.
Personal Data Protection Bill, India	TBD	Whatever the outcome, India's future privacy law will impact 1.3 billion people. It carries stringent privacy requirements for companies, but some say it gives complete carte blanche to India's government in terms of access to data.

○ DEEPER DIVE

Ethical Concerns

While we all seem to care deeply about our privacy, we continue using social media, websites and gadgets that don't necessarily put our privacy first. A great example: In the spring of 2019, millions of people uploaded photos of their faces to an app that would automatically age their appearance in the images. We learned later that the app, owned by a **Chinese** company, could legally use that database of biometric data as it pleased. A majority of Americans believe their online and offline activities are being tracked and monitored by companies and the government with some regularity, according to the **Pew Research Center**. And yet most people aren't confident that corporations are good stewards of the data they collect. Pew's research found that "79% of Americans say they are not too or not at all confident that companies will admit mistakes and take responsibility if they misuse or compromise personal information, and 69% report having this same lack of confidence that firms will use their personal information in ways they will be comfortable with."

Fragmented approaches

At the 2020 **World Economic Forum** in **Davos, Switzerland**, privacy and data ownership were key topics of conversation, with some policymakers and CEOs advocating for a new paradigm in which consumers would "own" their data. Others recommended a model in which consumer data would be treated as a public good. The regulatory environment will only grow more fragmented this year. In the **U.S.**, **California's Consumer Privacy Act (CCPA)** came into effect in January of 2020 and governs how businesses collect and share personal information. **Europe's General Data Protection Regulation** (or GDPR) is now being enforced. **Illinois** also has a restrictive state law on the books, preventing automatic face recognition and tagging, but if you cross the border into **Indiana**, you'll find much more lax restrictions on collecting and using an adult's data.

Celebrities including Tyrese Gibson, Ludacris and Courtney Cox participated in the FaceApp challenge.

THE IMPACT

Losing consumer trust is tantamount to losing their business. Once it's gone, it can be difficult to earn it back.

WATCHLIST FOR SECTION

Akamai Technologies, Alibaba, Amazon, American Civil Liberties Union, Anonymous, Apple, Byte, California Consumer Privacy Act, Carbon Black, Check Point Software, China's Personal Information Security Specification, CIA, CrowdStrike, DARPA, Def Con, Duo Security, Electronic Frontier Foundation, EPIC, Ethereum, Facebook, Facebook Messenger, FBI, Federal Trade Commission, FireEye, Fortinet, GDPR, GitHub, Google, Grindr, HackerOne, Huawei, iARPA, IBM, Immigration and Customs Enforcement, India's Personal Data Protection Bill, Instagram, Intel, International Consortium of Investigative Journalists, JPMorgan Chase, Kaspersky, Keybase, Krebs on Security, Match.com, McAfee, Microsoft, Oasis Labs, Ok Cupid, Oracle, Oxford University, Palantir, Palo Alto Networks, Princeton University, Qualcomm, Reddit, SAP, Sedicii, Senate Committee on Homeland Security and Governmental Affairs, Signal, Slack, Sony, Splunk, State of Illinois, Symantec, Technion Israel Institute of Technology, Tencent, TikTok, Tinder, Tor, Twitter, U.S. Census Bureau, U.S. Coast Guard, U.S. Computer Emergency Readiness Team, U.S. Cyber Command, U.S. Department of Defense, U.S. Department of Energy, U.S. Department of Homeland Security, U.S. Department of Justice, U.S. Marshals, U.S. National Security Agency, U.S. Supreme Court, Uber, Webroot, WeChat, Weibo, WhatsApp, WikiLeaks, ZTE.

⊘ TRENDS

The End of Biological Privacy

Open source genealogy website GEDmatch allows users to voluntarily share their genetic profiles for free, as a way to find relatives and trace their genealogies. Law enforcement used **GEDmatch** to track down Joseph James DeAngelo, the suspected Golden State Killer who over a period of years brutally raped 45 women and killed more than a dozen people. He himself never sent in a biological sample, but someone connected to him did. If someone you know—or someone who might in some way be connected to you—submits their information to an open source website, it can be traced back to you.

Public Entities Selling Private Data

In the **U.S.**, a number of DMV's—departments of motor vehicles—are selling the personal data of drivers to third parties, including insurance companies, private investigators, vehicle manufacturers, and prospective employers. In 2019, **Oregon's DMV** earned $11.5 million, while **California's DMV** reportedly earned $51 million. The **State of New York** sells license and vehicle information and earns roughly $2.2 million a year via pay-per-search as well as the sale of records. States are also beginning to update their laws governing how personal data can be used. For example, **Vermont** in 2018 passed a law that requires data brokers to disclose which data are being collected and to allow people to opt out.

Connected Device Security Loopholes

Throughout 2018, researchers showed how **Amazon's Alexa** and **Google Home** devices could be used to eavesdrop on users by employing techniques similar to conventional phishing attacks. Both Google and Amazon deployed countermeasures once the security vulnerability was discovered, but new loopholes were found yet again last year. As connected devices become more popular and ubiquitous, companies will have to redouble their efforts to secure our devices.

Tech Workers Fighting for Privacy

In 2018, when staff at **Google**, **Microsoft** and **Amazon** discovered their companies were engaged in programs to aid U.S. government agencies with surveillance, they published open letters, staged walkouts and protests, and formally organized into activist groups. As data collection and A.I. technology becomes more available, **Homeland Security**, **Immigration and Customs Enforcement** (otherwise known as **ICE**) and the **Pentagon** will rely more heavily on **Silicon Valley** tech giants for support. This isn't sitting well with workers. In 2019, Google fired five employees who were engaged in labor organizing.

Encrypted Messaging Networks

In response to social media hacks and government-sponsored surveillance programs worldwide, journalists have relied on closed, encrypted messaging networks like **Keybase** and **Signal** to send secure messages. However, many news organizations do not have guidelines on how these networks can and should be used at work. For example, a company may determine that emails are the intellectual property of the organization and are subject to professional codes of conduct; what about messages sent through encrypted networks? As hacks become more pervasive, private networks will continue to be popular in 2020. This could be problematic for ISPs: In the wake of net neutrality rollbacks in the U.S., clever users could engage a distributed browser system to prevent an ISP from throttling certain sites or users.

Vanishing Messages

"This tape will self-destruct in five seconds." Mission Impossible made vanishing messages famous in the late '60s, but this technology is no longer just for secret agents. On a consumer level, more and more apps give individuals the choice to have the messages they send be automatically deleted after a set period of time. **Snap** was one of the earliest social media companies to capitalize on this, with ephemeral photos and video messages that only last 24 hours. Now **WhatsApp**, **Facebook Messenger** and **Slack** are implementing "vanishing" messaging options to improve user privacy. In the **U.K.**, the conservative **Tory party** recently switched to using **Signal**, a privacy-focused open-source alternative to **WhatsApp**. With regulations like **GDPR** and **California's** newest privacy law, vanishing messages may become the norm.

Digital Eavesdropping Rights

As we connect more and more devices to the Internet of Things—fitness trackers, mobile phones, cars, coffee makers—those devices are having extended interactions with each other and with the companies that make them. Our devices aren't just talking to us anymore. They're learning about us, and starting to communicate with each other about us. Should consumers be given the right to eavesdrop on what their own devices are saying, and who else is listening in? News and entertainment companies must determine whether those devices, working as intermediaries, cross any ethical lines when consumer data changes hands. A debate over consumer rights and transparency

Privacy cont.

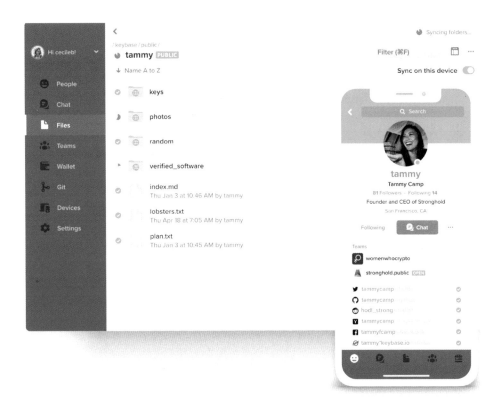

Tinder began offering photo verification in January 2020 as a way to curb catfishing.

is already underway in **Washington, D.C.**, and the outcome could affect those monetizing content via the internet of things.

Data Ownership

Who, exactly, owns our data is a topic of great concern worldwide. The reason: defining ownership would have huge ramifications for what can be done with our data, who could gain access to it and how it could be monetized. In a legal sense, data ownership has typically referred to intellectual property (IP) or copyright data. However, the rise of wearable smart devices and the internet of things boosted awareness about how large companies collect and monetize data related to our behavior, health statistics, and online activity. You do not own the site analytics that these tech giants make available to you, and you don't own any messages sent on a company email server or in your **Slack** channel. In a world where every device is smart and connected, surveillance is constant and ownership is unclear.

Digital Self-Incrimination

Whether it's a connected fitness device, a smart earphone, or a pair of smart glasses, consumers will find themselves continuously being monitored by third parties. Our legal system isn't keeping pace with technology, so we lack norms, standards and case law on how data collected from and produced by our wearables can be used. To date, fitness devices, pacemakers, and smart watches have been used as evidence in police investigation and criminal trials. In the U.S., judges get to decide whether to allow data from wearable devices—or whether individuals still have a reasonable expectation of privacy if they've been actively sharing their fitness stats in the cloud or with third parties.

Differential Privacy

Berkeley-based **Oasis Labs** develops cryptographic techniques that allow companies to use personal data in their algorithms without seeing our individual data points. This is an example of differential privacy, a mathematical concept that has been around for over a decade. Differential privacy is achieved by strategically introducing random noise into the dataset. It is most useful when answering simple (low-sensitivity) queries. Companies like **Apple** and **Google** now use the technique as a way to analyze aggregate data without compromising user privacy. It's good for finding out traffic patterns in Google Maps, determining the most popular emoji for iPhone users, and discovering ride sharing trends across **Uber's** global network—while keeping individual user behavior anonymous. The **U.S. Census Bureau** will be using differential privacy in the 2020 Population Census. A team of **Amazon** researchers recently proposed using differential privacy as a way to anonymize customer-supplied data. **Apple** set itself apart from its competitors by integrating differential privacy into its Safari browser, and **Google** uses its own differential privacy tool called RAPPOR as people search online. It is important to remember this method is still evolving. Depending on applications and data sets, differential privacy is harder to maintain when variables are correlated. And at the moment, there is scant regulatory guidance for use of the approach in the tech industry.

Defining Online Harassment

The #MeToo movement brought to light thousands of stories of sexual harassment and resulted in the takedown of several high-profile men. It's also sparked a global conversation about how we treat each other in person and online. A shared **Google** document, dubbed "The Shitty Media Men List," at one point circulated among female journalists, who entered the details of men who had allegedly sexually harassed women in the real world. When the list was leaked, some pointed the finger at the women, arguing that they were committing acts of online harassment simply by contributing to it. It's apparent that we don't yet have clear definitions for what constitutes harassment in the digital realm and especially as it relates to privacy. In the years ahead, we will continue to wrestle with what behavior is acceptable in virtual gaming worlds, in social media, in our mobile exchanges and in general digital discourse.

Safeguarding and Verifying Leaked Data

Many social movements worldwide have encouraged the leaking of sensitive information to the press, to hackers and to other governments. While many people seem eager to find and share information—not everyone agrees on what should be published, and by whom. In January 2020, a massive leak involving more than 700,000 documents implicated one of **Africa's** wealthiest people, **Isabel dos Santos**, in a massive scheme of fraud and money laundering. Before publishing it, **the International Consortium of Investigative Journalists** (ICIJ) launched a sweeping investigation into dos Santos, the billionaire former first daughter of **Angola**. Some 370 journalists from 76 countries collaborated on the investigation. She has since been accused of embezzlement, influence peddling, harmful management, forgery of documents and other so-called "economic crimes" by Angola's top prosecutor. Previously, the ICIJ spent a year reporting on a massive cache of 11.5 million leaked records they had received from a little-known law firm in **Panama**. These "Panama Papers" showed the offshore holdings of 140 politicians from around the world, 12 current and former world leaders, and more. In the summer of 2017, the **Senate Committee on Homeland Security and Governmental Affairs** issued a report titled "State Secrets: How an Avalanche of Media Leaks Is Harming National Security" and cited 125 stories with leaked information that the committee considered damaging to national security. Media organizations like the **New York Times** and the **Guardian** have secure sections on their websites where people can safely upload sensitive documents to journalists, and now political action groups and activists are seeking confidential document leaks, too. You can expect to see more coordinated efforts to leak—and to securely receive leaked data—in 2020 and beyond.

Promoting Anonymity

In the years since **President Donald Trump** was elected, the number of anonymous opinion pieces, sources and leaks rose dramatically compared to previous administrations. Notably, the **New York Times** published a rare and scathing anonymous Op-Ed essay entitled "I Am Part of the Resistance Inside the Trump Administration." For his part, President Trump in December 2019 retweeted a post that included the full name of the anonymous whistleblower whose complaint led to his impeachment by the **House of Representatives**. The world needs anonymity, because it enables whistleblowers to come forward and shields those who otherwise might be persecuted for their beliefs. Digital anonymity allows us to discreetly band together in times of need, whether that's to raise money for a good cause or to push back against injustices. But promoting and preserving anonymity will prove challenging as our digital publishing systems grow more complex and decentralized.

Trolls

Trolling is a specific type of cyber-bullying that often involves spamming, hate-speech, doxxing attacks, and other forms of harassment. Early in 2019, trolls found a video of newly-elected **U.S. Rep. Alexandria Ocasio-Cortez** that was taken when she was a college student in 2010. They edited a short clip to make her look provocative, and then helped it go viral. (In reality, the video showed her and a friend recreating the benign dance sequence from The Breakfast Club movie.) Controlling trolls online has forced many of us—as well as media outlets—to take a position on the line between freedom of speech and censorship. **Twitter**, **Facebook**, and **Instagram** updated their

community standards to limit hate speech. **Reddit** has banned groups like r/incels for violating the site's community standards (though there is plenty of awful content still to be found on the rest of the site). And yet, neo-Nazi site **Daily Stormer** resurfaced in February 2018 after being effectively shut down by their domain host. State-sponsored trolling is most often linked to **Russia** but according to research from **Oxford University**, 28 countries and counting have cyber troops of humans and bots for the purpose of manipulating public opinion on social media. (For further reading, we recommend accessing Oxford's full report "Troops, Trolls, and Troublemakers.")

Verification

In an era of deepfakes and digital mistrust, some networks are building new tools to verify real people. For example, dating app **Tinder** introduced a new Photo Verification feature in January 2020 that compares a series of real-time selfies to a cache of existing profile photos using both A.I. and humans. Those who pass the test receive a blue check mark verifying that the user is a real person. Who and what is real online is becoming harder to determine, which is why authenticity is an important trend going forward.

Data Retention Policies

A data retention policy is a formalized protocol for retaining information, and historically companies have enacted them for regulatory compliance. Now that companies regularly use consumer and other sources of data, they are building more protective policies. Regulatory frameworks such as the **General Data Protection Regulation** and the **California Consumer Privacy Act** both compel companies to update their policies.

Compliance Challenges and Unrealistic Budgets

The historical tension between security and privacy will unleash new challenges in the near future. Consumers shed more data each day, and as more connected devices enter the marketplace, the volume of available data will balloon. Yet those organizations creating devices and managing consumer data aren't planning for future scenarios. Managers must develop and continually update their security policies—and make the details transparent. Most organizations aren't devoting enough budget to securing their data and devices. Those that haven't carved out enough budget to se-

cure their internet of things environment will find themselves dealing with vast recalls, remediation and lawsuits. A fragmented regulatory landscape promises significant headaches for compliance officers and risk managers, who must ensure current policies and procedures for governments, companies, nonprofits and news organizations.

Revenge Porn

Revenge porn is the practice of uploading an individual's intimate, typically explicit photographs or videos without their knowledge or permission, as an act of vengeance. As of publication, 46 states and the **District of Columbia** now have revenge porn laws in the U.S., but a national law could soon arrive. The issue: the constitutionality of revenge porn on **First Amendment** grounds. **The U.S. Constitution** protects freedom of speech, even when it is offensive. But obscenity isn't covered, and neither is the disclosure of private information. We've seen many documented cases of revenge porn: In 2018, several **Los Angeles Police Department** officers were under investigation for allegedly distributing explicit images of one of their female colleagues—her ex-boyfriend had taken photos without her knowledge and then shared them in revenge after they broke up. Unfortunately, revenge porn is also regularly posted online to dedicated websites. Staff within the **U.S. Senate**, the **U.S. Navy**, and even **President Donald Trump's Executive Office** have accessed revenge porn websites. In the U.S., there is no national law banning revenge porn, but that could change this year. The **U.S. Supreme Court** may decide to take up a case involving a woman who, after learning that her fiancée had an affair, sent a four-page letter to family and friends detailing text messages and explicit photos of the mistress. She was charged with a felony for violating **Illinois's** strict revenge porn law, and she later argued that the law was unconstitutional.

Drone Surveillance

Drones now come in all shapes and sizes, and they can be used in a variety of settings for surveillance. Advanced camera technology can capture photos and video from 1,000 feet away, while machine learning software can remotely identify who we are and lock on to and follow our bodies as we move around—all without our knowledge. They can also intercept mobile phone calls, gather license plate information and determine whether someone is carrying a weapon. In the U.S., drones are regularly used by federal, state and local public safety agencies including the **FBI**, **ICE**, **U.S. Marshals** and **Coast Guard**. Wide-area motion imagery technology allows police to surreptitiously track any person or vehicle without being seen. Drones will soon enable the mass tracking of people at concerts, vehicles on the highway, amusement park attendees—the sorts of crowded public settings we may already expect to be under some form of surveillance by law enforcement. (See also: Drones Section.)

Influencing Future Privacy Laws

In September 2018, **Facebook** revealed that a breach had affected more than 30 million people's user information, while a month later **Google** reported that it discovered a glitch in its now-retired **Google+** network that could have exposed the private data of 500,000 users. Perhaps anticipating a wave of regulatory proposals, some of the big tech giants have made privacy a core message to both consumers and lawmakers. In October, **Apple CEO Tim Cook** warned of a "data-industrial complex" in which private information is weaponized against us, and he called for comprehensive privacy laws in the U.S., publicly shaming Facebook and Google in the process. **IBM CEO Ginni Rometty** followed by criticizing the other big tech companies for abusing user data, and similarly called for action. It would be a mistake to think that IBM and Apple are leaving fully up to lawmakers the work of crafting data privacy regulations. They'll offer industry-leading advice on what ought to be done next, which would likely put their competitors at a big disadvantage.

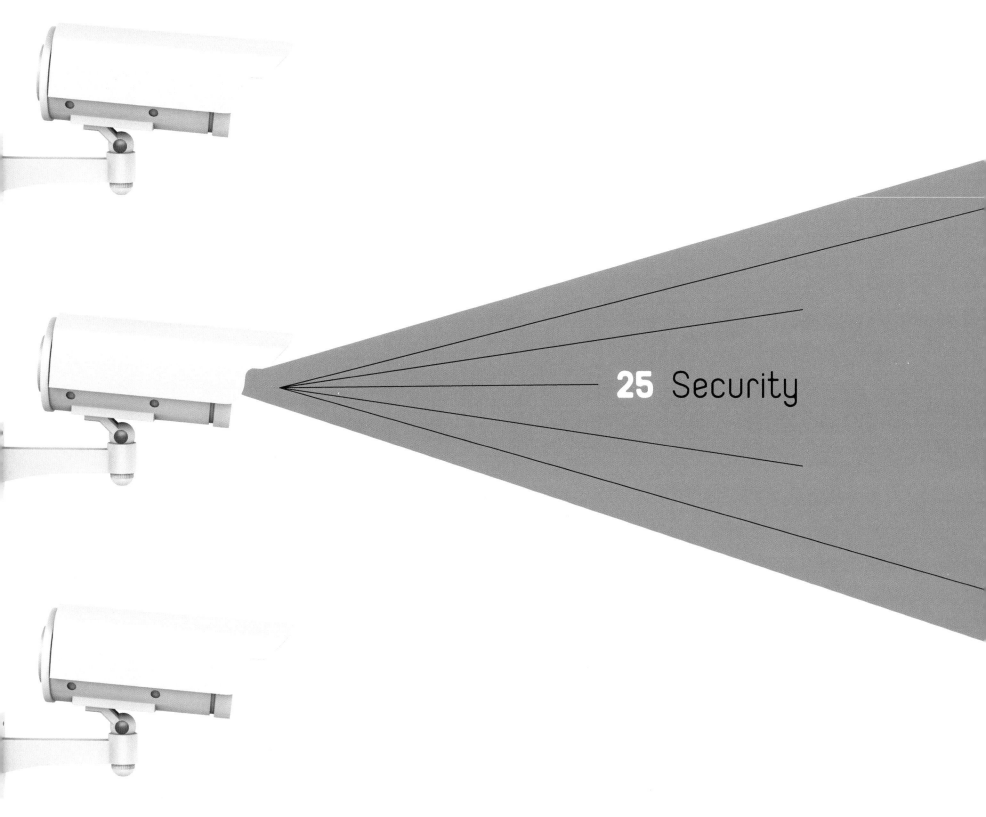

25 Security

Security

ForAllSecure, a Pittsburgh-based software company, won DARPA's 2016 Cyber Grand Challenge, the world's first all-machine cyber hacking tournament. (Photo courtesy of DARPA.)

KEY INSIGHT

From ransomware attacks that targeted municipalities, to data breaches that exposed the personal details of hundreds of millions of people, to supply chain attacks that crippled global trade, malicious hacking was on the rise in 2019. You can expect to see a continual stream of attacks throughout 2020.

WHAT YOU NEED TO KNOW

Hackers can gain access to critical systems and data through unsecured databases left open on the internet, out of date firmware and software patches, bugs in operating systems and software and vulnerable utilities—in addition to using methods that exploit human vulnerabilities like weak passwords. Sometimes accidents happen: In February 2019, a USB drive containing the tax information for 42,000 **Salt Lake Community College** students fell out of an envelope and made its way into malicious

hands. That same month, **Ohio government** employees accidentally sent 9,000 tax forms with personal information to the wrong people. Too often, breaches are the result of employee sloppiness. A misconfigured government database in **Ecuador** containing the private data of the country's citizens—about 20 million people in total—was left completely accessible to the public on the internet.

WHY IT MATTERS

The cost of data breaches is significant. According to **IBM**'s annual Cost of a Data Breach study, in 2019 the average breach costs an organization $3.92 million, up 12% from five years ago. Notification and compliance, expenses that stem from forensic investigations, systems repairs and the inevitable lawsuits all contribute to the cost, and fewer than half of all organizations are equipped to prevent against and properly and efficiently respond to a cyber attack.

A very brief list of 2019 glitches, hacks, leaks, malware attacks, ransomware attacks, backdoor attacks and data breaches.

January

• Glitch: A **Fortnight** player discovered an iOS bug: A teenager added a friend to a group call, and while that friend didn't pick up he was able to listen in on the conversations happening where the iPhone was located.

• Ransomware attack: The City of Del Rio (Texas) was attacked with ransomware, taking many of its digital systems offline.

• Backdoor attack: **BlackMediaGames** had the personal data of 7.6 million users stolen via multiple backdoors.

February

• Ransomware attack: **Cabrini Hospital** in **Malvern, Australia** had 15,000 patient files remotely locked.

March

• Hack: Someone breached the tornado warning systems in two **Texas** towns and set off 30 false alarms.

• Data breach: **Facebook** announced that hundreds of millions of users might have had their passwords stolen because the company had mistakenly stored the passwords in a readable, plain text format.

April

• Data breach: **Evite** announced that some of its users' personal data had been harvested and sold on the Dark Web.

• Data breach: **Facebook** announced that 540 million records were exposed on two AWS servers, and that the data had been collected by two third-party companies.

May

• Ransomware: The city of **Baltimore** was attacked with ransomware that was so powerful it crippled much of the city's digital infrastructure. It took several months before the city was mobilized to act, and even then some billing systems weren't fully restored.

• Hack: Someone broke into **GitHub** repositories, removed source code and demanded a ransom.

• Data breach: **First American Financial Corp.**, a real estate company, accidentally leaked hundreds of millions of insurance documents with bank account information, mortgage and tax records and other private information.

June

• Ransomware: Hackers crippled more than 40 U.S. municipalities over the summer—including **Albany**, **New York** and **Laredo**, **Texas**, and small towns like **Lake City**, **Florida**.

• Data breach: The **Nova Scotia Health Authority** discovered that 3,000 patients had their personal health information stolen.

July

• Data breach: **Capital One** disclosed a massive data breach involving 100 million customers in the U.S. and six million in Canada.

• Hack: A hacker broke into the **Los Angeles Police Department** and reportedly stole personal information for 2,500 recruits, trainees and officers.

August

• Glitch: The popular dating app **Grindr** was discovered to have a security flaw that could expose the location of a user in real-time.

• Leak: A biometric database used by the **U.K. Metropolitan Police** accidentally leaked millions of records.

• Ransomware: **Wilmer, Texas**, a smaller town outside of Dallas, was among 22 small cities across Texas that came under attack, prompting a widening **F.B.I.** inquiry and a statewide disaster response-style mobilization from the **National Guard**.

September

• Leak: A misconfigured database belonging to the government of **Ecuador** leaked the personal data of 20 million citizens.

October

• Data breach: **UniCredit**, an **Italian** bank, disclosed that it exposed the personal information of three million customers.

• Glitch: An **Israeli** cybersecurity firm was accused of selling spyware that exploited a vulnerability in **WhatsApp**.

November

• Data breach: **Facebook** inadvertently gave 100 developers access to private user data.

• Hack: **Macy's** was involved in a week-long attack and had customers' credit card information stolen.

• Hack: Hours after the new **Disney+** service launched, hackers began offering accounts on the Dark Web.

December

• Ransomware: The city of **New Orleans** was hit with a cyberattack which crippled its digital systems.

• Malware: **Chinese** hackers used sophisticated malware to take down a Cambodian government agency.

THE IMPACT

In January 2020, the **City of Las Vegas** was attacked, a sign that attacks are continuing.

WATCHLIST FOR SECTION

Akamai Technologies, Amazon, Anonymous, Apple, Carbon Black, Check Point Software, CIA, CrowdStrike, DARPA, Def Con, Duo Security, Ethereum, FBI, FireEye, Fortinet, Fujifilm Holdings, GitHub, Google, HackerOne, Huawei, iARPA, IBM Intel, In-Q-Tel, JPMorgan Chase, Kaspersky, Krebs on Security, McAfee, Microsoft, Oracle, Palo Alto Networks, Princeton University, Qualcomm, SAP, Sedicii, Sony, Splunk, Symantec, Technion Israel Institute of Technology, Tor, U.S. Computer Emergency Readiness Team, U.S. Cyber Command, U.S. Department of Defense, U.S. Department of Energy, U.S. Department of Justice, U.S. National Security Agency, Uber, Webroot, WikiLeaks, ZTE, municipalities, counties and civil agencies everywhere and the governments of Russia, China, Singapore, North Korea, Ukraine, Israel, United States, Iran and the U.K.

Security cont.

○ TRENDS

Zero-Day Exploits on the Rise

A zero-day vulnerability is a flaw within a hardware or software system that developers didn't discover during the testing process. That vulnerability can be exploited by malware to cause all sorts of problems. Zero-days are dangerous, prized vulnerabilities, and exploiting them is a favorite activity of malicious hackers. Once the flaw is revealed, programmers have "zero days" to do anything about it. In January 2020, a **Microsoft** zero-day was discovered, involving Internet Explorer, that would allow someone to gain remote access to a computer. Also in January, **Chinese** hackers used a zero-day in the **Trend Micro OfficeScan** antivirus system used by **Mitsubishi Electric** to gain access to the company's network. The **Italian** spyware maker **Hacking Team** (HT) helped bring zero-days into the spotlight when it was found selling commercial hacking software to law enforcement agencies in countries all over the world. Data leaked from HT, along with a massive dump of 400 gigabytes of internal emails, revealed a number of zero-day exploits. The HT breach helped to shine a light on a growing zero-day marketplace,

with information identifying certain exploits being sold for as much as $500,000. Tools to exploit vulnerabilities will be in greater demand in the near future.

Zero-Knowledge Proofs Go Commercial

With all of the hacking scandals that have plagued us in the past several years, we will see an increase in popularity of something called "zero-knowledge proofs," which allow one side to verify data without conveying any additional information (such as how or why something is true). It's a mind-bending approach to security, allowing you to verify your identity without revealing who you actually are. In essence, this eliminates the need for a company to store private identity data during the verification process. Zero-knowledge proofs aren't new, but they're becoming more popular as a method to protect our credit cards and online identities. **JPMorgan Chase** is using zero-knowledge proofs for its enterprise blockchain system, while cryptocurrency startup **Ethereum** uses zero-knowledge for authentication. **Irish** startup **Sedicii** now has zero-proof software in the marketplace, and researchers at **Microsoft** and **Princeton University**

are working on a zero-knowledge proof that would let inspectors identify something as a nuclear weapon without requiring them to take it apart, which risks spreading information about how to build one.

Gaining Access to Backdoors

While they sound malicious, backdoors—purposely programmed entry points to access the inner workings of an app, operating system, device, or network, meant for internal usage or in cases of extreme extenuating circumstances—aren't necessarily bad. Often, developers intentionally install them into firmware so that manufacturers can safely upgrade our devices and operating systems. But backdoors can also be used surreptitiously to access everything from our webcams to our personal data. Backdoors have been a recurring issue for **Apple**, which has had a history of disagreeing with the **U.S. Department of Justice** over unlocking iPhones. In 2019, after a deadly shooting involving Mohammed Saeed Alshamrani at the **Naval Air Station** in **Pensacola, Florida**, **U.S. Attorney General William Barr** asked Apple to help unlock two iPhones that were used by the gunman. Apple refused, and the government pressed further—but ultimately,

the **FBI** already had the tools necessary to break into the phones. The incident was reminiscent of another shooting that pitted the FBI and Apple against each other. In the wake of the deadly **San Bernardino** attack in December 2015, the FBI and Apple found themselves debating so-called "backdoors" in public. The FBI demanded that Apple unlock the assailant's phone, and Apple refused, arguing that creating a software update to allow a backdoor would endanger the privacy of all iPhone users. It's a debate that was never settled—and we'll likely see more cases pitting government agencies against big tech companies in the years to come. Given the rise of zero-day exploits, we should question whether backdoors are the best way forward. Government officials worldwide have been advocating for a set of "golden keys," which would allow law enforcement to bypass digital security measures using backdoors. But even without public agreement, some agencies may find their way into our machines. In 2013, the **U.S. National Security Agency** made a deal with security company **RSA** to include a flawed algorithm in their product, effectively giving the **NSA** a backdoor into various systems. The challenge is that the simple act of creating a backdoor would leave ordinary people vulnerable to everyday attacks by a wide swath of malicious actors.

Remote Kill Switches

As our technology becomes more immersive, we'll have an increased need for remote kill switches. Kill switches, found on smartphones and connected devices, will soon come in handy for the enterprise and for government agencies. **Uber** developed its own software program called Ripley that could be activated by staff in **San Francisco**, should any of its overseas offices be raided by police. It also deployed uLocker, a remote kill switch that could lock all company devices, including laptops and phones. On the consumer side, both **Apple** and **Android** now allow users to remotely wipe all the information on their phones and tablets using a web interface. The benefit would come with a cost, however. Kill switches would mean that nobody could gain access to what was inside a lost or stolen phone—not even law enforcement.

Insecure Supply Chains

Security expert **Bruce Schneier** has been warning of an ongoing problem: The supply chain is insecure. Consumers aren't willing to pay for security features or upgrades, while product manufacturers aren't as strict as they could be in safeguarding the integrity of every single component that goes into the systems we use. It's been cheaper to fix hacks after they happen and to ask for forgiveness, rather than to address the problem in advance. But as hackers grow more sophisticated and as more of our appliances, systems and databases are connected, we ought to think about the downstream implications of insecure supply chains in our infrastructure, hospitals, power grids—even our kitchens. Some hope that wider adoption of blockchain and distributed ledger technology will help solve these problems, but as of now, there aren't scalable solutions.

Data Manipulation Becomes The Greater Threat

Rather than malicious actors simply stealing data, in 2020 you can expect to see new kinds of attacks, in which hackers access and then manipulate data for long-term damage. The implications are more concerning than you might realize at first: If a company's data integrity comes into question, it could lose customers and partners quickly. Alternatively, if companies don't realize their data has been compromised, hackers could alter that data gradually to undermine the company or its users in subtle, pernicious ways over extended periods of time.

Consumer Device Targeting

With the proliferation of smart devices—connected speakers, mirrors, and fitness gadgets—hackers have a wellspring of new targets in 2020. Attackers might hijack your smart TV for ransom on the day before a big televised event (national elections, Eurovision, the Super Bowl) and refuse to unlock it until you've paid a fee. Or they could take control of your fitness device and hold years of personal workout data and in-app milestones and achievements for ransom.

Cyber Risk Insurance

New forms of insurance, intended to help businesses protect against hackers, will begin to enter the marketplace. Rather than simply covering the theft of basic information, insurers will also offer protection against damage to reputation, the loss of operational capacity, and the costs for system upgrades, as well as liabilities due as the result of lawsuits. As organizations develop their FY 2020-2021 budgets, they should investigate cyber risk insurance.

A.I.-Powered Automated Hacking Systems

Thanks to advancements in A.I., one of the big trends in security is automated hacking—in short, software that's built to out-hack the human hackers. The **Pentagon's** research agency **DARPA** launched a **Cyber Grand Challenge** project in 2016, with a mission to design computer systems capable of beating hackers at their own game. DARPA wanted to show that smarter automated systems could respond and develop fixes far faster than a human—in just a few seconds. A white hat hacker might spend months or years to spot and fix critical vulnerabilities, but the machine that won the Grand Challenge proved its might in just a fraction of the time. The winner became the first non-human entity to earn **DEF CON**'s black

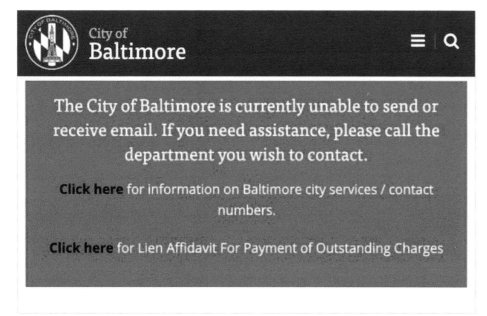

The City of Baltimore struggled to resolve a ransomware attack that stretched on for several weeks.

badge, which is the hacking community's equivalent of an Oscar. Very soon, malicious actors will create autonomous systems capable of automatically learning new environments, exposing vulnerabilities and flaws, and then exploiting them for gain—or any other objective, which could simply be generalized mayhem.

Hijacking Internet Traffic

The protocols underpinning the web were written long before we had connected microwaves and billions of daily users. In November 2018, hackers created a massive internet traffic diversion, rerouting data through **China**, **Nigeria** and **Russia**. It disrupted **Google**, taking its business tools offline, slowing down search and making its cloud unreachable. It was an example of Border Gateway Protocol (BGP) hijacking and while in this case the error exploited was related to an outdated Nigerian ISP, the incident points to a vulnerability in our web infrastructure. We anticipate new cases of internet traffic hijacking in 2020, especially during the numerous high-profile streaming events planned for the year ahead: big sports events (**World Series**, **Super Bowl**, **Olympics**), the **U.S. election** in November,

grand finales or premieres of series, and more.

DDoS Attacks on the Rise

A Distributed Denial of Service Attack (DDoS) attack happens when a hacker sends so many requests to machines that the entire network goes down. In the past several years, the number of DDoS attacks have spiked, increasing in both breadth and duration. A massive DDoS attack in 2016 took down **Dyn**, a major internet provider for companies that included **AirBnB**, **Netflix**, **PayPal**, **Visa**, **Amazon**, **The New York Times**, **Reddit**, and **GitHub**. All of them went offline for a day. While daylong or multi-day attacks aren't as common as their shorter cousins, which tend to last a few hours, they are on the rise. To date, half of the world's DDoS attacks have originated in **China**. Hackers are beginning to use more sophisticated tools, which means that future attacks will be larger in scope and could achieve greater impact.

Third-Party Verified Identities

In the **U.S.**, citizens must continually hand over their social security numbers as a means of identity authentication. But in the wake of the massive **Equifax** data breach, it has become clear that our social security numbers—a single identifier used in everything from our bank accounts to our health insurance profiles, and even shared with university registrars—isn't secure. Social security numbers were never intended to be used as general-purpose passwords. We'll see the emergence of third-party, non-governmental providers of identity verification. One example that's already in the marketplace is **CLEAR**, the trusted traveler program that lets verified customers get through airport security faster.

Ransomware-as-a-Service

Last year, ransomware devastated companies and even entire cities. Entertainment and news media organizations could be next. In a ransomware attack, hackers deploy malicious tools to hijack data, effectively locking administrators and users out of systems and devices, until a fee is paid. Since cash and online bank transfers are easy to track, the currency of choice is now bitcoin, which is transferred through an encrypted system and can't be traced. The

emergence of the blockchain and cryptocurrencies have transformed ransomware into a lucrative business. In the spring of 2019, **Baltimore** became the latest city to have some of its critical services held for ransom. Since it hadn't prepared in advance for such a scenario, it took several months for the systems to come back online. Residents couldn't pay water bills for months, email their city representatives, or schedule trash pickups, among other things. Ransomware attacks target mostly cities, financial services and healthcare organizations because their data and services are so valuable. Simply backing up your organization's data probably won't be enough of a failsafe going forward. Researchers have already found "doxware" floating around the internet—in those cases hackers, rather than simply holding your data hostage until you pay up, threaten to publish it to the web for everyone to see.

Decentralized Hacktivists

Hackers-turned-activists have had a busy few years, hacking in support of causes they believe in. They launched DDoS attacks against governments, corporations and

banks. Hacktivist organizations, including **Anonymous**, **WikiLeaks** and **DC Leaks**, see themselves as durable forces of change. Glamorized by the TV show "Mr. Robot," hacktivism is on the rise—and, given heated political tensions during a year in which many elections are being held, we'll likely see more of these operations. Hacktivists will use their skills to help shape local, state, national and international politics, conversations, and business practices.

Targeted Attacks on Voice Interfaces

Now that **Alexa**, **Siri**, and **Google Assistant** have moved from the fringe to the mainstream, we can expect to see targeted attacks of these popular voice interfaces. In 2018, professors at **Technion Israel Institute of Technology** and researchers at **McAfee** independently found flaws in **Microsoft's Cortana** voice assistant. When security testing firm **Checkmarx** conducted penetration testing on Alexa, it inadvertently allowed potential hackers to make Echo listen continuously, rather than only when prompted by a user. (**Amazon** fixed the vulnerability as soon as it was notified.)

Weird Glitches

Glitches are so common now they don't always make the news. Glitches don't have an immediate, obvious cause but nonetheless can cause frustrating problems. From customs and border protection terminals going dark to technical malfunctions on assembly lines, glitches affect every industry. And now, they're popping up in our homes, too. In the summer of 2019, at-home exercise platform **Peloton** pushed several updates to its smart stationary bike that resulted in weird closed captioning and exercise classes that would suddenly drop out—even with a strong internet connection. With so many people working on complex systems, errors no one planned for are causing major headaches. Glitches often have to do with degraded network connectivity or a miscalculation of the bandwidth needed. But a lot of times, glitches result from newer technologies that can break in unexpected ways.

Open Source App Vulnerabilities

Companies that use open source tools will need to perform daily, rather than occasional, security checks this year. Early in 2019,

Security cont.

the **EU** offered $1 million in bug bounties—rewards for hackers that identify vulnerabilities and report them to the affected organization—for open source software. Why? **OpenSSL** bugs like **Heartbleed** caught the government's attention. In 2017, a data scientist revealed a new kind of malware capable of infecting an open A.I. system like **OpenAI Gym**, which is **Elon Musk's** open-source toolkit for machine learning algorithms. It's just one example of a booming market for malicious tools that exploit vulnerabilities in open source applications and software. As the A.I. ecosystem grows to incorporate more open source code and community-built tools, it will be especially important to spot problems in advance.

Global Cybersecurity Pacts

Late in 2018, more than 200 companies (including **Microsoft**, **Google** and **Facebook**) and 50 countries signed an international agreement on cybersecurity principles to end malicious cyber activities in peacetime. While non-binding, the agreement attempts to develop norms and standards for how countries behave in cyberspace. Noticeably absent from the list of signers:

Russia, **China**, **North Korea**, **Israel** and the **United States**.

Proliferation of Darknets

Many people confuse the deep web—hidden parts of the internet that aren't usually indexed by search engines—with darknets, which are niche spaces promising anonymity, often for illegal activities. People go there to sell and buy drugs, guns, ammunition, security exploits (malware, ransomware) and your hacked data (passwords, credit card numbers and more). Cryptocurrencies have fueled activity in these dark corners of the internet, since they're encrypted and make tracking transactions nearly impossible. You can't just hop on to a darknet and find what you need the way you might **Google** your high school sweetheart. To access the hidden crime bazaars, you need special software, such as **Tor** or **Freenet**, you need to know where you're headed, and you do need a bit of technical knowledge. It isn't illegal to take a walk through dark marketplaces, and there's plenty of good activity that takes place there: whistleblowers hoping to shine a light on wrongdoing, political dissidents looking for asylum

and investigative journalists hunting down leads. As cryptocurrencies gain popularity, we're likely to see more activity in darknets. Activists with legitimate concerns will advocate for new layers of protection, while law enforcement will receive training on how to navigate the dark web. For government and law enforcement, the challenge of training is staying current—darkets are continuously changing, which means that training can quickly become outdated. Also problematic: Those who spend the most time on darknets are typically also the ones building them.

Bounty Programs

The past several years have been dramatically successful for hackers. Security expert **Brian Krebs** says that the "market for finding, stockpiling and hoarding (keeping secret) software flaws is expanding rapidly," and he went so far as to advocate for a compulsory bounty program. In response, a number of white hat (read: good hacker) bug bounty programs are becoming popular. In some cases, businesses solicit friendly hackers for paid work through platforms like **HackerOne**, which is being used by the **U.S. Department of Defense**, **Wordpress**, **Coin-**

base, **Shopify** and **GitHub**. In 2019, **Google** paid 461 different security researchers $6.5 million for bug bounties.

Magnetic Tape Supply Shortages

It's odd to think that in 2020 the world still relies on magnetic tape—those clunky old cartridges that were used decades ago to store data. And yet that's still the preferred method of backup for many companies needing to safeguard their most precious information. Our critical financial data and scientific records may be kept on cloud servers at **Microsoft**, **Amazon** and **Google**, but duplicate copies are often backed up to tape. The problem is that consolidation has left us with just two companies—**Sony** and **Fujifilm Holdings**—who still manufacture tape. In May 2019 the companies became embroiled in a patent lawsuit in which Fujifilm accused Sony of infringement. Fujifilm won, and the court banned Sony from importing media tape. The case was settled in the fall, but it caused widespread shortages of tapes. Tape isn't a big business unit within these otherwise sprawling companies, and potential shortages could lead to problems down the road for the world's data archives, especially given that the amount of critical data created every year increases significantly.

Biometric Malware

Kaspersky researchers found that in the third quarter of 2019 alone, about 33% of the systems that use and store biometric data were targeted by malware attacks. Biometric data aren't stored as securely as they should be, opening the door to theft and manipulation. Plenty of attacks have occurred in recent years: In 2018, a malware tool scraped photos from social media and used them to launch sophisticated phishing attacks. In Brazil, malware called CamuBot targeted bank customers, bypassed biometric hardware protections, and took over devices.

State-Sponsored Security Breaches

It's now well known that Russian hackers have targeted voter registration databases in more than 20 U.S. states, and there is evidence that the Russian government had a long list of targets that went far beyond American politicians running for office—targeting thousands of people, from defense contractors at Lockheed Martin and Raytheon, to Ukrainian lawmakers, to the Pope and his executive team. Russia is home to some of the world's most gifted and prolific hackers. Elite hackers in China spent 2018 carrying out some of the biggest and most damaging breaches in history, including attacks on U.S. Navy contractors and Marriott. They haven't just been hunting down individual people or companies—they're targeting managed service providers that provide IT infrastructure. And they aren't necessarily covering their tracks as they did in the past. Beyond the state-sponsored cyber initiatives, there are plenty of talented people who are motivated both by a lack of economic opportunity and ineffective law enforcement. It's created a perfect storm: Enormous talent, weak laws and economic stresses have brought about a growing pool of successful hackers.

Critical Infrastructure Targets

Researchers recently discovered critical security flaws impacting infrastructure—bridges, traffic systems, radiation monitoring, dams, power grids, etc.—in major U.S. and U.K. cities. Many cities lack the resources to repair roads and subways and they are woefully behind in building cybersecurity programs to prevent attacks. Every year, cybercriminals target critical infrastructure and facilities around the world and threaten to potentially disable dams, power plants and traffic lights. In 2018, it was publicly acknowledged that Russia targeted critical infrastructure sectors in the U.S., including the power grid—though efforts to gain access started in 2016. They succeeded in gaining access to a power plant's control system. Late in 2017, security firm FireEye discovered a new form of malware called Triton, which had taken control of an energy plant in the Middle East. In a separate attack, hackers targeted Ukraine's power grid, using malware called Industroyer. Cybersecurity company Symantec warned that hackers have already penetrated the U.S. power grid, exploiting staff at nuclear energy facilities with phishing attacks. The U.S. Computer Emergency Readiness Team issued a sternly-worded notice which was the extent of their punitive capabilities, but without any enforcement, companies and utilities managing our critical infrastructure haven't yet been jolted into action.

Offensive Government Hacking

Last year marked the tenth anniversary of the U.S. and Israel joining forces to deploy a devastating worm known as Stuxnet, which took down parts of Iran's covert nuclear weapons program. Rather than simply pursuing cyber deterrence, governments are going on the offensive. Singapore's Ministry of Defense is hiring white hat hackers and security experts to look for critical vulnerabilities in its government and infrastructure systems. In the U.S., the two agencies responsible for cyberwarfare—the U.S. Cyber Command and the National Security Agency—are playing offense, especially as artificial intelligence becomes a focus for U.S. cyber strategy. But there is a data scientist shortage globally, and it's especially hard for the government to attract gifted hackers to public service. That's due in part to a bad public image in the wake of Edward Snowden. To make matters worse, with a severe shortage of domestic cybersecurity workers—there are roughly 270,000 unfilled jobs in the field—skilled hackers can command perks and big paychecks in the private sector.

57 Cybersecurity Terms Everyone Should Know

○ Adware
Software that automatically generates online ads; it can also include spyware that tracks your browsing habits. Adware, in turn, has driven the demand for ad blocking software. (See the earlier "Blocking the Ad Blockers" trend.)

○ Air gap
A system that is physically separated and isolated from all other computers, networks and the internet for security reasons.

○ Anonymous
A collective of hackers, best known for its use of the Guy Fawkes mask and distributed denial of service (DDoS) attacks. Anonymous typically uses the hashtag #Ops when announcing a new campaign. Past ops included a takedown of the Church of Scientology and the Westboro Baptist Church.

○ Autorun worm
A malicious program that takes advantage of vulnerabilities in the Windows OS AutoRun feature. Autorun worms are often distributed on USB drives. (As a safety measure, Microsoft sets the AutoRun feature to off by default.)

○ Backdoor
Developers intentionally install backdoors into firmware so that manufacturers can safely upgrade our devices and operating systems. But backdoors can also be used surreptitiously to harness everything from our webcams to our personal data.

○ Black hat
A malicious hacker; someone who hacks for personal gain.

○ Bot
An automated program that performs a simple task. Some—simple chatbots, for example—are completely harmless. Others, however, can be programmed to repeatedly guess passwords to break into a website, for instance.

○ Botnet
A group of computers controlled by a third party for nefarious purposes. For example, malware installed on your computer can run, undetected, in the background while hackers use your machine as part of a large spamming network.

○ Breach
The moment a hacker gains access to a device or network via a vulnerability.

Browser hijacking

An attack that changes a user's default homepage and search engine without permission, often to gain clicks to websites for ad revenue or to inflate a page's ranking in search results.

Brute force attack

A laborious, methodical process in which software automatically guesses every potential password to gain unauthorized entry into a network or computer.

Bug

A flaw in a program that either could be harmless, or could allow hackers to exploit a system.

Compiler

A program that translates source code into executable machine language. Hackers use them as an easier way to surreptitiously gain access to various systems or networks without changing the source code, and without being noticed.

Cookie

A small file sent from your computer's web browser to a server that helps websites recognize you and helps third parties track audiences.

Cracking

A basic term that describes breaking into a security system. Anyone "cracking" a system is doing so maliciously.

Crypto

Cryptography (or "crypto") is the art and science of encrypting data—as well as breaking encryption.

Data leakage

The unauthorized access of information resulting in leaks, theft or loss.

Deep web/net and Dark web/net

The deep and dark net/web are actually two different things, though they're often conflated. The deep net or deep web is the vast trove of data that isn't indexed by search engines. Spreadsheets, databases and more that are stored on servers make up this space. The dark web/net is made up of sites that are invisible unless you know how to use a special network, such as Tor, which can find the dark site. Once there, you'll find what you might expect: pirated software and content, job listings for hackers, illegal drugs, human trafficking and worse.

Denial of service attack (DoS)

When a hacker sends so many requests to a website or network that the traffic temporarily overwhelms the servers, and the site or network goes down.

Distributed denial of service attack (DDoS)

A denial of service attack using a battalion of machines.

Digital certificate

These authenticate and approve the identity of a person, organization or service.

DNS hijacking

A category of attacks that change a computer's settings to ignore a domain name system (DNS) or to use a DNS that's controlled by malicious agents.

Doxing

The practice of hackers rooting out and publishing personally-identifying information about someone online.

Dump

A trove of data released by hackers.

Dumpster diving

The practice of hackers going through garbage looking for information that could help with an exploit. Organizations and individuals who don't consistently use a shredder leave themselves vulnerable to dumpster divers.

Encryption

The scrambling of data using special code or software so that it cannot be read by a third party, even if it is intercepted.

End-to-end encryption

When an encrypted message is scrambled on both ends, as it is sent and again as it is received.

Exploit

The successful leveraging of a vulnerability in a piece of code, software, hardware, or computer network.

Firewall

A system of software and hardware that's designed to prevent unauthorized access to a computer or computer network.

Hacker

This term means different things to different people. People who tinker with code to purposely manipulate it are hackers. Some are good, and some are bad. In popular culture, "hacker" has taken on a distinctly negative connotation.

Hacktivist

Someone who hacks for social or political reasons.

Honeypot
A system or network designed to look like a high-value target, but built to watch hackers do their work and learn from their techniques.

InfoSec
An abbreviation for "information security." InfoSec can refer to companies and professionals that work in the field of cybersecurity.

Jailbreak
To remove the restrictive manufacturer's code from a device so that you can reprogram it to function as you desire.

Keys
The code which, just like a physical key, is used to lock or unlock a system, encrypted message, or software.

Malware
Any software program that's been designed to manipulate a system by stealing information, augmenting code, or installing a rogue program. Rootkits, keyloggers, spyware and everyday viruses are examples of malware.

Man-in-the-middle (MitM) attacks
Attacks involving a hacker that impersonates a trusted connection in order to steal data or information, or to alter communications between two or more people.

Metadata
Data that explains what's in another set of data, such as a jpeg photo, or an email or a webpage.

Password managers
Third-party tools that remember one master password to unlock a database of all your other passwords, while using completely different passwords for every site and service. While managers are a good idea in theory, many are cloud-based. If a hacker gains access to your password manager, you're in big trouble. If you do use one, make sure to use a complicated password at least 36 characters long with lots of special characters, numbers and capital letters.

Patch
An after-market fix to address vulnerabilities.

Penetration testing
The practice of trying to break into your own computer or network in order to test the strength of your security.

PGP
PGP stands for "Pretty Good Privacy," and you've probably seen a lot of PGP numbers showing up in Twitter and Facebook bios lately. PGP is a basic method of encrypting email (and other data). In order to receive and read the message, your intended recipient must use a private key to decode it.

Phishing
Phishing attacks exploit human vulnerabilities that usually coerce people into sharing data, login credentials or credit card numbers.

Plaintext
Text without any formatting. In the context of cybersecurity, it also refers to text that isn't encrypted.

RAT
Remote Access Tool. If you've used a remote login service to access your office computer while away from work, you've used a RAT. But RATs can be malicious, too—just imagine a hacker using a RAT to take over your workstation.

Ransomware
Malware that allows a hacker to break into your computer or network and then take away your access until you pay a specified fee or perform a certain action.

Root
The central nervous system of a computer or network. It can install new applications, create files, delete user accounts and so on. Anyone with root access has ubiquitous and unfettered access.

Rootkit
Malware designed for root access. Often undetected, rootkits start running when you start your computer, and they stay running until you turn off your machine.

Spearphishing
A more targeted form of phishing to smaller groups, typically within social networks or work environments.

Spoofing
Spoofing is changing a real email or web address to make it look like it is a trusted source. Examples include cnnn.com instead of cnn.com, or changing the "from" section or header of an email to make it look as though it was sent by a coworker. In general, any time data is changed to mimic a trusted source, it's being spoofed. Hackers spoof emails by impersonating people you know, and then launch phishing attacks.

Verification

Ensuring that data, and its originators, are authentic.

Virtual Private Networks

Networks that use encryption to create a private channel for accessing the internet. These "VPNs" are necessary when connecting to public networks—even those at airports, hotels and coffee shops.

Virus

Malware intended to steal, delete or ransom your files. Mimicking the flu, this type of malware spreads like a biological virus.

Vulnerability

A weakness in computer software that hackers can exploit for their own gain.

White hat

White hats are security experts who work on highlighting vulnerabilities and bugs in order to fix them and protect us.

Worm

A certain kind of invasive malware that spreads like a virus.

Zero-day exploits

In the hacking community, these exploits are valuable because they are undisclosed vulnerabilities that can be exploited. Once the flaw is revealed, programmers have "zero days" to do anything about it. (Also written as "0day.")

Zombie

A computer, connected device, or network that's been infected by malware and is now being used by the hacker, probably without your knowledge. Just like the White Walkers in Game of Thrones, but machines!

For more resources and definitions, we recommend NATO's cooperative Cyber Defense Centre of Excellence's online database: https://ccdcoe.org.

26 Geopolitics,
Geoeconomics
& Tech Policy

Antitrust Probes and Lawsuits

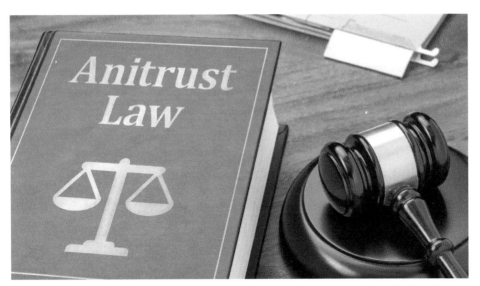

Big tech companies will face antitrust probes and lawsuits in 2020.

Key Insight

Antitrust laws exist to ensure and promote fair competition between companies, in part to protect consumers. Regulators in many countries are planning to take action to limit the reach and powers of the world's largest, most dominant technology companies.

Why It Matters

Facebook, Apple, Amazon, and Google have all faced pressure from lawmakers and federal agencies over their expanding power and their control of data.

Examples

In general, antitrust authorities are concerned with six key areas: big tech companies' ability to control data; the power they have to impose terms on competitors; the fact that they are both participants in and owners of their platforms; their potential use of algorithms to thwart competition; their habit of infringing on small competitors' patents; and their merger and acquisition activity, which has helped them to consolidate power.

The U.S. Department of Justice's Antitrust Division began hiring more staff in January 2020 to support their probes into big tech companies. The Federal Trade Commission is examining Amazon's retail and cloud businesses and Facebook's acquisitions. Numerous state attorneys general are investigating Google and Facebook. Meanwhile, the House of Representatives Judiciary Committee is investigating Apple, Amazon, Facebook, and Google. There is some debate in the U.S. regarding the Sherman Act, which was originally written to regulate and break apart the enterprises of railroad and oil tycoons, who had built America's biggest monopolies. What U.S. courts have yet to decide is whether big tech companies are indeed monopolies, which would trigger the Act's application. So far, the big tech companies have argued that there is plenty of competition—if people or organizations don't want to use **Facebook**, there are plenty of other social media companies to choose from. Except at this point, the services these tech firms provide aren't quite so simple or interchangeable: companies like Yelp, Spotify, Airbnb, and Tinder use Facebook and Twitter for authentication. Facebook is launching a cryptocurrency platform that can be used within Facebook's ecosystem. **Google** and Facebook effectively control the entire market for digital advertising, and **Amazon** is the undisputed leader in e-commerce in most markets. (Exceptions include Alibaba and Baidu in China.)

In the **European Union**, the argument against big tech has been gaining more traction. In 2017, the E.U. fined **Google** a record-breaking $2.7 billion for what adjudicators said was illegally nudging users to its comparison shopping site rather than to off-platform retail sites. In September 2018, the **E.U.'s Competition Commissioner Margrethe Vestager** began an investigation into how **Amazon** uses customer data. This year she and her division will review the E.U.'s antitrust parameters and could change how member governments anti-competitiveness—a new law could be on the books by mid-year.

What's Next

The problem with existing antitrust laws is that they don't always mesh with our ever-evolving business landscape. For example, **Amazon** recently acquired **Zappos**, **Diapers.com**, and **Whole Foods**. Together, all three give the company a much larger retail footprint, but individually, each acquisition doesn't amount to unfair competition. (It's not the same as **Walmart**, a retailer that sells related items—home goods, clothing, gardening supplies and foodstuffs—buying grocery stores **Publix** and **Safeway**.) Several new tech antitrust policies will take effect in 2020 in an attempt to modernize our approach to antitrust for the digital era.

The Impact

Breaking apart big tech companies could prove difficult. For example, as Amazon continues to build digital payments, logistics, and package delivery infrastructure, it could indirectly crush other retailers who use other, inferior platforms. But that still wouldn't be illegal. At the moment, we don't have any laws against being really, really smart.

Watchlist

Big tech companies (especially Amazon, Apple, Facebook, and Google), Congress, Federal Trade Commission, E.U. Competition Commissioner Margrethe Vestager, U.S. Department of Justice Antitrust Division.

Tech companies are "too big, and we've allowed them to exercise monopoly power."

– David Cicilline,
U.S. House of Representatives Antitrust Division chairman.

Policy Uncertainty

HIGH DEGREE OF CERTAINTY

INFORMS STRATEGY	ACT NOW
REVISIT LATER	KEEP VIGILANT WATCH

LONGER-TERM IMPACT · IMMEDIATE IMPACT

LOW DEGREE OF CERTAINTY

Key Insight

In our current and near-future political climate, there is great uncertainty in what key technology, environmental, and trade policies will be—not just in the U.S., but in other markets around the world as well.

Why It Matters

One of the biggest threats to the continued expansion of our economies is confidence. When it comes to technology—whether to regulate privacy, security, data, and trade—policy uncertainty is a trigger that could cause the market to overreact.

Examples

At the start of the **Trump** presidency in 2017, the White House promised a "comprehensive review of all federal regulations" for policies involving the environment, such as whether to continue tax credits for electric cars and solar panels, and how much to limit carbon dioxide emissions. Without further

specification or guidance, businesses can't make decisions. In the past few years, leaders across varied industry sectors have bemoaned uncertainty. Automakers are still recovering from whiplash: In 2012, there were new rules mandating 39 miles per gallon fuel consumption rates by 2025, but then in 2018 the Trump Administration proposed scrapping the requirement for new cars. Then in January 2020, fuel efficiency policy was reintroduced: Required miles per gallon standards will now increase 1.5% per year from 2021-2026. For the past several years, Americans have been eligible for tax credits for the purchase of new electric vehicles, but this year the credit is being phased out. At the start of the year, automakers will offer $7,500 in credits for each electric vehicle they sell up to 200,000 units. The available credit then gets cut in half six months later, and then it's halved again (down to $1,875) six months after that. Finally, the credit goes to zero. If democrats win big in November, the entire scheme could change yet again.

What's Next

Policy uncertainty exists in other critical areas of the U.S. economy: how we will build out 5G networks and how we will interact with countries using networks built on Chinese-made components; how personal data will be used by big tech companies; whether big tech companies will be allowed to continue to operate as they are today, and so on.

The Impact

Imagine trying to convince a board of directors to take a chance on innovative new ideas and areas of research when they have no real sense of what direction corresponding legislature and regulations might take. Companies could start to blame policy uncertainty for a lack of critical investment in R&D and innovation, which would put countries like the U.S. at a strategic disadvantage compared to nations with less fluctuation in their national leadership. Leadership teams who commit to strategic

foresight and long-term planning know how to weather policy uncertainty, but companies without a process in place could find the next several years challenging.

Watchlist

Big tech companies (especially Amazon, Apple, Facebook, and Google), car manufacturers, renewable energy companies, government agencies.

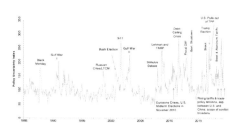

The U.S. economic policy uncertainty index, 1985 - 2019, from www.policyuncertainty.com.

Regulating Data Ownership

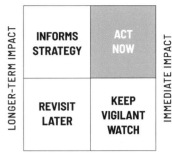

HIGH DEGREE OF CERTAINTY

LONGER-TERM IMPACT

INFORMS STRATEGY	ACT NOW
REVISIT LATER	KEEP VIGILANT WATCH

IMMEDIATE IMPACT

LOW DEGREE OF CERTAINTY

Key Insight

Who, exactly, owns your data? This is a matter of contention, as tech companies, advocacy groups, and governments start to define who has ultimate power and control over our information.

Why It Matters

In a digital economy, data is currency.

Examples

In recent months, we've seen a flood of headlines about personal data security, as **Google**, **Facebook**, and **Apple** strive to convince us—despite mounting evidence to the contrary—that their privacy policies and data management systems can be trusted by all users. "Privacy shouldn't be a luxury good," wrote Google CEO **Sundar Pichai** in a 2019 **New York Times** op-ed.

There are real-world business implications when it comes to the future of data ownership. In most countries, "data ownership" has typically referred to the legal rights to intellectual property, or copyrights. Determining what can be done with the personal data at a company's disposal, and under what circumstances, should be a topic of conversation in every boardroom. Data governance may sound boring, but it should be a centerpiece of every corporate strategy.

In a world where every device is smart and connected—essentially "paying attention" to you at all times—surveillance is constant and boundaries of ownership are unclear. Those bits and bytes we constantly shed may originate from us, but that doesn't mean they necessarily belong to us, which brings up thorny questions: Who is the legal guardian of our data? Do companies have the right to change end-user agreements without actively notifying users with a clear explanation of what is changing, and the potential impact? We could even go down a more philosophical road. What does owning a piece of data look like? Is "ownership" itself a misnomer, and does stewardship or guardianship better describe our relationship with data? What about your genetic data? If you take a **23andMe** DNA test, who owns your genome? What happens to your enormous trail of data when you die?

When it comes to IoT in our homes, is the data generated within our walls and physical spaces governed by privacy rights? Does the **Fifth Amendment** mean that wearables—our fitness trackers, connected bras, smart watches—can't be used to self-incriminate us in court? How, ultimately, should we define privacy in a digital era? These are questions that still must be answered collectively by companies, government officials, and, frankly, any living, breathing human being.

What's Next

Initiatives spearheaded by **former U.S. presidential candidate Andrew Yang**, as well as projects at the **World Economic Forum** and **United Nations**, aim to create guidelines for data ownership. The big tech companies will continue to face regulatory scrutiny in the coming year, and investors are paying attention. Most of the focus is on antitrust concerns and privacy. Meanwhile, most people may continue to be oblivious to just how much data they're generating, what might be done with it, and how it might be used against them.

The Impact

Without careful thought and planning today, we could wind up robbed of a valuable currency we helped create.

Watchlist

Big tech companies (especially Amazon, Apple, Facebook, and Google), government agencies.

Data ownership will be debated throughout 2020.

SCENARIO · MARC PALATUCCI

You're Saddled with Data Debt

MID-FUTURE CATASTROPHIC SCENARIO

Tech companies take a page from today's banks, which are incentivized to encourage consumer debt that, when compounded, leads to more profit for the financial institutions. Just as bank customers can become hopelessly buried in financial debt, nowadays average citizens find themselves drowning in "data debt," committed to providing deeper and deeper levels of personal data in exchange for arguably indispensable services. Eventually, every thought and action is quantified, seized, and made available for sale by the new debt collectors of the tech sector.

Digital Dividends to Fund Universal Basic Income Plans

HIGH DEGREE OF CERTAINTY

INFORMS STRATEGY	ACT NOW
REVISIT LATER	KEEP VIGILANT WATCH

LONGER-TERM IMPACT · IMMEDIATE IMPACT

LOW DEGREE OF CERTAINTY

Former presidential candidate Andrew Yang offered universal basic income and data ownership proposals during his campaign.

Key Insight

A digital dividend would give citizens a cut of the profits derived from their personal data.

Why It Matters

The idea of an unconditional guaranteed income for every citizen of a given country is now being discussed both as a means of encouraging entrepreneurial innovation, and as a response to workforce-displacing automation, advanced robotics, and artificial intelligence.

Examples

All eyes were on a test of this idea of universal basic income (UBI) in **Finland**, but the program came to an early close in 2018. It targeted only 2,000 randomly unemployed citizens and gave them 560 euros a month (that's about $675) for two years. The model didn't work there—but some experts believe that's because other social welfare programs weren't adjusted alongside the UBI program. Early in 2019, then Democratic presidential candidate **Andrew Yang** launched a pilot UBI program in **New Hampshire**—if it is successful, and if he ends up in a future presidential cabinet, he would work to ensure that every American aged 18 to 64 would receive $1,000 every month, regardless of employment status. The money to pay for this UBI initiative would come from consolidating social service programs and from a value-added tax (similar to current taxes in Europe) of 10% passed on to the consumer based on the value added at various steps in the production of goods. There are city-scale experimental UBI programs now running in **Oakland** and **Stockton, California**. The Stockton project will give 100 randomly selected low-income families $500 a month for 18 months.

What's Next

UBI programs may not be feasible going forward in many places, due in large part to sizeable aging populations and too few new workers entering paying jobs. A "digital dividend," on the other hand, could be a viable alternate path to the future. Researchers at **Oxford's Institute for Humanity**, researchers at the **Future Today Institute**, and former presidential candidate Andrew Yang separately published works outlining different versions of this digital dividend—a way for companies to pay back to society a portion of the profits derived from A.I. (See also: A.I. and digital dividends.)

The Impact

As the workforce changes due to automation, governments worldwide will need to find new alternatives to existing public support programs.

Watchlist

Future Today Institute, Oxford Institute for Humanity, Stanford Center for Philanthropy and Civil Society.

U.S. and Global Election Security

HIGH DEGREE OF CERTAINTY

INFORMS STRATEGY	**ACT NOW**
REVISIT LATER	**KEEP VIGILANT WATCH**

LONGER-TERM IMPACT

IMMEDIATE IMPACT

LOW DEGREE OF CERTAINTY

Key Insight

This is an election year, and security experts are warning that our election systems could be vulnerable to outside attacks as well as domestic technical incompetence and mismanagement.

Why It Matters

In January 2019, **House Democrats** introduced new election security measures as part of the **For the People Act**, which mandates that states revert to using paper ballots in elections, which must be hand-counted or counted using optical character recognition. It will also authorize the **Election Assistance Commission** to support smaller districts with grants to upgrade their systems, and it also tasks the **Department of Homeland Security** to run a security and threat assessment audit ahead of all future elections. The bill will still need a vote and funding for implementation, but it's a sign that our elections systems are now in transition.

Examples

Russia interfered with elections around the world during 2016 and 2017, and safeguarding our voting systems is an ongoing challenge that has yet to be fully resolved. It's now clear that Russia meddled in the 2016 **U.S.** election. This included pilfering local and national election databases, hampering registration operations in districts around the country, and deliberately spreading false or misleading information to target political candidates. Unfortunately, we made it easy for hackers to break in—during the 2016 election, 43 states used electronic voting machines that were perilously out of date.

In 2020, the **Iowa Democratic Party** used an app, called **Shadow**, built to simplify and streamline caucus results reporting. The system failed at the most critically important time, challenging the accuracy and integrity of the results. Meanwhile **Voatz**, a blockchain-based voting system that was piloted during **West Virginia's** 2018 general election and has been heralded as a new,

secure way for people to vote from their living rooms, was shown to have multiple vulnerabilities. Researchers from **MIT** found that an attacker could hack into phones via Voatz's Android app and then observe, suppress and alter votes cast. The research team also detailed how the Voatz API could be compromised to alter ballots before a final count was made.

What's Next

A January 2020 **NPR/PBS NewsHour/ Marist Poll** revealed that 41% of those surveyed said they believed the U.S. is not very prepared or not prepared at all to keep November's election safe and secure.

The Impact

Cybersecurity experts have repeatedly demonstrated that our existing internet voting systems aren't impenetrable. Lawmakers will likely debate mandatory voting technology standards: technology, connectivity, and security.

Watchlist

Caltech/MIT Voting Technology Project, Central Intelligence Agency, Department of Homeland Security's Cybersecurity and Infrastructure Security Agency, National Conference of State Legislatures, MIT, National Security Agency, Presidential Commission on Election Administration, Russia, Shadow Inc., Voatz, local voting commissions everywhere.

Election security was an area of concern during the 2020 election cycle.

Interoperability Initiatives

HIGH DEGREE OF CERTAINTY

INFORMS STRATEGY	ACT NOW
REVISIT LATER	KEEP VIGILANT WATCH

LONGER-TERM IMPACT / IMMEDIATE IMPACT

LOW DEGREE OF CERTAINTY

U.S. Sen. Mark Warner has led efforts to make mandatory the interoperability of platforms, devices and services.

Key Insight

Amazon, Apple, and Google use different operating systems for their various devices and ecosystems, which some regulators argue is anti-competitive.

Why It Matters

Lawmakers have threatened to break up big tech companies, but there may be less disruptive ways forward that involve increasing interoperability amongst these firms.

Examples

A bipartisan group of lawmakers led by Senators Mark Warner (D-VA), Richard Blumenthal (D-CT), and Josh Hawley (R-MO) proposed a new bill to encourage competition by making big tech's platforms interoperable. The Augmenting Compatibility and Competition by Enabling Services Switching Act (or ACCESS, for short) would require Google and Facebook to maintain API-like interfaces so that users could port their information over from one platform to another if they want, and so that smaller companies could more easily make use of our data. (With our permission, of course.) Meanwhile Apple, Amazon and Google joined the Zigbee Alliance to develop a shared connectivity standard allowing hardware from different companies to work together.

What's Next

Incentivizing companies to make their protocols and hardware interoperable could help curtail some of the antitrust probes the big tech firms will face this year.

The Impact

Interoperability and data portability could eventually lead to new business opportunities and a bigger device ecosystem.

Watchlist

Amazon, Apple, Google, Facebook, U.S. government, Zigbee Alliance.

Corporate Foreign Policy

HIGH DEGREE OF CERTAINTY

INFORMS STRATEGY	ACT NOW
REVISIT LATER	KEEP VIGILANT WATCH

LONGER-TERM IMPACT · IMMEDIATE IMPACT

LOW DEGREE OF CERTAINTY

Microsoft president Brad Smith wants to restore trust in technology companies.

Key Insight

Big tech companies are standing up departments dedicated to geopolitics.

Why It Matters

Some lawmakers are asking if our tech companies are so expansive and powerful that they now function like nation states.

Examples

In the **U.S.**, our largest companies have always engaged in lobbying for the purpose of influencing policy and regulation. But as the tech giants amass power and wealth, delegations from foreign governments are establishing small outposts in **Silicon Valley**. **Austria** and **Denmark** both maintain missions in **San Francisco** so that they can actively engage with the tech community, while China maintains several offices for venture funding all throughout Silicon Valley.

In 2019, **Apple CEO Tim Cook** met with China's head market regulator in Beijing; the company subsequently removed a live app map from its app store that was being used by protestors in **Hong Kong**. **Microsoft president Brad Smith** spearheaded a corporate foreign policy group within the company, and he champions multi-stakeholder approaches to geopolitics. He regularly meets with foreign ministers and heads of state. In 2017, Smith introduced a **Digital Geneva Convention**—an international treaty intended to protect citizens against state-sponsored cyberattacks—and his team actively works on a tech-focused approach to foreign policy. Tech companies are actively poaching staff at the **State Department**, especially those who have become jaded under the chaotic and confusing working conditions of the **Trump Administration**.

What's Next

In a globalized world, tech companies could wield great influence on the future construction of wireless networks, device ecosystems, artificial intelligence, and more. As they consolidate power in the commercial sector, big tech could wind up consolidating power in the public sector, too.

The Impact

It's one thing for a big company to lobby domestic lawmakers, but some are wondering what the longer-term implications would be for corporations trying to influence geoeconomics. What if a company's priorities differ from the national priorities of its government at home?

Watchlist

Amazon, Apple, Facebook, Google, Microsoft, U.S. Department of State, governments worldwide.

Multilateral Science and Technology Acts

HIGH DEGREE OF CERTAINTY

INFORMS STRATEGY	ACT NOW
REVISIT LATER	KEEP VIGILANT WATCH

LONGER-TERM IMPACT

IMMEDIATE IMPACT

LOW DEGREE OF CERTAINTY

Lawmakers, researchers and ethicists are calling for multilateral acts to help guide the future of science and technology.

Key Insight

Throughout history, multilateral efforts have resulted in nations working together toward a shared purpose.

Why It Matters

With debates about the future of CRISPR, ocean plastics, climate, autonomous vehicles, A.I., and space exploration reaching fever pitch, there will be new multilateral science and technology acts proposed.

Examples

The Geneva Conventions, the League of Nations, International Monetary Fund, United Nations, and World Health Organization started as a result of multilateral agreements between sovereign nations. After somewhat recent revelations that a pair of genetically engineered twin girls had been born in China, some now wonder whether international norms are enough.

What's Next

Now that many fields of science and technology have started to produce transformational new developments, lawmakers, researchers, and ethicists are calling for some kind of consensus, proposing international deliberations that could lead to international treaties and protocols.

The Impact

Proposals to create multilateral initiatives on artificial intelligence, genomic editing, and blockchain could prevent future conflict between researchers, companies and countries.

Watchlist

American Association for the Advancement of Science, International Social Science Council, International Union of Biological Sciences, United Nations, the United Nations Educational, Scientific and Cultural Organization (UNESCO), the World Economic Forum.

Overhauling Government Tech Infrastructure

HIGH DEGREE OF CERTAINTY

LONGER-TERM IMPACT

INFORMS STRATEGY	ACT NOW
REVISIT LATER	KEEP VIGILANT WATCH

IMMEDIATE IMPACT

LOW DEGREE OF CERTAINTY

Some departments in the U.S. government still use legacy computer equipment.

Key Insight

Parts of the federal government rely on comically old technology that is vulnerable and very difficult to maintain.

Why It Matters

Overhauling federal technology infrastructure has bipartisan appeal.

Examples

In 2017, **President Donald Trump** signed an executive order to modernize the **U.S. government**. To kick off the process, he invited 20 tech CEOs to the White House to discuss how to make the transition. But the idea of overhauling government IT didn't start with the Trump White House. **President Barack Obama** created the **U.S. Digital Service** to attract tech sector experts to federal jobs and to fix the broken system from within. There's a financial incentive to do so: A 2016

Government Accountability Office (GAO) report estimated that we spend $80 billion annually on IT because of obsolete technologies and sweeping inefficiencies. The GAO report included a sobering technology audit. It found that the **State Department** uses a 26-year-old system to track visa information for 55,000 foreign nationals—software that has since been decommissioned by the vendor who built it.

What's Next

In a perplexing move, President Trump acknowledged that government systems need to be overhauled—but then didn't name key advisors who would have the authority to make needed changes, casting doubt on the future of the initiative. The problem isn't just about legacy systems, it's about keeping pace with the changing nature of technology. Old software, machines, and systems are expensive to maintain.

The Impact

There aren't many technicians who have enough institutional knowledge to make the necessary fixes, which means re-hiring retired employees at high contract wages. Until significant updates are made, these legacy systems are vulnerable to attack.

Watchlist

Government Accountability Office, Internal Revenue Service, Office of Management and Budget, Office of Science and Technology Policy, and U.S. departments of Defense, Energy, Health and Human Services, Homeland Security, Housing and Urban Development, Justice, State, and Transportation, U.S. Digital Service, as well as lawmakers.

New Policy Questions We Need to Ask in 2020

⊘ Can the government force big tech companies to make A.I. explainable?
Should A.I. systems carry something akin to a nutritional label, detailing the training data used, the processes used for learning, the real-world data being used in applications and the expected outcomes? For sensitive or proprietary systems, should trusted third parties be able to assess and verify an A.I.'s transparency?

⊘ Who should own our data?
What should data governance look like in an era when companies act as data brokers, profiting off of the information we give them, often without us fully realizing the extent of what we've shared?

⊘ How should we define privacy in a digital era?
Can law enforcement agencies use the Fourth Amendment to compel a company to jailbreak a device? If citizens use spatial computing systems in their homes, are the data generated by walls and physical spaces governed by privacy rights?

⊘ Can bots break the law?
If a digital assistant or bot breaks a law without your direct involvement—automatically purchasing illegal drugs or using hate speech against another person—who's to blame? You? The individual developers who created the assistant or bot's code? Or the technology company that built the platform?

⊘ Who owns your biology?
You are shedding biometric data every day, either intentionally or unwittingly. Every time you speak to Alexa, use your fingerprint or face to unlock a device, or allow a photo to be automatically tagged when you upload it to social media, you are voluntarily sharing your bioinformation with for-profit companies. What legal right do they have to change end-user agreements? Who is the ultimate legal guardian of that data? Can a company take ownership of your DNA and other biodata in perpetuity? Can it be given the perpetual, royalty-free worldwide license to our data?

⊘ Can your Fitbit plead the Fifth?
Does the Fifth Amendment mean that wearables—our fitness trackers, connected bras, smart watches—can't be used to self-incriminate us in court?

⊘ Do anti-slavery protections extend to Alexa?
Our Thirteenth Amendment declares that "neither slavery nor involuntary servitude, except as a punishment for crime whereof the party shall have been duly convicted, shall exist within the United States, or any place subject to their jurisdiction." It doesn't specifically reference humans. Do anti-slavery protections extend to our artificially intelligent agents?

China's Quest for Global Cybersovereignty

HIGH DEGREE OF CERTAINTY

INFORMS STRATEGY	ACT NOW
REVISIT LATER	KEEP VIGILANT WATCH

LONGER-TERM IMPACT / IMMEDIATE IMPACT

LOW DEGREE OF CERTAINTY

China is building a new set of digital tools and networks for the future.

Key Insight

Cybersovereignty refers to a government exerting its control over how the internet is run, who gets access to it, and what can be done with all of the data generated.

Why It Matters

In 2019, **Chinese President Xi Jinping** pushed forward an agenda of strict control, censorship and suppression, and it is starting to export its systems to authoritarian leaders elsewhere in the world.

Examples

China has always restricted what can be posted digitally and by whom, but last year there were serious repercussions for those who violated the **Communist Party of China's (CPC)** content preferences. A "South Park" episode critical of the Chinese government quickly went viral, which prompted cen-sors to remove not just the episode—but all instances of South Park content on the internet, social media, and in discussion rooms. In China, **Twitter**, **Facebook**, and **Google** are impossible to access without a VPN—citizens instead use home-grown apps like **Baidu** and **WeChat** to surf the web and chat with friends. The CCP argues that China is an enormous country in the midst of the fastest economic transition in modern history, and their unique controls are meant to promote social and economic stability. But there's more to it than that: In 2019, Xi also announced that the government would wean itself off of foreign-made computers and operating systems, replacing familiar brands (**Microsoft**, **Dell**, **Apple**) with Chinese products.

What's Next

President Xi has said that China's digital and information systems can serve as a new model for other countries around the world, and now other authoritarian regimes are following suit. **China's Belt and Road Initiative**, which has been a huge success in expanding trade throughout emerging economies, also has boosted the country's digital initiatives. **Russia** passed "sovereign internet" laws in 2019 that allow authorities to track and block information as it pleases. **Vietnam** passed a law that, like China, allows the government to block content it deems problematic to society.

The Impact

Within a decade, the digital world could be split in two, a free system in the West, and a closed system led by China.

Watchlist

Governments worldwide.

AMY WEBB

Strategic Guidance:
The Case for Establishing the U.S. National Office of Strategic Foresight

The federal government has at its fingertips an abundance of technical experts spread across myriad agencies. But the U.S. still lacks a centralized office that's charged with long-range, comprehensive, streamlined planning to address critical science and technology developments.

Without a more coordinated approach, we will continue along the status quo, which results in a misalignment between agencies and redundant strategic work. At the start of the next presidential term, the new President should create a new, centralized office championing strategic foresight.

This office would bring strategic leadership and processes and use data-driven models to analyze plausible futures—continually evaluating macro sources of change, finding emerging trends, and mapping the trajectory and velocity of those changes. The focus of the office would be to bring authoritative, unbiased insights to the executive branch, facilitate forward-leaning research, lead strategic conversations, disseminate knowledge and capabilities, and drive the kind of rigorous quantitative and qualitative proceedings that result in real, concrete actions.

The Challenge

The U.S. government has no blueprint for articulating long-term research and development funding targets at a critical time in our country: Emerging technologies in A.I., genomics, autonomous transportation, home automation, and biometric data collection are fast changing and coalescing, and they will have serious societal implications that reach far beyond the existing mandate of federal science and technology agencies.

For example, numerous initiatives, agencies, councils, and centers now work independently on the future of A.I. on behalf of the United States. Yet interagency collaboration on these efforts is inadequate, just as coordinated efforts to streamline goals, outcomes, R&D efforts and funding tend to be. For instance, The National Institute of Standards and Technology (NIST) and various congressional offices are all separately trying to define technical specifications for A.I., while the Joint AI Center and National Security Commission on A.I. each focus on artificial intelligence used primarily in national security and defense.

When it comes to planning for the future of A.I., there's even more duplication: specifically between the National Artificial Intelligence Research and Development Strategic Plan and the National Security Strategy and the National Security Commission on A.I.

In addition, top tech executives are often asked to serve on multiple commissions or to participate in similar efforts across government. This overlap actually creates a glaring gap: With so many groups working either redundantly or even at odds with each other, the U.S. will miss key opportunities to coordinate efforts between tech, finance and government—efforts that could otherwise drive significant forward progress within a reasonable timeframe.

Without a central strategic foresight office, we won't establish the norms, standards and regulations desperately needed for the future. Worse, we will squander important opportunities to leverage new technologies that could spur economic development and that could help us prepare our future workforce, augment our national security, and promote civic well-being. Existing mechanisms for science and technology within the executive branch lack the scope, mandate, and expertise necessary to do strategic forecasting, and they lack the cross-cutting approach needed to meet tomorrow's challenges.

Here's a look at the competing federal agencies and councils, their oversight and scope of existing duties:

White House Office of Science and Technology Policy (OSTP)

This group is charged with advising the President on science and technology issues and with leading interagency policy coordination efforts. The OSTP can tap deep technical expertise and has the institutional mandate to lead federal science and technology agencies in strategic planning processes.

Yet OSTP is not organized for a strategic forecasting role, and it lacks the authority to articulate future budget targets—a role that falls to the Office of Management and Budget. Nonetheless, OSTP leads strategic planning processes through the National Science and Technology Council, a coordinating entity for science and technology policy across federal R&D agencies. Together, these two organizations are responsible for the following:

○ Taking on domain-specific strategic planning, such as the federal government's recently updated National Artificial Intelligence R&D Strategic Plan.

○ Overseeing national coordinating offices responsible for cross-agency initiatives. This includes the National Information Technology R&D (NITRD) Program and the National Nanotechnology Initiative. For example, NITRD acts as the nation's primary plan to coordinate federally funded research and development for advanced information technologies (IT), computing, networking and software. It's scope is broad: 21 federal member agencies. Yet still, its charge doesn't include strategic forecasting functions, such as modeling the next-order implications.

National Security Council "Stratplan" team
This is the White House's body for coordinating national security-related strategic planning on a wide range of issues, including emerging technologies.

President's Council of Advisors on Science and Technology
The Council acts as a formal advisory group to provide the President with advice on a broad range of science and technology issues. Though it lacks formal authority, it nonetheless can elevate critical issues and propose federal strategies to address them.

Science and Technology Policy Institute
This independent federally-funded research and development center serves as OSTP's think tank. It receives annual appropriations from Congress to inform OSTP on policy decisions. But its function is dramatically underutilized.

Government Accountability Office
The GAO recently reorganized to strengthen its science and technology and forecasting functions, and it may be a source of strategic expertise on emerging technologies. Yet the organization's mandate is more of an oversight role—rather than a strategic one.

While each of the above entities marshal some aspect of a strategic foresight function, no single group is charged with a single focus on strategic foresight across domains nor given the resources needed to undertake a comprehensive approach to the emergence of a range of new platform technologies.

A Proposal

Regardless of who occupies the Oval Office in 2021 and beyond, our President must champion a foresight process that positions our leaders to plan for the long-term future. A new Strategic Foresight Office (SFO) will position leaders to articulate and drive a positive future—one in which the United States remains a powerful global force.

The new SFO would exist within the White House Office of Science and Technology Policy (OSTP) and would use the convening power of the National Science and Technology Council to implement a plan with the President. This structure would mimic that of the Office of the Chief Technology Officer created in 2009 by President Barack Obama that elevated the importance of technology, data, and innovation in policy making. The head of the SFO would report directly to the President, serving as an assistant to the President.

The SFO's responsibilities should be educational, strategic and tactical. The office would gather administration officials, department heads, members of Congress and other stakeholders regularly and facilitate strategic conversations, prototype policy and model impact scenarios for the future. It would further build a culture of foresight in the federal government to inform the long-term vision for our country.

The SFO would pave the way for a dedicated team of individuals to think exclusively about long-term science and technology issues of national importance and their broader implications. While OSTP staff members oversee policy topics, they don't always have the same long-term strategic perspective, in part because of limited time and intense, competing demands. The SFO could provide the people and resources needed to provide that long-term planning and strategic thought that is often absent in policy discussions, simply because of limited bandwidth.

To give this office real teeth, its responsibilities should include:

Report to President
The head of the SFO would co-chair the NSTC with the OSTP director and serve as an assistant to the President, responsible for providing strategic advice on a full range of science and technology topics.

Staff
The SFO would employ people with strategic forecasting expertise and varied backgrounds in emerging science and technology issues. Staff members could be drawn from other agencies or institutions through detail and IPA arrangements.

Budget Authority
The office would have a mandate to create an emerging technologies budget crosscut in the President's annual budget and would articulate a series of forward-looking budget requests that extend five to 10 years in the future.

Strategic Planning
The SFO would use a standardized, rigorous, data-driven foresight methodology and would work through the NSTC's committee structure to work with agency leaders and their teams on strategic planning and drive execution with accountability.

Cross-Agency Priority Goals
The SFO would work with OMB to create a suite of cross-agency priority goals, which could drive progress on interagency efforts.

National Coordinating Offices
The SFO would create establish new coordinating offices and oversee existing domain-specific offices, such as NITRD that would drive cross-agency strategic priorities.

External Expertise
The SFO must draw on considerable outside expertise, too. In addition to convening technical advisory committees, the SFO would access outside, world-class expertise in science and technology on an ad hoc basis. This has long been the domain of the OSTP—via the Science and Technology Policy Institute.

Report to Congress
The SFO would be held accountable to Congress through regular reporting on its work, including dissemination of the strategic plans it creates.

Strategic Foresight Office: Where to Start?

The SFO for emerging science and technology should start with a focus on artificial intelligence and then begin adjacent work on a few other pressing science and tech issues, including biotechnology and gene editing, autonomous transportation, microsatellites, smart cities and the internet of things, quantum technologies and robotics. Because all of these domains are adjacent to or directly involve A.I., focusing first on A.I. as a platform technology would help the SFO develop a baseline of workflows and processes for how it will cover other areas of science and technology.

The SFO should clearly define A.I. as a public good. When economists define a "public good," they use a very strict definition: It must be *non excludable*, meaning it's impossible to exclude an entity from using it, because to do so would be impossible; and it must be *nonrivalrous*, meaning that when one entity uses it another can use it too.

If we formally define A.I. as a public good, this doesn't preclude large companies from earning revenue. But it does offer an opportunity to develop and enforce a common set of norms and standards for those companies, schools and researchers that are operating within or in partnership with the United States. We are now at the beginning of A.I.'s modern evolution, and we cannot continue to think of A.I. as a platform built by big tech companies in the U.S. and China for digital commerce, communications and cool apps. We must envision A.I. broadly as a non-excludable, non rivalrous public good that is developed in the best interests of all citizens, rather than just a few tech giants.

The following immediate executive actions can be taken by the SFO

1. Adapt or develop a rigorous, data-driven methodology for strategic foresight that shares common frameworks, models and vocabulary—one that can be used throughout all government and military offices. It should include frameworks and methods for: time horizon analysis, broadly-defined stakeholder analysis, defining weak signals, defining and verifying emerging trends, quantifying the velocity and trajectory of change, identifying areas of deep uncertainty, developing data-driven scenarios to confront those areas of deep uncertainty, using those scenarios to backcast near- and long-term strategic actions, quantifying

priorities based on established key indicators, and incentivizing continual, incremental action. This methodology, its frameworks and lexicon should become the accepted process for strategic foresight throughout the U.S. government and military.

2. Develop guidelines for the rigorous, data-driven modeling of risk and opportunity. Every science and technology domain studied must incorporate intersections with other areas: education, public health and medicine, workforce, energy and climate.

3. Conduct thorough audits and assessments of government funding in critical areas of science and technology.

4. Develop a tactical, durable plan for driving interagency collaboration.

5. Forge meaningful public-private sector relationships that incentivize collaboration and transparency.

As part of its initial agenda, the SFO should focus on developing the following immediate A.I. actions:

1. Define a national priority to establish principles, norms and standards for developing and deploying A.I. in the public interest. Failing to treat A.I. as a public good—the way we do our breathable air—will result in serious, insurmountable problems. Treating A.I. as a public good does not preclude the private sector from earning revenue and growing. It just means shifting our thinking and expectations. Someday we will not have the luxury of debating and discussing automation within the context of human rights and geopolitics. A.I. will have become too complex for us to untangle and shape into something we prefer. A public good must meet a standard set of criteria set by a global body, one that has the power and ability to enforce compliance.

2. Develop federal A.I. capacity. All levels of government—leaders, managers, people who work on budgets, those who write policy—should demonstrate a working knowledge of A.I. and, ideally, should incorporate those with technical expertise.

In such varied places as the Department the Interior, the Social Security Administration, Housing and Urban Affairs, the Senate Foreign Relations Committee, Veterans Affairs, and beyond, there must be A.I. experts embedded and emboldened to help guide decision-making.

3. Develop and implement a whole-of-government A.I. strategy. Coordinating everything from federally-funded research to the application of A.I. for citizen services, such an effort would ensure a comprehensive federal approach.

4. Spearhead international collaboration on setting guardrails for A.I. and enforcing standards, testing advanced systems before their commercial release, and monitoring activity as A.I. progresses from narrow to general to super intelligence. One way to do this would be through a new international entity, the Global Alliance on Intelligence Augmentation, which I describe in greater depth in my recent book, *The Big Nine: How the Tech Titans and Their Thinking Machines Could Warp Humanity.*

Learnings from the A.I. pilot should be used to expand the SFO's area of coverage to include genomics, space, agriculture, education, autonomous transportation and other areas.

The establishment of a Strategic Foresight Office would require significant bipartisan support. However, failing to develop strategies for emerging science and technologies in advance will result in untenable outcomes, pitting our legal and governing systems against the public sector. Waiting until game-changing science and technology hits the mainstream will guarantee that the U.S. falls behind other countries. Yielding strategic thinking to special interest groups makes our future dependent on politicking, which always results in poor long-term decisions. The SFO offers an alternative, one in which long-term strategic planning will set us on a responsible course for the future.

Excerpted from "A National Office for Strategic Foresight Anchored in Critical Science and Technologies," Stanford University, Geopolitics, Technology and Governance Cyber Policy Center, October 2019.

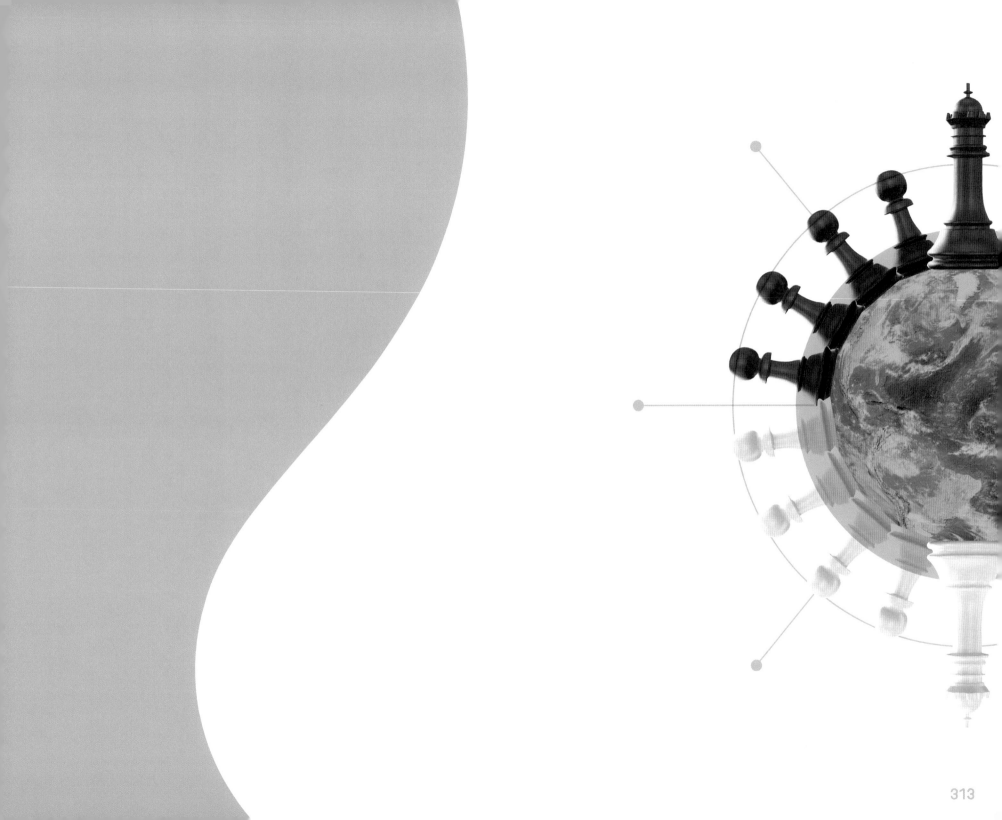

27 Smart Cities

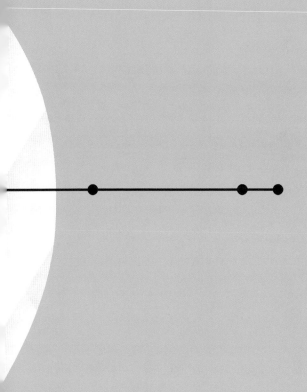

Smart City Initiatives

HIGH DEGREE OF CERTAINTY

	INFORMS STRATEGY	ACT NOW	
LONGER-TERM IMPACT	REVISIT LATER	KEEP VIGILANT WATCH	IMMEDIATE IMPACT

LOW DEGREE OF CERTAINTY

The market for smart city projects could increase to more than $1 trillion by 2025.

Key Insight

From smart city grids to car-free zones and flying taxi parking lots, cities are poised for transformational updates to their technological systems and related infrastructure.

Why It Matters

By 2050, there will be twice as many citizens living in cities than in rural areas. As the Internet of Things ecosystem matures, there will be new opportunities for city managers to learn from, influence, and optimize infrastructure, traffic, and daily living.

Examples

In the **U.S.**, a growing number of smart city initiatives are underway. The city of **Austin, Texas** debuted an open data directive in 2013, launched a series of smart city goals, and last year began trialing a city-wide 5G network. **Boston** created an Office of New Urban Mechanics to spearhead local public-private innovation partnerships. **Las Vegas** made itself a testing ground for self-driving vehicles, while **NYC Mayor's Of-**fice of Technology and Innovation (MOTI) is overseeing a number of different initiatives, which include smart water metering, citywide trash cans with wireless sensors, and new air quality monitoring systems. **Vietnam, Indonesia**, and **Myanmar** have inked smart city partnerships with **Japan**, which has pledged to help **Southeast Asian** cities ease traffic congestion, introduce cashless payments, and harness environmental data to improve the quality of life. It's an alternative to **China's** Belt and Road infrastructure initiative, which is dedicating billions of dollars in loans for various projects to help modernize its many partner countries.

What's Next

In cities throughout the **U.S.**, universities are starting to partner with city councils on a wide range of experiments. The **Argonne National Laboratory** and the **University of Washington**, for example are deploying a variety of sensors around **Seattle** to improve hyper-local weather forecasting due to climate change. But not everyone is eager for smart upgrades in their cities—**Alphabet**-owned **Sidewalk Labs** faced pushback from citizens regarding the company's plan for a heavily tech-integrated smart district in **Toronto**, ultimately scaling back elements of their plan and agreeing to more outside oversight in response to privacy concerns.

The Impact

Globally, the market for smart city projects could increase to more than $1 trillion by 2025, driven in part by multinational partnerships as well as public-private collaborations.

Watchlist

Airbus, AT&T Wireless, Audi, Continental Automotive Systems, Cora, Ericsson, Flyer, General Motors, General Motors' Cruise, Google, Huawei, Hyundai, Lilium, Mercedes-Benz, Mobile, NASA's Urban Air Mobility project, Nissan, Nokia, Sprint, T-mobile, Toyota, Uber, Volvo, Waymo, Waze, Wisk, local business leaders, local municipal agencies, universities and colleges.

Strengthening Municipal Cyber-Security Efforts

HIGH DEGREE OF CERTAINTY

LONGER-TERM IMPACT			IMMEDIATE IMPACT
	INFORMS STRATEGY	ACT NOW	
	REVISIT LATER	KEEP VIGILANT WATCH	

LOW DEGREE OF CERTAINTY

Cities are not yet prepared to deal with the coming onslaught of municipal cyberattacks.

Key Insight

Historically, cybersecurity hasn't been a top priority for cities and towns. However, as more local government services move online, municipal managers are investing in new technologies and better policies to protect against attacks.

Why It Matters

More than 40 **American municipalities** were hacked in 2019.

Examples

In 2019, the city of **Baltimore** was targeted by hackers—for several months, residents could not pay their water bills or traffic tickets online, and police officers had to write and submit warrants by hand. When the city government of **Lake City, Florida**, got hacked, it decided to pay $460,000 in bitcoin rather than try to rebuild all of its compromised systems, which would have cost significantly more. Clever bands of hackers know that local governments don't have formal cybersecurity policies—and few employ enough trained experts to safeguard systems and train employees on how to avoid attacks.

What's Next

There is a significant talent shortage—those who have the right skill set and experience to develop and implement municipal cybersecurity programs tend to take much higher-paying jobs in the private sector. If cities are committed to improving cyber-security, they must carve out a budget to invest in qualified staff. Another avenue being tested in some cities is public-private partnerships. Whatever the approach, cities must act quickly: the longer they wait, the longer they're exposing themselves to the damaging and costly threat of cybercrime.

The Impact

Municipal ransomware attacks are now so lucrative that hackers are funding their own R&D to build more powerful tools. At their most organized and resourceful, they have the power to cripple critical infrastructure and wreak havoc in major cities.

Watchlist

Local city and town agencies, local business leaders, local universities and colleges.

Landscrapers Are on the Horizon

FAR-FUTURE NEUTRAL SCENARIO

In the future, architects may choose to build laterally, rather than vertically. Advancements in the technology that moves elevators now allows a new kind of device to move omnidirectionally. Given what we know to be true about extreme weather and climate change, it's plausible that economic centers will move inland from the coasts, and that "landscrapers" will become more mainstream over the next 20 years. Spanning massive areas the size of several football fields, these new buildings could withstand high winds and structural pressures due to sudden, extreme temperature changes. They will create entirely new city footprints we haven't seen before in the U.S.

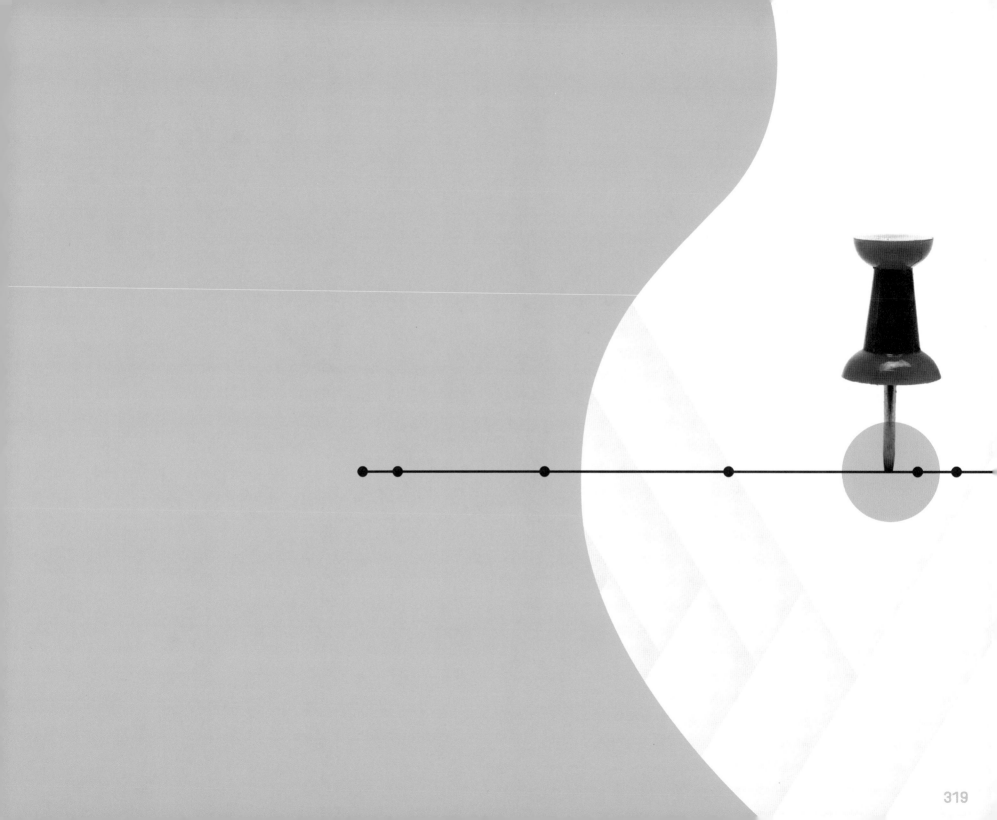

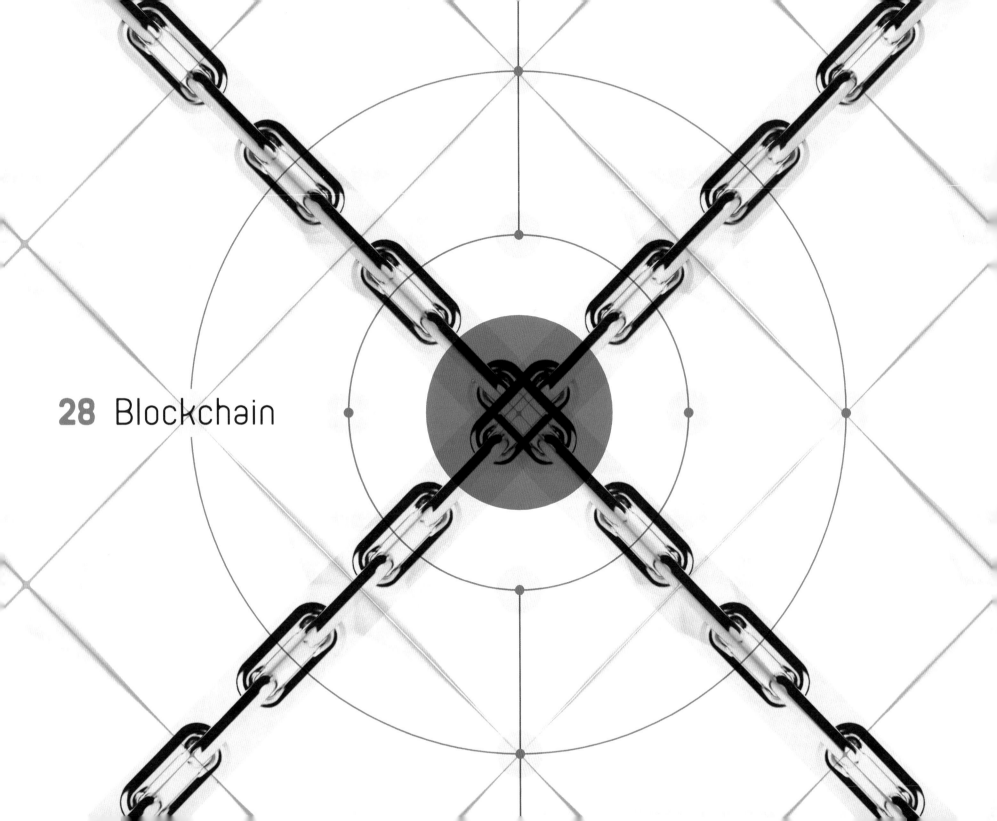

28 Blockchain

Blockchain

HIGH DEGREE OF CERTAINTY

INFORMS STRATEGY	**ACT NOW**
REVISIT LATER	**KEEP VIGILANT WATCH**

LONGER-TERM IMPACT — IMMEDIATE IMPACT

LOW DEGREE OF CERTAINTY

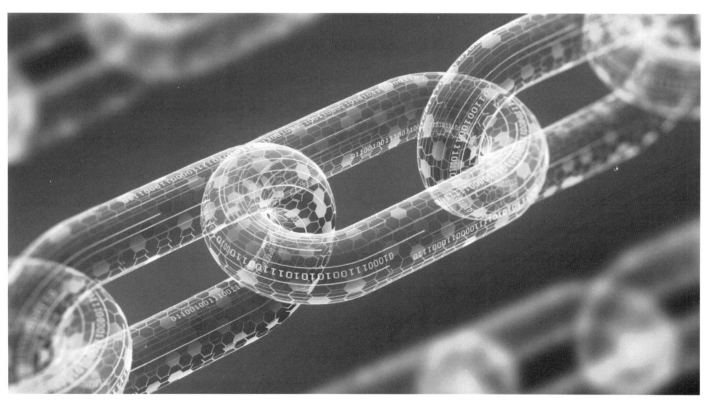

Blockchain technology is a method of sharing and storing information on a distributed ledger.

KEY INSIGHT

Blockchain technology hit an inflection point in 2017. It evolved beyond a fringe format of storage and exchange for a digital asset—Bitcoin—and broke into public consciousness as a new way to share and store information. While this technology is still developing, its broad and far-reaching applications are poised to impact a range of industries. Though it's not yet mainstream, we will continue to monitor blockchain technology as it matures in 2020. For that reason, in this section we have outlined key themes within blockchain and distributed ledger technologies.

WHAT YOU NEED TO KNOW

Blockchain technology is a method of sharing and storing information on a distributed ledger where identities and transactions are cryptographically protected. At its core, blockchain enables multiple parties to agree on a single source of collective truth without having to trust one another individually. In theory, blockchain reduces the need for intermediaries such as banks to coordinate or verify transactions. Blockchains fall under the umbrella of distributed ledger technologies, a new family of technologies that are enabling radical advancements in the fields of data sharing and data management.

WHY IT MATTERS

Blockchain technology offers enormous opportunity to protect data, safeguard privacy, build trust in supply chains, and to automate transactions across numerous industries.

⊙ DEEPER DIVE

What's the Difference Between a Blockchain, a Token, and a Cryptocurrency?

The term "blockchain" refers to a specific type of data architecture—often in the context of a network or an ecosystem. It's on the blockchain where transactions occur. "Tokens" or "cryptocurrencies" can be part of a blockchain network: They represent units of value. They can be traded or spent to make purchases or investments, to facilitate transactions, or to reward work that benefits the network. Most people have heard about "bitcoins." These are units of cryptocurrency in the Bitcoin network.

Where Is "The Blockchain," Exactly?

There isn't just one blockchain. In fact, there are different types: private, public, and federated. (This is similar to how there isn't just one "internet"—there is internet architecture and protocols, but there are different versions, networks, repositories, sites, and services based all around the world.) Blockchains can be started by individuals, companies, or consortiums, and they live on multiple machines simultaneously. They can run on different protocols just like mobile phones can run on different operating systems. There is no singular place where "the blockchain" is hosted.

How Does It Work?

Imagine editing a **Google Doc** or a **Wikipedia** article. These are distributed systems where transactions—in these examples, informational transactions in the form of textual edits—are verified by a central authority—in this case Google and Wikipedia, respectively. Blockchain systems replace the central administrators with consensus algorithms and network miners.

Let's assume we have a network of 100 individual nodes (individual computers or clusters of computers) running a blockchain ledger. In a public blockchain, every node has access to see the full ledger because the ledger is *distributed*. No single node controls the network, and all nodes have the opportunity to verify transactions, in exchange for a reward. This is generally referred to as "mining." The more nodes that choose to become miners, the more the network is *decentralized*. As a reward for their efforts, every miner that verifies a block of transactions wins a block reward—this is represented by a cryptocurrency unit or a token. Miners can be anyone: people who want to help build the infrastructure, startups with spare computing resources, or even huge investment banks looking to get into crypto markets. Miners compete against each other to verify transactions. Once a miner verifies a set of transactions, or a "block," the node broadcasts the new block to the entire network. If the majority of the network agrees the block is valid, it is cryptographically added to the existing chain of blocks or "blockchain," which forms the ledger. Miners then can work on the next block.

Can Blockchains Get Hacked Easily?

Not in the traditional way. Since it is impossible to predict which miner will verify the next transaction, it is nearly impossible to collude against, attack or defraud the network. The network is secure as long as miners act independently of one another. However some clever hackers know that it's possible to manipulate a network by doing more of the work than anyone else. One known method of attack is to control greater than 51% of the mining activity. Believe it or not, this has happened in the past—in 2019 hackers took control of the **Ethereum Classic** blockchain with a 51% attack.

Bitcoin: A Peer-to-Peer Electronic Cash System

Satoshi Nakamoto
satoshin@gmx.com
www.bitcoin.org

Abstract. A purely peer-to-peer version of electronic cash would allow online payments to be sent directly from one party to another without going through a financial institution. Digital signatures provide part of the solution, but the main benefits are lost if a trusted third party is still required to prevent double-spending. We propose a solution to the double-spending problem using a peer-to-peer network. The network timestamps transactions by hashing them into an ongoing chain of hash-based proof-of-work, forming a record that cannot be changed without redoing the proof-of-work. The longest chain not only serves as proof of the sequence of events witnessed, but proof that it came from the largest pool of CPU power. As long as a majority of CPU power is controlled by nodes that are not cooperating to attack the network, they'll generate the longest chain and outpace attackers. The network itself requires minimal structure. Messages are broadcast on a best effort basis, and nodes can leave and rejoin the network at will, accepting the longest proof-of-work chain as proof of what happened while they were gone.

1. Introduction

Commerce on the Internet has come to rely almost exclusively on financial institutions serving as trusted third parties to process electronic payments. While the system works well enough for most transactions, it still suffers from the inherent weaknesses of the trust based model. Completely non-reversible transactions are not really possible, since financial institutions cannot avoid mediating disputes. The cost of mediation increases transaction costs, limiting the minimum practical transaction size and cutting off the possibility for small casual transactions, and there is a broader cost in the loss of ability to make non-reversible payments for non-

In 2008 a person or group of people using the name "Satoshi Nakamoto" published the seminal paper "Bitcoin: a Peer to Peer Electronic Cash System" and launched the Bitcoin movement.

A Very Brief History of Blockchains (With Caveats)

The concept of blockchains was first introduced in 2008 when a person or group of people under the name Satoshi Nakamoto published the seminal paper, "Bitcoin: a Peer to Peer Electronic Cash System." To this day, it's still not clear who **Satashi Nakamoto** really is, whether or not they are Japanese, and what their true motivations were in helping get blockchains started in the real world.

It took several years for the information in the paper to evolve from an interesting concept to usable code at scale. But once **Bitcoin** gained recognition as the first cryptocurrency, other versions soon followed. In 2015, **Canadian** computer programmer **Vitalik Buterin** released **Ethereum**, a blockchain-based protocol that allowed for more sophisticated functionality in the form of smart contracts, or self-executing agreements, the terms of which are written directly into lines of code. Ethereum was the first blockchain project to fundraise through an "Initial Coin Offering" or ICO, raising $19 million in 2014. An ICO is similar in some ways to an Initial Public Offering, but instead of shares in a company, investors receive tokens which may or may not eventually be of some value or use in the digital ecosystem that the money is being raised to develop. In 2017, more than 400 ICOs raised $5.6 billion.

The year 2018 was dubbed the "crypto winter," because the total market cap of cryptocurrencies fell by 85% over the course of 12 months. Despite the bear market, finance, tech, and retail heavyweights like **Fidelity**, **IBM**, **Facebook**, **Google**, **Microsoft**, **Amazon**, and **Walmart** all made significant investments in the industry. **Bank of America**, **Mastercard**, and **IBM** collectively owned more than 100 blockchain-related patents.

Opportunities and Challenges

Blockchain is still a nascent technology, and many challenges must be addressed before it can reach mass adoption—namely speed, scale, and regulation.

Decentralized systems are inherently less efficient than centralized systems, and there are trade-offs between security and scale.

Bitcoin and Ethereum process between three and six transactions per second, while **Visa** processes thousands of transactions in the same amount of time. As systems improve, this is changing—but there's still a long way to go.

However, the bigger challenge is likely to be regulatory. The fate of blockchains, cryptocurrencies, and tokens is uncertain, to say the least. In the **U.S.**, the **Securities and Exchange Commission (SEC)**, congressional offices, and local state governments all have specific and, at times, conflicting policies related to blockchains and cryptoassets. In fact, the SEC still does not have a regulatory framework ready for use in the crypto domain. In the summer of 2019, the **Internal Revenue Service** caused a mini-shockwave when it sent out 10,000 warning letters to the owners of cryptocurrencies. Some believe it may be a similar effort the agency took when it went after **Swiss** banks a few years ago, rooting out financial hideouts for people avoiding taxes.

While the primary use cases for blockchain technology evolved in the field of financial services, blockchains are proving their use in wider contexts where authentication matters. Many different industries are building new applications and uses for blockchain technology. We are paying close attention to what's happening in professional services, commercial real estate, financial services, supply chain management, logistics, healthcare, and identity management.

Blockchain is still a nascent technology, and many challenges must be addressed before it can reach mass adoption—namely speed, scale, and regulation.

How to Speak Blockchain

51% Attack
A hypothetical attack on a blockchain in which an affiliated group of miners working collectively controls more that 50% of the network's mining power. These miners could collude to verify fraudulent transactions.

Altcoin
Any blockchain-based coin or asset other than Bitcoin.

Bitcoin
The first cryptocurrency, mined, stored, and exchanged on the first blockchain. It was introduced in 2008 by Satoshi Nakamoto, and is abbreviated on exchanges as BTC.

Block Height
The number of blocks preceding a particular block. The first block on a blockchain, referred to as the genesis block, has a block height of zero.

Block Rewards
Tokens distributed by the network to the miner or group of miners that verifies a particular block. Block rewards are different from mining fees and tips, which are distributed by individuals (as opposed to the network) to incentivize miners to verify their transactions first.

Blockchain
A new distributed system to share and store information in which transaction and identities are cryptographically secured. Blockchains are a subset of distributed ledger technologies (DLTs). Bitcoin, Ethereum, and Litecoin are some of the more prominent examples of blockchain networks.

Cold Storage
The practice of storing a digital "wallet" or private keys offline, on a piece of hardware not connected to the internet.

Cryptocurrency
A crypto-asset typically designed to function as money, or a medium of exchange. Cryptocurrencies' value fluctuates depending on demand and supply, similar to traditional currency in the global economy.

DAO
A decentralized autonomous organization. Many coins use DAOs as a form of governance and decision-making among the network.

Dapp
Decentralized applications run on blockchain platforms.

Ethereum
The second largest coin by market cap, after Bitcoin. It was introduced in 2015 by Vitalik Buterin, and is abbreviated on exchanges as ETH.

Fiat
Government-issued currency.

Fork
The splitting of a single blockchain into two blockchains—identical up to the point of the split, but differing from that point forward—on different parts of the network. Forks can be accidental or intentional, temporary or permanent, and are often the subject of dispute. They can be the result of software upgrades or governance decisions that nodes refuse to acknowledge or forget to install.

Fork; Hard Fork
A software update on a blockchain protocol that is not backward compatible, creating a separate blockchain. Ethereum's hard fork resulted in Ethereum and Ethereum Classic.

Fork; Soft Fork
A software update on a blockchain protocol that is backward compatible with older versions.

FUD
Fear, uncertainty, and doubt, often used in the context of blockchains.

Full Node
A node on the network that can act as a miner, verifying transactions on the blockchain.

Governance
Set rules that govern the blockchain protocol. Governance structures can include on-chain rules like smart contracts and code specifications and off-chain rules like those designating a board of directors and annual meetings.

Hash Pointer
Unique alphanumeric strings linking blocks in the chain together with a one way math function.

Hashing
A one-way math function that takes any input and produces a unique alphanumeric string. It's used in blockchain technology to condense information into blocks, and it's useful for assigning any digital file or asset with a unique identifier.

HODL
Misspelling of the word "hold"—a term used by crypto investors to describe keeping coins despite market volatility and price crashes.

Hot Storage
The practice of storing a digital "wallet" or private keys online, usually within an application or exchange connected to the internet—examples include Poloniex, Coinbase, and Bittrex.

ICO
An initial coin offering, or IOC, is similar in some ways to an Initial Public Offering, but instead of shares in a company, investors receive tokens which may or may not eventually be of some value or use in the digital ecosystem that the money is being raised to develop.

Immutability
A primary characteristic of blockchains, this is the quality of a record of transactions being unchangeable, a quality that prevents "back-dating" in record keeping. Sometimes referred to as digital granite.

KYC/AML
An acronym for "know your customer" and "anti-money laundering." KYC/AML requirements are used by many financial service providers to confirm the identity of their customers and detect illicit and criminal activity in their networks.

Light Node
A node on the network that can transact with other nodes but cannot verify transactions.

Mempool
The aggregate number and size of unconfirmed transactions on a blockchain.

PoW PoS
Acronyms for Proof of Work and Proof of Stake, mechanisms that blockchain protocols use to choose the miner that gets to produce the next block.

Public Key + Private Key
A type of cryptography (similar to the method used in credit cards) for managing identities in the form of alphanumeric addresses used to send and receive transactions.

SHA256
The cryptographic hash algorithm used in most blockchains.

Shilling
Aggressively promoting a coin or crypto-to-asset.

Smart Contracts
Self-enforcing agreements, issued on a blockchain, the terms of which are built directly into the code.

Solidity
A programming language invented by Vitalik Buterin for smart contracts on Ethereum.

Stablecoin
A cryptocurrency that is valued relative to a "stable" asset or basket of assets, whether another cryptocurrency, fiat money, or commodities.

Token
A digital identity for something that can be owned.

TPS
An acronym for Transactions Per Second, a measure used to compare the speeds of different blockchains.

Wallet
A file that contains a collection of private keys.

Whitepaper
A technical paper outlining the governance, protocol and features of a project.

Digital Citizenship

HIGH DEGREE OF CERTAINTY

INFORMS STRATEGY	**ACT NOW**
REVISIT LATER	**KEEP VIGILANT WATCH**

LONGER-TERM IMPACT · IMMEDIATE IMPACT

LOW DEGREE OF CERTAINTY

One of Venezuela's digital citizenship cards.

Key Insight

Blockchain is being used to facilitate a new kind of digital citizenship in some countries.

Why It Matters

Governments are expanding the definition of digital citizenship with surveillance programs such as social credit scores and government-issued IDs that track everything from voting records to state pensions.

Examples

Estonia, a small northern **European** country of 1.3 million, was the first nation to move most of its government services fully online 16 years ago. From taxes, to voting, to healthcare, Estonia has created myriad digital tools to serve its citizens. In 2017, in an effort to attract more entrepreneurs and tech talent, Estonia began piloting a beta digital citizenship program (along with financial benefits such as favorable tax breaks) without requiring a physical residence in the country. While Estonia's digital citizenship is an example of positive government innovation, other countries have introduced more controversial initiatives.

Some 15 million **Venezuelans** allegedly have a *"Carnet de la Patria"* or a Fatherland Card, which was developed by **Chinese** telecom giant **ZTE**. Under the dictatorship of **Nicolás Maduro**, the country rolled out the cards four years ago, requiring Venezuelans to use this card to access government services, pensions, and food stamps. The card also tracks voting records and party registration.

Where does blockchain fit into all of this? Estonia incorporates distributed ledger technology in many of its digital citizenship services. In the **U.S.**, one startup called **Voatz** is applying blockchain technology to voting. In 2018, Voatz conducted a pilot program with the government of **West Virginia** in which 144 Americans living in 31 countries overseas cast ballots in the November midterm elections.

What's Next

In democratic countries with protections for individual freedoms and rights, digital citizenship can usher in a new age of innovation and improved public services.

The Impact

Many authoritarian and totalitarian regimes are also eager to adopt these technologies as well to maintain control and concentrate power.

Watchlist

Voatz, Utah, West Virginia, the governments of China, Estonia, and Venezuela, voting commissions worldwide.

DIGITAL CITIZENSHIP

In the next 10 years, blockchain technology advances enough to support key functions of citizenship, including identification cards, driver licenses, and voting. But these innovations are met with public distrust, and a lack of political coordination to effectively implement these blockchain applications. Communities define themselves by how "smart" they are (whether they embrace new technologies, such as automation, security, grid management, and more) or how "human" they are (whether they're unplugged, have internet-free zones and honor the right to digital invisibility).

Blockchain Empowers Democracies

Blockchain Empowers Authoritarian Regimes

MID-FUTURE OPTIMISTIC SCENARIO

In stable democracies, digital citizenship starts with the mundane, such as e-passports and virtual jury duty, and then gradually grows into more complicated systems like voting. Pilot tests continue for blockchain voting startups like Voatz in large counties and districts. These pilots target small groups such as the homebound elderly and active military stationed overseas, and eventually scale to wider populations. Voting processes are the primary indicator of a fully digitally engaged civic community, although it takes more than a generation to see a widespread shift to digital and decentralized systems.

Eventually, governments apply open-source algorithms and machine learning to other tasks, including balancing the budget and determining where to build new roads. Citizens will, in the words of Bitcoin maximalist Anthony Pompliano, "trust the governance of algorithms over the governance of humans."

Open-source technology and publicly-funded initiatives, like municipal internet projects, gain traction despite a few high profile failures. Governments pass data security and data sharing restrictions on any public-private partnerships to prevent corporations from harvesting data to further commercial interests. Open-source tools for government and civic life increase transparency and efficiency in government processes and usher in an era of more connected and civically engaged communities.

MID-FUTURE CATASTROPHIC SCENARIO

Blockchain evolves as a technology that makes it easier to track citizens and abuse power. Canada, Estonia, and India all launch massive digital identity programs for their citizens; some are voluntary opt-in programs, others are compulsory programs like the Aadhaar program in India. Once these digital citizenship programs are in place, it becomes hard to ensure that citizens maintain some GDPR-era digital rights, such as the right to be forgotten.

China and Russia establish large scale citizen surveillance programs, and they export them to countries in Southeast Asia, Latin America, and Africa. Venezuela launches a botched cryptocurrency. While it's ridiculed in the crypto community, it's a sign of things to come. Iran follows suit with plans to launch a sovereign-backed cryptocurrency. China, which initially outlawed cryptocurrencies, develops its own national cryptocurrency that can only be used by its preferred trading partners.

While the blockchain and Web 3.0 promised decentralization of power, in reality influence in these networks concentrates within two parties: the developers who write the code for core protocols and the miners who validate transactions. The number of people who can contribute to open-source blockchain projects is tiny relative to the potential size of the networks. Corporations and governments with majority control of either the miners or the developers manipulate the system and rewrite the rules on their own terms.

Self-Sovereign Identity

Key Insight

Identity management systems have seen a gradual evolution from government issued IDs to email providers and social media accounts.

Why It Matters

The average person uses between 27 and 130 unique online accounts. Companies like **Google**, **Yahoo**, and **Facebook** built their business models on managing troves of data on behalf of their users, but users suffered from large-scale security breaches. Case in point: The Yahoo hack impacted every single one of its 3 billion accounts. Last year alone saw 15 high profile data breaches affecting 2 billion accounts across government, healthcare, finance, and technology sectors involving organizations like Facebook, **CapitalOne**, **Singapore's Ministry of Health**, and **Bulgaria's Revenue Agency**.

Examples

Blockchains and distributed ledger technologies introduced a new approach to identity management: self-sovereign identity, a system in which the user is central to the administration of her data and owns her data outright. It is interoperable and transportable across applications, devices, and platforms.

Self-sovereign identity has two primary benefits. There's increased security, because decentralized identity solutions, in theory, are much harder to hack. And there's also increased control; because an individual manages her identity, she owns her data and can therefore decide what information to share and with whom—and, hypothetically, how to monetize it. Self-sovereign identity is a trend that touches on paywalls, authentication, and royalty tracking, as well as digital advertising.

Identity systems help individuals validate reputation, manage risk, and gain access to groups. Many rely on third-party "identity providers" such as governments, Facebook, or Google. Digital identity management has been a central point of vulnerability for individuals and corporations alike, with hackers using phishing emails and personally identifiable information (PII) to reset passwords and break into accounts.

In 2019, **Microsoft** launched Identity Overlay Network (ION), a decentralized identity solution. It's a collaboration between the **Decentralized Identity Foundation**, **IBM**, **Aetna**, **Mastercard**, and **Accenture**. **Samsung** has also created a decentralized identity project with a consortium of **South Korean** enterprises.

What's Next

Self-sovereign identity will likely be adopted in phases. The **Brave Browser**, for instance, gives users more control over their data as they surf the web. While not a "self-sovereign identity" platform, the Brave model illustrates how users could capitalize on their data if they had more control over their digital identities. With Brave, users get paid 70% of the ad revenue from the ads they watch and they can then choose to share their identities with the sites they visit—for not. There's strong incentive for businesses like Google and Facebook to consider this trend because of rising data breaches and security hacks that impact users. Identity is closely tied to data, which means these businesses must consider a business model shift if self-sovereign identity solutions become widely adopted.

The Impact

Since interoperability is a defining feature of decentralized identities, companies should look for partners instead of attempting to launch an identity product on their own.

Watchlist

Aetna, Accenture, AdEx, Brave Browser, Comcast, Decentralized Identity Foundation, Facebook, Google, IBM, Mastercard, Microsoft, Netflix, Spotify, Samsung, UPort.

Web 3.0

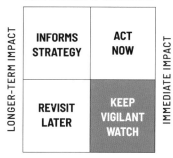

HIGH DEGREE OF CERTAINTY

INFORMS STRATEGY	**ACT NOW**
REVISIT LATER	**KEEP VIGILANT WATCH**

LONGER-TERM IMPACT · IMMEDIATE IMPACT

LOW DEGREE OF CERTAINTY

Key Insight

2019 marked the 30th anniversary of the world wide web. Decentralization and collaboration are driving its next iteration.

Why it Matters

Just as cloud computing revolutionized how businesses manage and store information, blockchain will enable a new wave of innovation for information technology and databases. Distributed ledgers can encourage massive collaboration on a larger scale and usher in Web 3.0.

Examples

The internet is always evolving. So far, it has seen three major waves of innovation. Web 1.0, the beginning of the internet age, introduced static web pages, e-commerce, and email. Web 2.0 enabled decentralized collaboration and creativity by ushering in social networks, sharing economies, cloud computing, and dynamic self-sustaining content repositories like **Wikipedia** and **Github**. Some collaborations pushed our imagination beyond what we thought was possible, like **Reddit's** April Fool's Day 2017 experiment or **Google's** six-month Quick Draw Doodling game.

With Web 3.0—in certain contexts referred to as the Semantic Web—collaboration and decentralized creation is accelerated for two reasons. First, gathering and understanding unstructured data will be much easier with advanced techniques in data mining, natural language processing (NLP), and text analytics. Second, machines will be able to collaborate directly with one another through artificial intelligence and machine learning. Eventually, machines will be able to teach one another as well.

Such projects are already underway. In media, **Otoy** is cutting the costs of 3D visual effects production with a decentralized, distributed network of partners that can chip in spare processing power with a digital token known as RNDR. The **Interplanetary File System (IPFS)** is a peer-to-peer hyper-media protocol that facilitates decentralized file-sharing and cloud computing. All this is possible because of what **Joel Monegro** from **Union Square Ventures** described as the "fat protocol layer." Web protocol layer is part of the full internet stack. "Full stack" refers to every stage of the computer programming/ web developers tool kit: front end (UX, design, HTML, Java, CSS) to back end (servers, databases, APIs, Python, Ruby). The internet stack has application layers and protocol layers.

In web 2.0, most of the value rested in the application layer, with little variability in the protocol layer. Examples of the most common protocols are HTTP used by browsers and SMTP and IMAP is used by email-clients.

What's Next

In web 3.0, protocols and platforms may have much more potential for value creation, hence a larger protocol layer. Companies like **Blockstack**, **Lightning Labs** and **RSK** are building layer 2 networking products.

The Impact

With web 3.0, web browsers and mobile applications can perform more complex processes and enable transactions that were previously not possible. In this new iteration of the internet, media companies could potentially set up micropayment systems or give users more control over their privacy and data.

Watchlist

Blockstack, Lightning Labs, RSK.

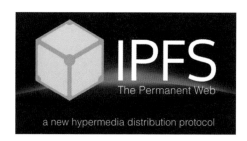

The Interplanetary File System (IPFS) is a peer-to-peer hypermedia protocol that facilitates decentralized file-sharing and cloud computing.

Making Money While You Sleep

NEAR-FUTURE NEUTRAL SCENARIO

Imagine getting into bed tonight and plugging your phone into its charger on your nightstand like always. You set the alarm, and just before sleep, you start up a special app—one that invites hackers to take over your phone. It isn't a dream—but it isn't a nightmare either. It's the future of the gig economy.

In the coming years, you're going to hear a lot about our new decentralized sharing economy. It's a clever way of distributing computing power over a wide network for a variety of tasks, which range from performing mathematical computations to mining for cryptocurrencies. All you need to get started is to install what we call "gigware." It's a benevolent use for the same kind of malware a hacker relies on to break into your computers and phones—except that it generates a tangible benefit, whether you're a company or individual user. Think of it as the next evolution of the sharing economy, powered by artificial intelligence.

At the moment, there are nearly four billion internet users spread around the world, and each of us owns three devices on average. That means there's a gigantic pool of processing power sitting dormant at any given time.

Gigware is like Airbnb for your computers and phones. It will someday allow third-party businesses to use your smartphones and computers in exchange for credits or real money you can spend elsewhere. And because the systems are distributed and decentralized, private data is safeguarded.

Tokenizing Value

HIGH DEGREE OF CERTAINTY

INFORMS STRATEGY	ACT NOW
REVISIT LATER	KEEP VIGILANT WATCH

LONGER-TERM IMPACT · IMMEDIATE IMPACT

LOW DEGREE OF CERTAINTY

The Basic Attention Token compensates internet users for their attention to ads.

Key Insight

In the context of blockchain technology, tokenization refers to the representation of a real-world asset or value with a digital token. These digital tokens carry the unique property of "digital scarcity," meaning that tokens cannot be counterfeited or duplicated.

Why It matters

In theory, asset tokenization allows businesses to reduce the friction associated with buying and selling securities to a greater network of investors.

Examples

Buzz around this trend started during the initial coin offering (ICO) boom of 2017, when startups raised millions of dollars in capital by tokenizing equity of their company or utility of their networks. While many of those ICOs proved unsuccessful, the underlying theory of using digital tokens to represent real-world assets is gaining traction. **Louis Vuitton** and **DeBeers** launched blockchain platforms to combat counterfeiting of luxury goods, and **Nike** has a patent for tokenizing sneakers. The **National Basketball Association** rejected **Brooklyn Nets** player **Spencer Dinwiddie**'s attempt to tokenize his contract to investors and fans. Companies are exploring ways to use their own tokens to capitalize on different business models and incentivize user behavior. The **Brave Browser** allows users to earn tokens—called BAT, or Basic Attention Token—based on the ads they watch. **Althea** is a startup using mesh networks to bring internet to rural and underserved communities using a system in which routers pay one another for bandwidth using, you guessed it, digital tokens. **Helium** pays customers in tokens to run internet hotspots and provide wireless coverage for smart scooters, bikes, and other IoT devices.

What's Next

Asset tokenization and token economies are based on mostly theoretical models. During the next five years, these networks will pilot and test different approaches to find the best product-market fit.

The Impact

Eventually asset tokenization could shift how we represent real-world assets in everyday transactions.

Watchlist

Althea, Blockstack, Brave, Debeers, Helium, Louis Vitton, Nike, NBA.

Tokens For Smart Royalties and Freelancers

HIGH DEGREE OF CERTAINTY

LONGER-TERM IMPACT

INFORMS STRATEGY	ACT NOW
REVISIT LATER	KEEP VIGILANT WATCH

IMMEDIATE IMPACT

LOW DEGREE OF CERTAINTY

Key Insight

Blockchain networks like **Ethereum** offer new ways to track ownership and licensing for content through smart contracts.

Why It Matters

Smart contracts are self-executing agreements in which the terms of the agreement are directly written into lines of code. In the music industry, for example, a smart contract could entail that every time a song is streamed, a small amount of money would be automatically sent to the artist from the listener.

Examples

Blockchains like **Ethereum** form the foundational infrastructure layer for new, low-friction ways to automate royalty payments for digital intellectual property. The **Open Music Initiative** (OMI) is a nonprofit consortium with members such as **Facebook**, **IBM**, **IDEO**, **IHEARTRADIO**, **Netflix**, **Pandora**, **Sony**, and **Spotify**. Based out of the **Berklee School of Music**, this initiative is focused on developing standardized open-source protocols and APIs for the music industry. Blockchain is a key part of the strategy. Meanwhile, the **KODAKOne** platform helps photographers manage the digital rights of images using blockchain technology. The platform works by recording ownership and creation of the images on a blockchain ledger, and then a web crawling service scans websites to see if a copyrighted image is being used.

News and media organizations may also have new opportunities to use smart contracts, digital intellectual property rights structures, and micro payments—and potentially revisit an economic model adopted by the news services on **CompuServe** in the 1980s. In that news structure, readers paid per view for articles, including paying extra for images. At the time, CompuServe offered high quality journalism that was easier to access and navigate. Ultimately the service failed because of the arrival of free, high quality journalism and free search services such as **Google** and **AOL**.

What's Next

Ownership of digital assets is evolving, with a growing movement in favor of content creators holding the rights to their content. In **Europe**, for example, **GDPR** legislation gives people greater ownership rights over the data they create, no matter what platform it is created on. We expect an increased demand for platforms that honor this ownership model, and also those that compensate creators for the engagement they drive on the platform—a shift that would affect creatives like musicians, photographers, videographers, writers, and others.

The change in ownership rights would be the equivalent of Instagram directly paying popular content creators to host them on their platform—it's a departure from the current model, in which Instagram does not need to pay content creators, ostensibly because of the free service the platform provides. Instead, content creators are paid by brands that want access to the creators' followers.

The Impact

Musicians may well be the first to publish content on platforms with smart contracts that remove intermediaries such as management and distribution companies. This could prove successful because of enduring consumer demand for music and the promise of more revenue for artists. News platforms will be fast followers, specifically for video and photo libraries—but they may struggle, because journalists tend to have more elastic followings than musicians or other artists. Regardless, there will likely be changes in methods of digital ownership and licensing playing out across all creative industries.

Watchlist

Associated Press, Ethereum, Getty, KodakOne, Mycelia, Open Music Initiative, Reuters, Facebook, IBM, IDEO, IHEARTRADIO, Netflix, Pandora, Sony, Spotify, the Berklee School of Music.

Immutable Content

HIGH DEGREE OF CERTAINTY

INFORMS STRATEGY	ACT NOW
REVISIT LATER	KEEP VIGILANT WATCH

LONGER-TERM IMPACT / IMMEDIATE IMPACT

LOW DEGREE OF CERTAINTY

Misinformation can be curtailed with blockchain technology.

Key Insight

Decentralized platforms for content will give more control to the people who originally created it, whether it be a social media post or a public speech. Think of this trend as a new way to build trust around critical information.

Why It Matters

Those political truth-o-meters that have become popular around the world in the past few years may soon be a thing of the past. That's because blockchain technology allows for the creation of a distributed immutable record of information, which means that information can never be deleted or modified; taken out of context, sure—but not twisted or changed into something different.

Examples

Decentralized platforms for content pave the way for information to be recorded and distributed in a way that is visible to all and cannot be changed without changing all records across most users. A distribution channel leveraging blockchain technology could make it more difficult to censor and limit access to information. Content creators could use distribution channels that can guarantee that their content does not get altered, filtered or blocked by a third party.

What's Next

We will soon have the ability to leverage blockchain-based platforms that can guarantee our content does not get manipulated or censored en route to its end consumers. Information archives or distribution companies—something akin to **WikiLeaks**, for example—will be able to disseminate information using a distributed system by recording the information on a blockchain ledger similar to Bitcoin's. The blockchain would also ensure that the information does not become inaccessible if the host servers are disconnected.

The Impact

As misinformation continues to spread, immutable content could help restore the public's trust.

Watchlist

Agora, Decent, Ethereum, Facebook, Internet Archive, reddit, Twitter, WikiLeaks, WordPress.

Content Provenance and Permanent Archiving

HIGH DEGREE OF CERTAINTY

LONGER-TERM IMPACT

INFORMS STRATEGY	ACT NOW
REVISIT LATER	KEEP VIGILANT WATCH

IMMEDIATE IMPACT

LOW DEGREE OF CERTAINTY

In 2018, Chinese activist Yue Xin at Peking University used the Ethereum blockchain to publish her letter detailing a pattern of abuse and intimidation from school administrators. Her letter had been routinely censored from social media sites like WeChat.

Key Insight

Blockchains can be used as a universal index of content authorship and edits.

Why It Matters

Blockchain technology enables the creation of a shared permanent ledger where nothing can be deleted. Because of this, adding original content or an index to the original content to the blockchain is a way that journalists can make their content permanent and traceable.

Examples

In 2018, **Chinese** activist **Yue Xin** at **Peking University** used the **Ethereum** blockchain to publish a letter that detailed a pattern of abuse and intimidation from school administrators. Her letter had been routinely censored from social media sites like **WeChat**. Her actions illustrated how to use blockchain to permanently archive content that would otherwise be subject to censorship or suppression. Other Chinese activists have since followed her example.

In an increasingly digital world, permanent archives are difficult to maintain for small newsrooms and large media companies alike. The **Wayback Machine** is a nonprofit that started in 2001 with a mission to digitally archive the world wide web. Despite archival efforts such as these, information on the internet is routinely deleted or censored by large corporations and governments.

In other initiatives, the **New York Times** is exploring blockchain as a way to combat misinformation, and **The News Provenance Project** is a project to help the public better understand the origins of journalistic content and detect when images and videos have been doctored or manipulated.

What's Next

We will see increasing experimentation with blockchain as a method of verifying the origins and unaltered condition of the content users consume online, and as a secure method of archiving.

The Impact

Blockchain-based tools could prove critical in efforts to restore order and reliability to online records and information, which has become increasingly challenging as the internet has evolved.

Watchlist

Associated Press, Internet Archive, New York Times, Washington Post, WikiLeaks, WordPress.

Distributed Computing For a Cause

HIGH DEGREE OF CERTAINTY

INFORMS STRATEGY	**ACT NOW**
REVISIT LATER	**KEEP VIGILANT WATCH**

LONGER-TERM IMPACT

IMMEDIATE IMPACT

LOW DEGREE OF CERTAINTY

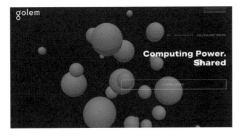

The Golem network is a distributed computing system that pools resources across many devices for shared projects and tasks.

Key Insight

Distributed computing is a process in which large computer problems are broken down into smaller segments that can be calculated on multiple standard computers, instead of on centralized supercomputers.

Why It Matters

With distributed computing technology, people can donate idle processor time on their personal laptops, cell phones, and other digital devices in support of certain causes or to help solve socially relevant problems.

Examples

Folding@home is a distributed computing project for disease research that was launched in 2000. Consumers donated idle processing power on their computers, PlayStation 3s, and some Sony smartphones to power the scientific research.

Since then, a number of other similar projects have popped up, demonstrating how idle computer resources can become a valu-able and monetizable asset. For instance, the Golem network was built upon the Ethereum blockchain and lets people rent out idle computing resources like storage, processing power, or bandwidth to render computer-generated images, conduct DNA analysis, and tackle machine learning tasks. GridCoin is another blockchain-based distributed computing platform providing resources to philanthropic scientific research.

What's Next

Expect to see more platforms that monetize idle computer resources, allowing consumers to earn income from underutilized resources that they already own.

The Impact

Distributed computing systems will drive down prices for developers and those who need greater processing power, and provide the average device owner with a new source of income and a novel way to support purpose-driven initiatives.

Watchlist

Apple, Android, AWS, Golem.network, Google, GridCoin, Intel, Microsoft, Monero, Samsung, SONM, ISPs and wireless carriers worldwide.

29 Financial
Technologies
& Cryptocurrencies

Tech Companies Acting Like Banks

HIGH DEGREE OF CERTAINTY

INFORMS STRATEGY	ACT NOW
REVISIT LATER	KEEP VIGILANT WATCH

LONGER-TERM IMPACT · IMMEDIATE IMPACT

LOW DEGREE OF CERTAINTY

In 2019 Apple launched its Apple Card, a credit card backed by the Mastercard payment network.

Key Insight

Big tech companies are building new services and tools for banking.

Why It Matters

In the near-future, the value of our everyday financial transactions will be eclipsed by the value of our data itself.

Examples

In 2020, **Google** will begin offering checking accounts. **Apple** has launched a credit card service with no late fees, and no wait to qualify—notably, the service is optimized for use with iPhones and Apple Watches, rather than a physical card. **Uber Money** is building a bank for Uber drivers. **Amazon**, which already offers branded rewards credit card in partnership with **Visa** and **Chase** on **Amazon.com**, is reportedly looking into its own checking account service. **Facebook** made headlines throughout 2019 for its foray into payments: It announced **Facebook Pay**, a system to transfer money to other users via **WhatsApp**. That will be separate from Facebook's new **Calibra** project, an attempt to build a digital wallet and standardized infrastructure for cryptocurrencies. And, of course, there is **Libra**, Facebook's controversial global cryptocurrency network. There's a good reason tech companies are moving swiftly into fintech: Our transactions not only offer new streams of revenue, but our sensitive personal data can be used to better understand our financial behavior. Knowing how, when, and why we'll spend money gives these companies a significant advantage in marketing products and services to us, and strategically targeting us with ads.

What's Next

To understand the future of big tech's role in financial services, look to **China**, where payment apps provided by **Ant Financial**—the banking arm of **Alibaba**—are now ubiquitous. Cash is quickly falling out of favor, and so are physical cards as many people in China and beyond now pay using biometric scanning or by tapping their phones against a computer screen. As a result, those consumers are paying twice: once with the money in their bank accounts, and once again with their personal data. Regulators in the **U.S.** and the **European Union**, however, are currently debating whether to keep big tech out of finance.

The Impact

Big tech companies have made payments easier, and this will put pressure on traditional companies to upgrade their products, customer service, and terms. It's possible the entire consumer banking industry could be disrupted before long.

Watchlist

Alibaba, Amazon, Ant Financial, Apple, Citi, Chase, Facebook, Goldman Sachs, Google, Mastercard, Square, Stripe, Tencent, Uber, Venmo, Visa.

Financial Inclusion

HIGH DEGREE OF CERTAINTY

INFORMS STRATEGY	ACT NOW
REVISIT LATER	KEEP VIGILANT WATCH

LONGER-TERM IMPACT   IMMEDIATE IMPACT

LOW DEGREE OF CERTAINTY

Key Insight

It is no accident that **Facebook's Libra** positions itself as a global cryptocurrency built to promote financial inclusion, a term used to describe equitable access to affordable financial services for the widest population possible. In theory that population includes those who are currently not served or minimally served by financial institutions, often referred to as the unbanked or underbanked. Financial inclusion is more than a positive social impact story, it's a forward-looking customer acquisition strategy and subsequent business model in an increasingly competitive global economy.

Why It Matters

Traditional financial institutions are facing competition and disruption from agile fintech companies and social platforms that are integrating payments and other financial features and services into their product ecosystem.

Examples

It's not just financial services vying to unlock the underbanked market. Mega-retailers like **Walmart** and **Alibaba** offer financial products to their customers. **Latin America** and **India** will be two markets to watch closely for innovation in financial inclusion. **The Reserve Bank of India** took such measures as licensing telcos as payment banks and instituting national standards for payment software. The result has been dramatic advancements in digital payments. **Amazon**, **Samsung**, **Facebook**, and **Google** all have products that are compatible with unified payment interfaces (UPIs, India's mobile-optimized payments system), and Indian mobile e-commerce company **Paytm** now boasts a $16 billion valuation. **The Center for Financial Inclusion** ranks **Colombia**, **Peru**, and **Uruguay** as the top three countries for financial inclusion (India took the No. 4 spot). In those countries and others, Latin American fintech companies are working to solve the region's most pressing problems, particularly around inflation and remittances.

What's Next

The role of a traditional financial institution is changing, and digital currencies are often cited as an opportunity for increased financial inclusion. **Kenya**-based **AZA Finance** allows cross-border payments and aims to cut the time and costs of those payments inside **Africa** and other frontier markets. In established markets, people are saving less and in some cases sidestepping banks entirely thanks to the gig economy, uncertain geopolitical conditions, and the rising cost of living. In emerging markets, mobile payments and remittances hold huge potential due to more internet and cell phone penetration. But financial inclusion is not just about getting users an app. The most successful companies build products that also bridge a knowledge gap and inform and empower users to be more financially literate.

The Impact

Lack of financial education will continue to be a barrier for people, excluding them from financial services and systems. Digital and mobile payments, meanwhile, continue to grow with promising pilot programs that leverage cryptocurrencies for remittances and humanitarian aid.

Watchlist

Afluenta, Alibaba, American Express, Ant Financial, AZA Group, Capital One, Carrefour, Center for Financial Inclusion, Citi, Facebook, Falabella, FICO, GoBank, IMF, Key Bank, JPMorgan Chase, mPesa, Ripio, TDBank, The United Services Automobile Association (USAA), Visa, Walmart, Wells Fargo.

Digital currencies provide an opportunity for increased financial inclusion.

The Rise of Quant Funds

HIGH DEGREE OF CERTAINTY

INFORMS STRATEGY	ACT NOW
REVISIT LATER	KEEP VIGILANT WATCH

LONGER-TERM IMPACT   IMMEDIATE IMPACT

LOW DEGREE OF CERTAINTY

Quant funds use algorithms to buy and sell stocks based on "factors," asset features determined to drive return and used to set trading parameters.

Key Insight

Quantitative hedge funds, also known as "quant funds," have been around since the 1990s. These algorithm-powered funds follow factors set by humans, and they're taking over more of the U.S. stock market.

Why It Matters

The algorithms powering quant funds, like the humans who develop them, are vulnerable to inherent biases.

Examples

In 2017, quant funds became the dominant method of institutional trading in the U.S. Quant funds use algorithms to buy and sell stocks based on factors, such as quality and value, that help forecast performance over a given period of time. Some use machines to mimic previous human strategies, while others use generative adversarial networks and advanced deep learning techniques to create new strategies on their own. The world's largest algorithmic hedge fund managers—AQR Capital, Bridgewater, Two Sigma—execute trades quickly and efficiently, and sometimes at lower costs than non-algorithmic funds. The world's best funds used to run primarily on human brain power, but today A.I. is increasingly taking on a greater role in their data-driven trading strategies.

What's Next

As A.I. systems become more sophisticated and powerful, quant fund investors are now asking computers not only to crunch numbers and execute trades, but to identify the decision-making factors, too. While machines might surface entirely new criteria for trades, it's important to note that the human programmers who originally built those systems made choices about which data to train and which algorithms to run. Those human decisions have downstream implications. Bias is a well-known problem in the A.I. ecosystem, which means that fund architects will need to redouble their efforts to ensure their systems aren't missing critical information or factors that might have been excluded due to human error or ignorance.

The Impact

As quant funds advance to include more machine-derived factors, there will be new strategic advantages—and risks—for investors and fund managers.

Watchlist

ARQ Capital, Bridgewater, Kensho, Man Group, Renaissance, Two Sigma.

Regulating Open Banking

HIGH DEGREE OF CERTAINTY

LONGER-TERM IMPACT			IMMEDIATE IMPACT
	INFORMS STRATEGY	ACT NOW	
	REVISIT LATER	KEEP VIGILANT WATCH	

LOW DEGREE OF CERTAINTY

In Europe, banks will soon be required to create APIs for developers.

Key Insight

Financial data systems are becoming more standardized and interoperable, facilitating access to banking infrastructure and analytics for third parties.

Why It Matters

The European Union and the **U.K.** recently passed laws requiring banks to create application programming interfaces (APIs) for third-party developers. This should bring standardization to open banking and give the E.U. and U.K. a competitive advantage over the **U.S.**, which has no such laws on the books.

Examples

In the E.U., a fintech company can access APIs by registering as an "account information service provider" (AISP) or "payment initiation service provider" (PISP). In November 2019, **Open Banking Europe**, an initiative operated by **EBA Clearing** subsidiary **Preta**, published a directory to list all publicly available bank APIs in the European Union. The European regulation known as **Payment Service Directive Two (PSD2)**, which went into effect in 2018, requires banks to enable third parties to access a customer's financial data. PSD2 lays the foundation for new players to use financial transaction data to improve analytics behind product development, predictive analytics, fraud analysis, marketing, and a la carte services within an ecosystem of providers.

What's Next

Regulation will change the ownership structures of financial data. Interoperability will make it easier for customers to aggregate finances and choose a la carte services from various providers to best suit their needs. We expect disruptive fintech innovators to build functionality that attracts a critical mass of consumers, which will then trigger large incumbents to seek partnerships or acquisitions. The most successful players will be those who can get access to the richest data and can effectively productize data-driven insights. This would likely be through personalized marketing and operating efficiencies, such as reducing fraud and chargeback rates.

The Impact

New standards will make it easier for vendor integration, compliance, reporting, and data management.

Watchlist

American Express, BBVA, Banco Santander, Citi, Clear, European Union, Fidor, HSBC, Intuit, iZettle, Klarna, Lloyds, N26, Mastercard, Monzo, Open Banking Europe, Plum, Square, Visa, Wells Fargo.

Social Payments

HIGH DEGREE OF CERTAINTY

INFORMS STRATEGY	**ACT NOW**
REVISIT LATER	**KEEP VIGILANT WATCH**

LONGER-TERM IMPACT · IMMEDIATE IMPACT

LOW DEGREE OF CERTAINTY

Social platforms are a preferred method of payment in China.

Key Insight

Financial service and payment providers are tapping into social interactions to facilitate financial transactions.

Why It Matters

As social payment offerings grow more robust, millennials may opt out of traditional banking services entirely.

Examples

Late in 2018, **Amazon** worked to expand **Amazon Pay** from the digital-only space to physical brick-and-mortar gas stations and restaurants. The move coincided with a rollout of new cashless (and cashierless) **Amazon Go** stores. While Amazon's system is new, the digital wallet model isn't, and consumers now prefer convenience to traditional point-of-sale transactions. **Venmo** launched nine years ago as one of the first social payment apps in the U.S., and incorporated social features into its interface. Users were required to caption their transactions with a comment or emoji, and could share publicly with whom they were transacting. **China**-based **AliPay** launched 15 years ago and now has amassed more than 870 million active users. Through its financial partner, **Ant Financial**, AliPay users get much more than emojis. They can access wealth management services, loan applications, and credit scores. Other popular peer-to-peer payment apps include **PayPal**, **Apple Pay**, **Square's Cash App**, and **Google Pay**. The most advanced players seek to embed seamless functionality into the customer experience, including chat applications. In the Chinese market, **WeChat** and **Alipay** drive mobile payment, thanks to a highly developed network of merchants that now accept chat-based payments. These apps blur the lines between sending money to a friend versus sending money to a store.

What's Next

Late in 2019, **Facebook** launched **Facebook Pay** for **WhatsApp**, **Instagram**, and **Facebook Messenger**—Facebook Pay exists separately from **Calibra**, the company's digital wallet, and its **Libra** cryptocurrency network. We expect to see more integrations for social payment systems from the big tech companies in 2020.

The Impact

Government regulation for all major tech companies is threatening to become more stringent in the wake of data breaches, privacy concerns, rampant fraud, and claims of antitrust violation. Social payment systems are a valuable way to transfer money, but they could face heightened scrutiny this year.

Watchlist

Alibaba, Amazon, Ant Financial, Apple, Baidu, Facebook, Google, Mastercard, Microsoft, PayPal, Tencent, Visa, WeChat.

Countries Creating Digital Decentralized Currencies

HIGH DEGREE OF CERTAINTY

INFORMS STRATEGY	ACT NOW
REVISIT LATER	KEEP VIGILANT WATCH

LONGER-TERM IMPACT · IMMEDIATE IMPACT

LOW DEGREE OF CERTAINTY

In 2017, Singapore's central bank trialed a distributed ledger system focused on inter-bank payments.

Key Insight

Countries including **China** and **Sweden** are researching how to develop their own decentralized currencies.

Why It Matters

The global monetary system is currently based on state-backed fiat currency.

Examples

In 2018, **the Marshall Islands** created a new digital currency called the Sovereign (SOV), which is now legal tender in the micronesian nation. **Singapore's Central Bank** created a digital currency backed by the Singapore dollar that runs on the Ethereum block-chain. **Canada's Central Bank** has been researching a central bank digital currency, or CBDC, and **China** is working on its own blockchain-based digital currency.

What's Next

One of the hot topics at the 2020 annual **World Economic Forum** in **Davos, Switzer-land** was the rise of central bank digital cur-rencies (CBDCs). At the close of the confer-ence, WEF published a policy-maker toolkit designed to help central banks investigate CBDCs, which "could potentially be used as a tool to achieve policy objectives such as improved safety and resilience in payments systems; increased efficiency, access and competitiveness of payments systems; better data transmission and reporting to central banks; and financial inclusion."

The Impact

According to a report from the **Bank of International Settlements**, 80% of the 63 central banks surveyed are researching whether and when to release their own digital currencies.

Watchlist

Bank of International Settlements, central banks worldwide, the World Economic Forum.

Additional Financial Technologies and Cryptocurrencies Trends

❯ TRENDS

Automated Credit Risk Modeling

Big banks now use artificial intelligence to automate credit risk modeling. Start-up **Spin Analytics** readies data first and then runs models as needed. It's just one example of the A.I.-powered automated credit risk modeling services that are now being studied by central banks and tested at commercial banks including **BBVA** and **Crédit Agricole**.

Crypto Trading Bots

Investing in cryptocurrencies isn't for the faint of heart. With significant volatility and complicated technical workflows, it can be exhaustingly difficult to trade cryptos. But trading bots can help by monitoring the crypto markets 24/7, since, unlike the stock market, they never close. Send instructions to the bot, and it will carry out its commands until you instruct otherwise. That said, as we've seen in other places, bots can be glitchy.

Crypto-Mining Malware

Crypto-mining malware pirates processing power on a computer, smartphone, or other connected device to mine cryptocurrencies. Hackers most often gain access to computers by hiding cryptocurrency mining software in what appear to be legitimate, mundane software updates from brands like **Microsoft** and **Adobe**. Once a machine is infected, it uses its computing resources to mine for currency on behalf of the hacker. We'll likely continue to see crypto-mining malware spread in 2020.

30 Space & Off-Planet Trends

Space

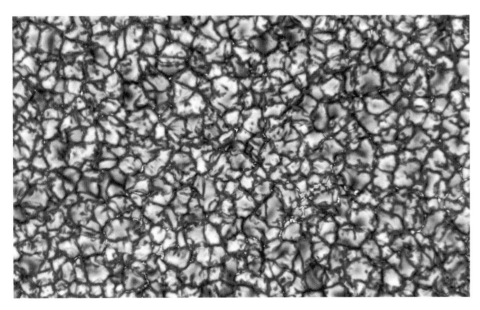

One of the first high-resolution images of the surface of the sun, taken by the Daniel K. Inouye Solar Telescope.
Photo courtesy of the NSO, AURA and NSF.

"Change is the essential process of all existence."

– Mr. Spock

KEY INSIGHT

Space: the final frontier. A new generation of astrophysicists, cosmologists, engineers, astrobiologists, planetary scientists, astrochemists, astrobotanists, atmospheric scientists, aerospace professionals, computer scientists, businesspeople, and government leaders hope to go where no human has gone before. Not just to the **Moon** and back, but to asteroids, black holes, Mars, and exoplanets beyond our solar system.

WHAT YOU NEED TO KNOW

This is an important year for space initiatives. Some of the planned missions involve humans, others are for robots only, and a handful will bring earthly agriculture into space. Some estimates value the space industry at $330 billion, with that figure potentially set to double by 2026.

WHY IT MATTERS

Human ambition, our quest for knowledge, and our curiosity have driven our endeavors to explore space. Last year marked the 50th anniversary of Apollo 11's historic voyage to the lunar Sea of Tranquility, which punctuated a space race that had pitted the **U.S.** against the **U.S.S.R.** Five decades later, the race has many more competitors. This year will see spacecraft launches from **India**, **Japan**, the **United Arab Emirates**, **China**, and **Israel**, as well as from commercial companies like **Blue Origin**, **SpaceX**, **Virgin Orbit**, and **Boeing**.

⊙ DEEPER DIVE

A Busy Year for Off-Planet Exploration

Sun

The long-awaited Solar Orbiter spacecraft, a joint mission from **NASA** and the **European Space Agency**, will take high-resolution images of the Sun's poles for the first time, and give us a better understanding of how our main source of energy, heat, and light works.

Moon

In humanity's first attempt at collecting lunar samples since 1976, **China**'s Chang'e 5 mission will head to the Moon.

Mars

Once every 26 months, the launch window for Mars missions opens, and July presents a new opportunity for **America**, **Europe**, the **United Arab Emirates**, and **China** to send up unmanned orbiters, research tools, and rovers. The ExoMars program, a joint effort by the **European Space Agency** and Russia's space agency **Roscosmos**, will send an exploratory spacecraft to Mars on a Russian Proton rocket. China's Huoxing 1 Mars rover and **NASA**'s Mars 2020 rover will both be launched to the Red Planet. The **UAE**'s Hope Mars Mission will send an orbiter to study the atmospheric chemistry of the planet from above.

Human cargo tests

For the first time since 2011, **American** astronauts are scheduled to launch into space from a U.S. launchpad. **SpaceX**'s Crew

SpaceX's Starman mannequin sits inside Elon Musk's red Tesla Roadster with Earth in the background, shortly after the initial launch of SpaceX's Falcon Heavy rocket on Feb. 6, 2018.
Image credit: SpaceX

Space cont.

SpaceX's Crew Dragon craft.

Dragon will launch an historic mission to the **International Space Station (ISS)** with people on board. **NASA** astronauts **Doug Hurley** and **Bob Behnken** are scheduled to make the journey. **Boeing's** CST-100 Starliner spacecraft will take its first crewed mission to the ISS, too. **China's** Long March 5B rocket will launch an unpiloted test flight with the ultimate goal of bringing humans back to the Moon. **Virgin Galactic** has said that it will start taking its first prepaid customers—six at a time, plus two pilots—for 15-minute space flights on its SpaceShipTwo craft this year. Though a date hasn't yet been announced, **Blue Origin** has said it expects to send humans into space sometime this year as well.

Satellites

From massive rockets carrying heavy satellite payloads to tiny microsats you can hold in your hand, there are thousands of satellites scheduled for launch this year.

IMPACT

Numerous industries and businesses, even those firmly rooted on the ground, will be impacted by space exploration: those working in insurance, on the 5G network expansion,

in finance and in science-fiction and game design, to name a few.

WATCHLIST FOR SECTION

3gimbals, Aerial & Maritime Ltd., Aerospace Corporation, Airbus D&S, Amazon, Astro Digital, Astrobotic, Astrocast, AXA XL, Boeing, California Polytechnic University, Capella Space, China National Space Administration, ConsenSys, Cornell University, DARPA, Delft University of Technology, DigitalGlobe, Earthcube, Elysium Space, European Space Agency, Fleet Space Technologies, GeoOptics, Google, Government of Luxembourg, Hera Systems, Hexcel, Indian Space Research Organization, Inmarsat, Interorbital Systems, Johns Hopkins Applied Physics Lab, Kanagawa University, Kepler Communications, Lancashire Holdings, Lawrence Livermore National Laboratory, Lockheed Martin, Los Alamos National Lab, Masten Space Systems, MDA, MIT, MIT Lincoln Lab, Morgan Stanley, Mojave Air and Space Port, NASA, NASA Ames Research Center, NASA Jet Propulsion Lab, National Geospatial Intelligence Agency, National University of Defense Technology (China), Naval Postgraduate School, Northrop Grumman, NRL Naval

Center for Space, OneWeb, Orbital Insight, Planet, Santa Clara University, Satellogic, Scaled Composites, Shanghai Engineering Center, Shanghai Engineering Center for Microsatellites (China), Shenzhen Aerospace Dongfanghong, Sky and Space Global, Space and Missile Defense Command, Spaceflight Industries, SpaceKnow, SpacePharma, SpaceX, SRI International, Stratolaunch, Technische Universität Berlin, Tokyo Institute of Technology, Toray, Transcelestial, University of Tokyo, U.S. Air Force, U.S. Space Command, Viasat, Virgin Galactic.

⊙ TRENDS

Imaging Space

In 2019, scientists did what they had always thought was impossible: They captured an image of a black hole's silhouette using the Event Horizon Telescope. A team of international astronomers and computer scientists spent a decade developing a new kind of imaging technique that revealed a dark black center surrounded by a massive ring of orange and yellow light. In early January, scientists in **Maui** used the new Daniel K. Inouye Solar Telescope for the first time, taking the highest-resolution photos of the sun ever recorded. (The surface looks like the cracked ground of the **Atacama desert**—if it were oozing lava and on fire.) Our abilities to image space using new techniques and equipment will advance the work of research scientists across a variety of fields.

Lots (and Lots) of Satellite Launches

Entrepreneurs are building and preparing to launch thousands of low-cost, high-value satellites in the next year. These satellite constellations are small, capable of communicating with each other, and they continue to work even when one satellite in the network goes down. They're referred to as microstats or cubesats, and they can be used for a variety of purposes, including taking photos and beaming internet access back down to Earth. Fleets of cubesats now take photos of farmland and beam them back down to earth to help farmers assess their crops. Image analysis software can find patterns in satellite images and tell big box retailers, such as **Walmart**, how many cars are parked in their lots and can look for trends over time. They can then do the same with a competitor's parking lots to gather strategic intelligence. Mining companies can survey a swath of land to see who's started drilling and whether they've struck oil. Satellites monitor traffic, polar ice caps, and even individual humans. Near-real time images captured from space, coupled with machine learning and analysis tools, is big business. Governments, big agricultural corporations, intelligence agencies, shipping companies, and logistics firms all want access, and they're willing to pay tens of millions of dollars a year for it. The combined valuation of companies such as **Planet**, **Airbus D&S**, **MDA** and **DigitalGlobe** is well into the tens of billions. In early 2020, the Starlink constellation, a project from **Elon Musk's SpaceX**, began sending clusters of 60 satellites into orbit every few weeks. By the middle of the year, there could be a fleet of 12,000 overhead. **Amazon** is planning a constellation of 3,200 microsats, while **U.K.**-based **OneWeb** is launching up to 700. And that's just a few examples—it would have taken us several pages to list every company planning to launch spacecraft over the next five years.

Crowded Skies

With thousands of planned spacecraft launches—microsat and cubesat constellations, in addition to heavier satellites, rockets, and spaceships with rovers and human cargo—astronomers are warning that our view of the sky, and our ability to research the cosmos, is under threat. Scientists have voiced concern that mega-constellations of microsats and cubesats will not only obstruct their view, but that they could also interfere with radio astronomy equipment. Some commercial spacecraft manufacturers, including **SpaceX**, are developing new coatings that would minimize reflection and other sources of interference.

Internet from Space

Apple and **Facebook** are working on satellite technology that would beam internet services directly to our devices, and in the process bypass our ISPs. Aerospace company **OneWeb** is one of the companies planning to power what it calls "fiber-like internet" coverage in the **Arctic**. New space-based internet services will rely on a complex array of microsat constellations and ground stations. **SpaceX** and **Amazon** are similarly working on services that could someday bring internet coverage to people in areas neglected by traditional wireless carriers and internet service providers.

Space-Based Quantum Internet

A quantum computer uses special equipment and algorithms to perform wildly complicated computations faster and more efficiently than classical computers. (See also: Quantum Computing.) While we are still some years away from quantum computing, some physicists believe that quantum networks are possible—and that they would provide security, privacy, and safety unmatched by today's internet. Delft University of Technology in the Netherlands is currently working on a quantum network, while China is building a quantum communications satellite program.

Space Junk

Space is our next dumping ground. As many as 170 million fragments of metal and astro debris encircle the Earth as a result of human behavior. That includes 20,000 pieces larger than a softball, and 500,000 about the size of a marble, according to NASA. This debris will pose a navigation hazard for many centuries to come. At least 200 objects roar back through the atmosphere toward earth each year, including pieces of solar panels and antennas and fragments of metal. All of them pose dangers for future astronauts: One plum-sized piece of gnarled space trash traveling faster than a speeding bullet could rip a five-foot hole into a spacecraft. That collision would then spawn its own batch of shrapnel, adding to the rushing river of junk already circling the planet. It's not just Americans doing the dumping, China and Russia each have dozens of decommissioned satellites overhead. Where all that junk winds up isn't something we can predict accurately. We could be unintentionally wreaking havoc on civilizations far away from Earth, for all we know catalyzing future intergalactic wars. Or, we might cause far less grandiose problems. Space junk could start to behave in unpredictable ways, reflecting sunlight the wrong direction, changing our atmosphere, or impacting the universe in ways that don't fit into our current understanding of physics.

Bigger, Bolder Telescopes

In 2018, a review board found that NASA's James Webb Space Telescope project was already $8.8 billion over budget and still many years away from taking flight. Even so, there are four new NASA space telescope concepts that could find their way into development soon. One of the concepts will be funded and built to launch in the mid-2030s, but they're all designed to help scientists discover supermassive black holes, planet-forming disks, new galaxies, and of course earth-like exoplanets that might sustain life.

Asteroid Mining for Resources

Mining asteroids for resources will prove invaluable to researchers back on Earth. In September 2017, Arizona State University astrophysicist Dante Lauretta and his team launched the OSIRIS-REx spacecraft to Bennu, an asteroid that might offer secrets about the early history of the solar system. In January of 2020, the craft successfully completed a flyover of its designated mining site; the probe will take its sample in August and then begin its three-year journey home.

The New Space Economy

New spacecraft, rockets, and other technologies are helping private commercial companies to achieve liftoff—with plenty of eager venture capitalists footing the bill. Investors, including Morgan Stanley, are eyeing a new space gold rush, now that a critical mass of commercial space companies and their technologies have matured enough to move beyond proof of concept into testing. Some estimates project the value of the space industry to reach more than $1 trillion in the next two decades. We anticipate investment into commercial space companies, especially in the areas of insurance, satellites, defense, aerospace technologies, and materials (manufacturing and mining).

Made in Space

As the cost of sending payloads into space decreases, we will start to see more products made in space. Sure, it sounds cool—imagine the label possibilities!—but making products in space has more to do with leveraging microgravity than marketing. For example, printing muscle tissue, such as a heart, is difficult on Earth because the delicate tissues required tend to collapse under their own weight. Space-based organ printing using bio-inks and gels would be possible in microgravity. The first bioprinter was sent to the ISS last July and printed a tiny portion of a heart muscle. Similar techniques could be used in microgravity to culture meats more easily. Another candidate for space production is fiber-optic cables made from fluoride glass, which is difficult to work with terrestrially because our gravity can cause crystals to form when the glass is being heated and stretched. Researchers believe that in space, the necessary fibers could be created more easily.

Space Tourism

Test launches for manned commercial space flight are now underway, which will help usher in a new era of space tourism. In December 2018, Virgin Galactic successfully launched a human crew 51 miles into the sky over the Mojave Desert in California. Two pilots, Mark Stucky and former NASA astronaut Rick Sturckow earned the first ever commercial astronaut wings from the Federal Aviation Administration. As of the publication of this report, more than 600 people had pledged $250,000 each to take a ride aboard Virgin Galactic's tourist spacecraft, which is set to begin flights this year. But not everyone has the physical or mental fortitude for space flight. Carl Sagan wrote about the disconcerting "Overview Effect" in his book *Pale Blue Dot*: "Our planet is a lonely speck in the great enveloping cosmic dark. In our obscurity, in all this vastness, there is no hint that help will come from elsewhere to save us from ourselves." There are practical limitations, too: the estimated travel time for a trip to Mars and back is currently set at three years. Getting to and from the Moon is much faster—just a one week round trip—but still challenging. Lunar travelers would contend with something called "space adaptation syndrome" (like car sickness, but a lot worse) and elevated levels of radiation. One nine-day mission to the Moon would result in radiation exposure equivalent to 35 chest x-rays.

Galactic Ride Sharing

New technologies have spawned a new trend in space transportation: galactic ride sharing. Spaceflight Industries launched its first rideshare mission, called SSO-A SmallSat Express, aboard a SpaceX Falcon 9 in 2018. The company purchased all of the available payload space on the rocket to service customers who wanted to launch things into space. It included microsats and cubesats from 17 countries—but there were some unusual projects aboard, too. Artist Trevor Paglen sent a self-inflating sculpture that reflects sunlight and can be viewed by the naked eye here on earth. A separate spacecraft from the Los Angeles County Museum of Art sent up a 24-karat gold jar with a bust of the first African American astronaut to reach space. Yet another craft, the Elysium Star 2 sent by Elysium Space, contained the cremated remains of people who wanted to become shooting stars. As more researchers, artists, and everyday people need to hitch rides on a rocket, we anticipate new business models—and more potential regulation.

Seeking a New Life in the Off-World Colonies

NASA said it wants to send humans to Mars by 2030, and in 2016, it selected six private U.S. companies, including Boeing, Lockheed Martin, and Bigelow Aerospace, to develop prototypes for deep space habitats. At the beginning of the year, Tesla CEO and SpaceX founder Elon Musk discussed sending 1 million people to colonize Mars by the year 2050 by scheduling three Starship launches a day. That may sound like science fiction, but SpaceX has taken preliminary steps toward making it a reality—this year, the company will ramp up testing of its manned spacecraft by bringing astronauts to the ISS. However, astrophysicists have been quick to point out that human travel to Mars would have some difficult hurdles to overcome, not the least of which is radiation. As Columbia University astronomer Caleb Schart said, explaining of the perils of space travel, "in the worst case scenario (which may or may not be a realistic extrapolation) there's a chance you'd end up dead or stupid on Mars. Or both."

Fuel-Free Space Propulsion Systems

Researchers at the Naval Research Laboratory are working on a concept that could not only help steer satellites back down to earth when they're decommissioned, but also clean up space clutter in the process. The idea is to outfit new satellites with thin tethers about a kilometer long. Running an electric current through the cord would enable a satellite to steer itself using its own electric field as well as the magnetic field from Earth. Think of it as an invisible rudder that could someday guide old satellites home.

Space cont.

Blue Origin's reusable launch vehicles and rocket engines will lower the cost of access to space.

Mercury Rain

New propulsion systems for rocket engines would use mercury as a fuel, which could run the risk of spreading toxic chemicals through Earth's atmosphere. **NASA** experimented with mercury in the 1960s because it's a low-cost, high-power option for ion engines. Startup **Apollo Fusion** has discovered a new approach to using mercury—but again, there's a catch. Mercury is heavier than the xenon and krypton powering other ion engines in use today. What customers might save on costs could pollute the atmosphere in potentially harmful ways. While the **U.S. government** has tried to reduce our mercury emissions since the 1990s, longstanding regulations do not specifically cover spacecraft hovering above us. **The Federal Aviation Administration** requires companies to disclose hazardous materials, but this doesn't include satellites. It's an area where, yet again, technology has leapt beyond our governing agencies and the policy they write.

Galactic Gas Stations

Some satellites require fuel, and, as it turns out, fuel is very heavy. Once a satellite runs out of said fuel, it's no longer fully operational. For that reason, researchers are developing refueling stations for use in space with new techniques to overcome some challenging hurdles in liquid dynamics. Last year, startup **Orbit Fab** successfully completed the first set of experiments to see if water could be transferred between two satellite test beds. Orbit Fab has been working with satellite manufacturers on something called the Rapidly Attachable Fuel Transfer Interface, or RAFTI, which is a new kind of valve system that would allow satellites to be fueled on the ground before launch and, someday, refueled in space. This would eventually allow more satellites to stay in orbit and help reduce the creation of new space junk.

Space Forces

The **U.S.** announced the launch of a new **Space Force** in 2019. Its purpose: to secure our satellite communication networks that not only power our information ecosystems, but also control the navigation and positioning systems we use. **President Donald Trump** signed a $738 billion defense bill, a portion of which will be earmarked for the new agency, which is also expected to have up to 15,000 military personnel. But the U.S. isn't the only country with a military space program; both **Russia** and **China** maintain their own space forces. It's unlikely that a traditional war would be fought in space—these departments are about securing critical network and communications infrastructure from government-sponsored cyberhacking.

China's Space Ambitions

In January 2019, China became the first country to land a robotic mission on the moon's far side. It was an historic accomplishment—and a clear sign of new leadership in aerospace from China. The country showed up late to the space race—China didn't send its first satellite into orbit until 1970, long after the **U.S.** and former **Soviet Union** had already been to the moon and back—but it's certainly making up for lost time. **President Xi Jinping** said "the space dream is part of the dream to make China stronger...the Chinese people will take bigger strides to explore further into space." China doesn't just want to be seen as a powerful Asian nation—it wants to set the global pace for numerous geoeconomic initiatives, for environmental causes, and for societal development. Chinese officials have said that by 2030, China hopes to be among the major space powers of the world.

Ultra-Long Space Missions

If climate change escalates, and we are unable to mitigate its effects, humanity is going to need a plan B to planet Earth. Some scientists think our next best option is a 1000-year space mission to save future generations from extinction. Their target is a planet called Proxima Centauri b, an exoplanet in a habitable zone of a star similar to our sun. This means that theoretically water could exist in liquid form there and, the thinking goes, thus it could support human life. We don't know what the atmosphere is like, or whether the planet's surface is too hot or too cold to sustain living organisms as we know them. A program founded by science philanthropist **Yuri Milner** and the late **Stephen Hawking** is building a spacecraft weighing only a few grams that would be propelled by a 100-billion-watt laser fired at it from earth. The craft would take 20 years to reach the Alpha Centauri solar system, where Proxima Centauri b is located. It's a step toward building a new kind of spacecraft, one big enough to transport us deep into space on a 1,000-year journey to reach humanity's new home.

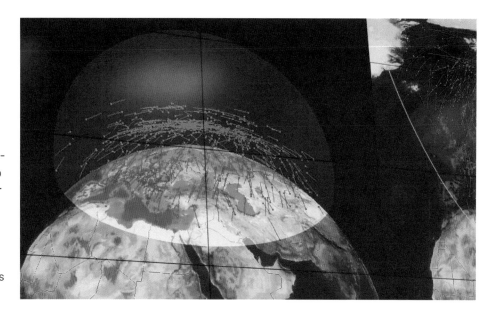

A computerized projection of space objects monitored by Russian space radar, Sofrino, Russia.

➔ WEAK SIGNALS FOR THE 2020'S

At the Future Today Institute, our goal in the first step of forecasting is to identify weak signals. Because we know that technology is deeply intertwined with a number of other areas of modern change—the economy, education, government, media, and more—we cannot think about the future of a given technology without simultaneously considering how it relates to all these other areas.

To do this, we use a series of questions to guide our research on emerging technology, science, and other areas of change. We categorize our research using a network of nodes and connections. Creating a network map of signals forces us to think very broadly—not just about an emerging trend, but about how that trend relates to a broader ecosystem. Taking this wider view, where nodes and relationships are considered in tandem, is critical. This approach can be used to map the fringe for a product, or even an entire industry.

We're headed into a new decade that will bring scientific and technological breakthroughs, emerging ecosystems, and new businesses. Here are some of the weak signals that we will be tracking throughout the 2020s:

01 Artificial intelligence detecting and acting on our emotions, especially in advertising.

02 An Internet of Behaviors that mines, refines, and productizes our behavioral biometrics for use in personalizing our devices and networks.

03 A new constellation of connected devices—that doesn't include smartphones.

04 Blockchain applied to news in an effort to deter misinformation and deepfakes.

05 City-scale spatial computing functionality that acts as a giant municipal operating system, helping citizens with their day-to-day activities.

06 "Unhackable" computers that make use of quantum mechanics.

07 Fully autonomous public transportation systems.

08 Engineered, factory-grown food and beverage at scale.

09 Five-axis additive manufacturing (5D printing for short) that prints curved layers.

10 Computational pharmacies that employ specially trained pharmacists with backgrounds in bioinformatics, medicine, and pharmacology.

Events That Will Shape 2020

Your guide to the events that will shape the year ahead.

March

- More than 100,000 techies, filmmakers, journalists, game designers and musicians flock to Austin, Texas for the annual South By Southwest festival.

- Super Tuesday narrows the Democratic field of presidential candidates, and by the end of the month, nearly half of U.S. states will have selected their candidate for the primary nomination.

- The Vatican releases the archives of Pope Pius XII, which will provide researchers insights into the Catholic Church's thinking and work during World War II.

- It is the 250th anniversary of the Boston Massacre, when Bostonians argued "no taxation without representation."

April

- April is a month of important anniversaries. It is the 150th anniversary of the birth of Vladimir Ilyich Ulyanov. You know him by his nickname: Lenin. It's also the 50th anniversary of the U.S. invasion of Cambodia, in which Richard Nixon helped set into motion events that brought the Khmer Rouge to power.

- Fifty years ago this month, the first Earth Day was held. Former U.S. Senator Gaylord Nelson (D-Wisconsin) came up with the idea after witnessing a catastrophic oil spill off the coast of Santa Barbara, California. And 10 years ago, the iPad debuted.

- The Quibi platform—a much-anticipated mobile video service founded by HP ex-CEO Meg Whitman and Walt Disney Studios ex-chair Jeffrey Katzenberg—will launch publicly.

May

- May is an important month for tech announcements. Google's annual I/O conference will bring together developers from around the world, and will tout Android releases, updates to various consumer products and services, and prototypes will be revealed. Microsoft's annual Build conference highlights all of the company's upcoming devices, gaming updates and OS releases for developers. Facebook returns to San Jose for its annual F8 developer conference. And the annual IBM Think conference in San Francisco will reveal IBM's plans for A.I., cloud, security, and IT infrastructure.

- It is the 200th birthday of Florence Nightingale, a pioneer in statistical evidence communication, data visualization and the nursing profession.

- Government leaders, business tycoons, philanthropists, and sovereign wealth fund managers head to Los Angeles for the Milken Institute's Global Conference.

- It's the 10th anniversary of the Augmented World Expo, which brings together AR experts, researchers and vendors from around the world.

June

- It's the 50th anniversary of Anna Mae Hays and Elizabeth P. Hoisington becoming the first women promoted to general officer in the U.S. military.

- June is another important month for tech announcements. AI. researchers gather in Long Beach, California to present their latest research at the annual IEEE conference on Computer Vision and Pattern Recognition.

- At Apple's annual WWDC, company leaders take the stage to showcase new OS versions and Apple products. Computex, the world's largest PC and hardware manufacturing show, will be held in Taipei. And Amazon's re:MARS Conference brings together world leaders in home automation, robotics, space exploration, and A.I.

- The U.S. hosts the G7 summit—though not at a Donald Trump-owned resort as originally planned.

- It is the 75th anniversary of the signing of the United Nations charter.

- For sports fans, the UEFA Euro 2020 football championship begins.

July

- The 2020 Summer Olympics opens in Tokyo, which will feature rock climbing, surfing, skateboarding, and karate as new competitive sports. The games will end in August.

- The United Nations World Population Day asks us to consider global population issues.

- A hundred years ago on July 25th, chemist Rosalind Franklin was born. Her research in DNA and x-ray images enabled Watson and Crick to deduce the double-helix DNA architecture.

- The Democratic National Convention takes place in Milwaukee, Wisconsin and will announce its presidential nominee to face off against Donald Trump in the fall.

- Once every 26 months the launch window for Mars missions opens, and July presents a new opportunity for America, Europe, the United Arab Emirates, and China to send up unmanned orbiters, research tools, and rovers into space.

- Tech, media, and business moguls trek to Sun Valley, Idaho for Allen & Co's annual confab.

August

- The Paralympic games begin in Tokyo, with taekwondo and badminton added as new competitive events.

- It's the 75th anniversary of the World War II nuclear strikes on Hiroshima and Nagasaki, which killed more than 200,000 people.

- It's 100 years since the passing of the 19th amendment, which gave American women the right to vote.

- Professional hackers gather in Las Vegas for the 28th annual DEF CON conference.

- The Republican National Convention takes place in Charlotte, North Carolina. The RNC will confirm their candidate—which as of publication is incumbent Donald Trump—and will release their national platform.

September

- It is the 400th anniversary of the Mayflower voyage.

- It's also the 25th anniversary of the Beijing Declaration, which was a conference that produced what was then the most progressive blueprint ever for advancing women's rights. The declaration was adopted unanimously by 189 countries, but there hasn't been a follow-up summit since then.

- This month marks the 50th anniversary of Black September, when members of the Popular Front for the Liberation of Palestine hijacked three commercial jets bound for NYC.

- A new successor to Live Aid—Global Goal Live—will take place around the world to help raise money for the world's 59 poorest countries. The 10-hour concert will bring together artists and celebrities from five continents and will be livestreamed globally.

- The UN General Assembly's 75th annual meeting takes place in New York.

- The IFA—Europe's largest consumer electronics trade show—is held in Berlin.

October

- Dubai will host the Expo 2020, which will include pavilions from 180 countries, a massive-scale vertical farm, and many other technological wonders.

- The world's largest and most important book fair, the Frankfurter Buchmesse, takes place in Frankfort, drawing 300,000 visitors from around the globe.

Events That Will Shape 2020

Your guide to the events that will shape the year ahead.

November

⊙ In November, world leaders will meet to discuss various initiatives. The United Nations' COP 26 climate change conference takes place in Glasgow with 200 world leaders in attendance. A massive gathering of G20 nation representatives and leaders from the International Monetary Fund and World Bank gather for a summit in Saudi Arabia. Leaders from the world's 20 largest economies gather in Riyadh for the G20 summit to discuss trade and technology. And celebrations will honor the 50th anniversary of the founding of UNESCO, the United Nations Educational, Scientific and Cultural Organization.

⊙ Presidential and congressional elections decide America's next slate of political leaders.

⊙ November 11 marks Singles' Day in China—the annual shopping event that dwarfs both Black Friday and Prime Day in the United States.

⊙ The AWS re:Invent draws the largest gathering for the cloud computing community, while Dreamforce, the annual mega-conference produced by Salesforce, brings more than 170,000 people to San Francisco.

December

⊙ New Zealand decides whether to legalize cannabis.

⊙ It's the 250th anniversary of the birth of Ludwig van Beethoven. Concerts and celebrations are planned around the world.

⊙ It's also the 50th anniversary of an infamous meeting between President Nixon and Elvis Presley, who shook hands for a photographer. To date, it is the most-requested item from the National Archives— more than the Bill of Rights or Constitution.

⊙ A.I. luminaries gather at the annual Neural Information Processing Systems conference in Montréal to talk about the future of artificial intelligence.

January

⊙ The World Economic Forum Annual Meeting is held in Davos-Klosters, Switzerland, bringing together 3,000 of the world's most powerful government, business, and academic leaders.

⊙ The Consumers Electronics Show, the world's largest convention for electronics and digital media, is held in Las Vegas, Nevada. Expect countless roundups and think pieces about the future of consumer media.

February

⊙ Some of the biggest thought leaders will gather in Europe for the Mobile World Congress, which typically unveils big mobile network announcements.

About the Authors

Authors

Amy Webb
Future Today Institute Founder

Amy Webb is a quantitative futurist. She is the founder of the Future Today Institute and is a professor of strategic foresight at the NYU Stern School of Business. Webb is a Visiting Fellow at Oxford University's Säid School of Business, a Fellow in the United States-Japan Leadership Program and a Foresight Fellow in the U.S. Government Accountability Office Center for Strategic Foresight. She was a Visiting Nieman Fellow at Harvard University, where her research received a national Sigma Delta Chi award. She was also a Delegate on the former U.S.-Russia Bilateral Presidential Commission, where she worked on the future of technology, media and international diplomacy. She has written several award-winning books, including *The Signals Are Talking: Why Today's Fringe Is Tomorrow's Mainstream*, which explains the Future Today Institute's forecasting methodology and how any organization can identify risk and opportunity before disruption hits, and *The Big Nine: How The Tech Titans and Their Thinking Machines Could Warp Humanity*, a long-view assessment of artificial intelligence which was longlisted for the Financial Times & McKinsey Business Book of the Year award and shortlisted for the Thinkers50 Digital Thinking Award.

Marc Palatucci
Senior Foresight Analyst

Marc Palatucci is a futurist and associate with the Future Today Institute specializing in technology, culture and business. He holds a BA in linguistics and languages from NYU's Gallatin School of Individualized Study, an MBA in emerging technology from NYU's Stern School of Business, and he serves as editor-at-large for an arts, fashion and culture magazine and creative media agency in New York.

Elena Giralt
Foresight Affiliate

Elena Giralt is a researcher at the Future Today Institute and is currently the product marketing manager for the Electric Coin Company, where she focuses on Zcash and privacy-preserving technology. Elena co-founded Blockchain Latinx, a monthly meetup group that explores what blockchain means for Latinos and for Latin America. She has an MBA from New York University Stern School of Business.

Sam Guzik
Foresight Affiliate

Sam Guzik is a digital strategist and journalist. He works as a product director for Hearst Newspapers, leading development of subscriber experiences and newsroom tools. Previously, he was editor for strategy and platforms at Newsday. He is a graduate of the NYU Stern School of Business, Columbia University Graduate School of Journalism and Washington University in St. Louis.

Kriffy Perez
Foresight Affiliate

Kristofer "Kriffy" Perez has over a decade of experience as a payments strategy consultant with leading global banks and retailers across Europe and the Americas. Kriffy has worked for Visa, MasterCard Advisors, the Boston Consulting Group, IBM, and co-founded a startup. He has accumulated more than 120 projects across eight countries and filed 15 patents. He received a degree in mechanical engineering from Lehigh University and an MBA from New York University's Stern School of Business.

Additional Research

Kara Lipsky
Ryo Hashimoto

Production Staff

Jennifer Alsever
Editorial Director

Jennifer Alsever is an award-winning journalist, who, for more than two decades, has written about technology, business, consumer trends and startups as a contributor to the New York Times, Fortune Magazine, Fast Company, Inc Magazine, Wired and more. She is also the author of the award-winning young adult fiction trilogy, The Trinity Forest Series. She is a graduate from the University of Colorado at Boulder.

Emily Caufield
Creative Director

Emily Caufield is an award-winning graphic designer and illustrator. At the Future Today Institute, she applies design thinking and computational design to complex research and forecasting scenarios. She is a graduate of Boston University's College of Fine Arts.

Cheryl Cooney
Director of Operations

Cheryl Cooney has served as the Future Today Institute's director of operations for the past decade. She manages workflows, planning, and logistics. Previously, she worked at various law firms in New York and Washington D.C., where she supported attorneys and managed back office operations. Cheryl has had various poems and stories published in Dream Chaser's Magazines, along with various poems published in an Australian anthology called "Prints Rhyming - Singing the Year" published by Prints Charming Books.

How To Think More Like a Futurist

We invite you to develop a culture of strategic foresight within your organization. The following tools are open source and available for download at **futuretodayinstitute.com**. Our Future Today Institute foresight methodology is published in detail in *The Signals Are Talking*, available in hardcover and paperback at most bookstores and on Amazon. For bulk orders of *Signals*, contact our office.

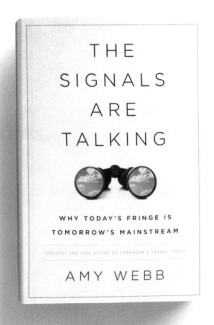

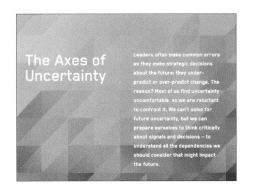

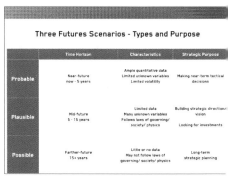

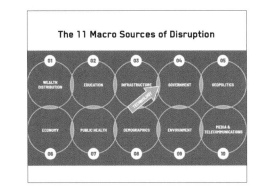

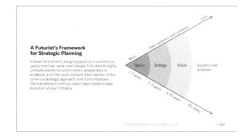

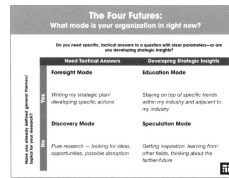

About The Future Today Institute

Founded in 2006, the Future Today Institute helps leaders and their organizations prepare for deep uncertainty and complex futures. We focus exclusively on how emerging technology and science will disrupt business, transform the workforce, and ignite geopolitical change. Our pioneering, data-driven forecasting methodology, trend identification framework, scenario writing process and risk/ opportunity matrix empowers leaders to make better decisions about their futures, today.

Contact Us

The Future Today Institute
120 E. 23rd Street
5th Floor
New York, NY 10010

hello@futuretodayinstitute.com

267-342-4300

www.futuretodayinstitute.com